AMERICAN MEDICINE

Books by Dr. Henry E. Sigerist

AMERICAN MEDICINE

THE GREAT DOCTORS

MAN AND MEDICINE

I. WILLIAM H. WELCH, WILLIAM STEWART HALSTED, WILLIAM
OSLER, AND HOWARD A. KELLY

Portrait by John Singer Sargent in the William H. Welch Medical Library,
The Johns Hopkins University

AMERICAN MEDICINE

by

Dr. Henry E. Sigerist

THE WILLIAM H. WELCH PROFESSOR
OF THE HISTORY OF MEDICINE
THE JOHNS HOPKINS UNIVERSITY

Translated by Hildegard Nagel

W · W · NORTON & COMPANY, INC.

NEW YORK

To
FIELDING H. GARRISON
PIONEER IN MEDICAL HISTORY
IN THE
UNITED STATES
CO-WORKER AND FRIEND

CONTENTS

INTRODUCTION   xi

I.   THE SOIL   I

II.   COLONIAL TIMES   14

III.   THE UNITED STATES   52

IV.   PIONEERS   75

V.   MEDICAL EDUCATION   131

VI.   THE PHYSICIAN AND THE PATIENT   169

VII.   HOSPITALS AND NURSING   204

VIII.   PREVENTIVE MEDICINE   230

IX.   MEDICAL SCIENCE   267

EPILOGUE   287

BIBLIOGRAPHY   289

INDEX OF PERSONS   305

INDEX OF SUBJECTS   310

☆ ILLUSTRATIONS ☆

1. Doctors Welch, Halsted, Osler and Kelly   *Frontispiece*
   Portrait by John Singer Sargent
2. Medicine Man of the Blackfoot Indians   4
3. Magic Sand Painting of the Navajo Indians   5
4. Pennsylvania Hospital in Philadelphia   48
5. John Morgan   80
6. Benjamin Rush   81
7. Ephraim McDowell   90
8. Daniel Drake   91
9. William Beaumont   100
10. Samuel David Gross   104
11. James Marion Sims   105
12. Oliver Wendell Holmes   116
13. Silas Weir Mitchell   117
14. John Shaw Billings   121
15. Sir William Osler   128
16. Johns Hopkins Hospital   129
17. Johns Hopkins University School of Medicine   142
18. Ground Plan of the Same   142
19. Welch Medical Library and Institute of the History
    of Medicine, Johns Hopkins University   142
20. New York Hospital and Cornell University Medical
    College   142
21. Columbia-Presbyterian Medical Center, New York   142
22. Medical Arts Building, St. Paul   176
23. The Old Mayo Clinic   178
24. The New Mayo Clinic   179
25. New York Hospital, 1791   206
26. Massachusetts General Hospital, 1821   207

Illustrations

27. Johns Hopkins University School of Hygiene and Public Health   244
28. Rockefeller Institute for Medical Research   276
29. Rockefeller Institute for Medical Research, Department of Animal and Plant Pathology   277
30. William H. Welch   284

On a bright morning in the late spring of 1927, I met Dr. William H. Welch for the first time. It was in Leipzig, where I was professor of the History of Medicine at the University, and in charge of the Institute of the History of Medicine, as successor to Karl Sudhoff. Dr. Welch intended to create a similar institution at the Johns Hopkins University; and he had come to Leipzig to discuss his plans with Karl Sudhoff and to see for himself what we were doing.

I had heard a great deal about Dr. Welch. I knew that he had contributed more than anyone else to the advancement of medical science in America. I was most anxious to meet him; and there he was, short, rotund, with a big cigar, a man whose great modesty and extreme kindliness captivated all who met him from the very first moment.

Those were pleasant days in the Leipzig Institute, showing Dr. Welch around, telling him about our work, what we had done so far, and what we intended to do in the future, asking for his advice, discussing the present situation in medicine. We agreed that modern medicine had become so specialized and so technical that some place had to be established in the medical schools where medicine would be studied, not from the specialist's point of view, but as a whole, as an entity—and in its relationship to the other sciences, and to society as a whole.

Dr. Welch never said much, but there was not a thing that he did not observe. He met our classes, went every day through the library and the collections. You never saw him with a pencil in hand; he never made a single note. But after a morning spent at the Institute you would find him in a nearby bookshop, ordering from memory hundreds of books, so many books in fact that there were later rumors that he had far exceeded his budget.

One day we had lunch in one of the historical Leipzig inns, "Auerbach's Keller," and it happened that we were seated at the same table where, more than half a century before, Dr. Welch had met John Shaw Billings. He looked around and suddenly said: "After all, this is the place where my career started." And he began telling me of his career—the days spent in Ludwig's laboratory in Leipzig, the work with Cohnheim in Breslau, the small laboratory at Bellevue Hospital in New York; then, in 1884, the Johns Hopkins, his pathological institute, the courses he gave long before there was a medical school, the Hospital erected after Billings' plans; then, in 1894, the Medical School, what it meant to them and to the country, and—much later—the School of Hygiene and Public Health; and now, as a new step in the development, the Library that was to bear his name and the Institute of the History of Medicine.

He talked for hours. We were quite alone. I listened entranced, and certainly had no idea that five years later I would succeed him at the Hopkins, and that my American career had started at the same table where he had once met John Billings.

Before leaving Leipzig, Dr. Welch invited me to come to Baltimore some day as a visiting lecturer, to give a few courses and to see what they were doing in America.

The idea of a lecture tour through the United States fascinated me. The average and even the cultivated European knows very little about America. He knows a few names, a few dates; but otherwise his notions are very vague. The scientist of course will be conversant with the work done in his special field of research, and will have noticed the tremendous development of the last decades, but his picture will necessarily be very fragmentary, and limited by the narrowness of his subject. There is no lack of books on America; some of them are quite excellent. The great majority however merely render fugitive impressions of superficial travellers, emphasizing over and over again the surface aspects of American life—skyscrapers, chain-stores, jazz and the movies. If, after a few weeks of ill-tempered travelling, you write a book condemning the country, you have a good chance of being rewarded with an Academy prize.

To me, as a student of the history and sociology of medicine, a trip through the United States held the promise of a great experience. Having lived and worked in a good many different countries, I was thoroughly familiar with the medical conditions in Europe, past and present. What would they be in America? How would they compare with the European conditions?

I was well aware that America was becoming an ever increasingly dominating factor in world medicine. At the turn of the century, America hardly counted in medicine. A few great contributions had come from over the ocean—ether anaesthesia, to mention only one: but they were not numerous. American students came over to study in Europe, and once home again little more was heard of them, as a rule.

A few decades later the situation had changed entirely. The great advances of the last years, insulin treatment in diabetes, liver treatment for pernicious anaemia, had their origin in the new world. In ever-growing numbers, European physicians went to America, and American publications were read with increasing attentiveness. America was undoubtedly beginning to return what it had received from Europe for so many years.

What had happened? What had been the process? This I wanted to study, and several years before I came to America I began to prepare myself for the trip. My approach to a new subject has always been the historical approach. To me the best way to understand a complex phenomenon has been always to study its genesis. As a teacher it has been my task for many years to introduce young students into the vast field of medicine, and it has always been my experience that unfamiliar and complicated concepts immediately become clear the moment I have traced the development for them.

I realized that if I wanted to get more than a superficial picture of American medicine, if I wanted really to understand it, I would have to study it not merely in its present aspects but in its peculiar development. And so I began to read whatever I could find in Europe on the history of American medicine. Great figures like Daniel Drake, William Beaumont and so many others, men of whom I hardly knew more than the names, before, became alive. I read their books. I followed their struggles against a hostile nature, and adverse conditions, and admired their accomplishments.

But then I also knew that medicine is but one aspect of the general civilization of a country—that it is always determined by the general cultural conditions and by an underlying philosophy. Whether a country has a high standard of physicians, whether it is ready to take an active part in medical research, whether the profession is able to apply its knowledge efficiently or not—all these are factors which depend, not so much on medicine as on society at large. I therefore had to make a study of the political, economic, and social history of the American nation. I read the philosophers, the poets, acquainted myself with the songs of the negroes on the Mississippi, of the cowboys in Texas. And gradually I began to visualize a great world, a gigantic historical process, strange and alluring.

Finally, in September of 1931, I landed in New York. I saw autumn on the hills of Maryland, saw the maples turning red in New England. I found a country so different from anything that I had read about—the beauty of its nature, the variety of its landscapes, the individuality of its cities. I had been told that American cities were all alike. As soon as you look under the surface, you see that there is nothing more erroneous: Boston, New York, Philadelphia, Baltimore, Washington, Richmond, are all within a few hours of each other, and yet how dissimilar are their physiognomies, which still show the mark of the Puritan, the Quaker, the English aristocrat. Further west, and everywhere in the South, one finds the same variation. An historic process has assumed a visible form. This process—the opening up of a gigantic continent, the building of a nation out of the most heterogeneous elements—forms an epic the like of which history has not seen. This is not generally recognized because it happened only yesterday. It is the World War which perhaps marks for us the end of a period. Moreover, this epic has found no Homer, as yet. Homer, for that matter, was born centuries after the Trojan War.

I spent two months as visiting lecturer at the Johns Hopkins and had a splendid opportunity to continue my previous studies at the Welch Medical Library. Then, for half a year, I travelled all over the country; went west, went north, went to Ohio, Michigan, Illinois, Wisconsin, Minnesota, Iowa, Nebraska, Colorado, and California, and wound up with a trip to the Hawaiian Islands. A delightful episode was a week spent in Santa Fé and Taos, where one comes in contact with America's ancient history. I had the great advantage of travelling, not as a specialist who would get to see only one section of medicine; for I was as interested in medical schools, laboratories, hospitals, nurses' schools, conditions of medical practice, public health service, as I was in the non-medical aspects of American life. And everywhere I met with an enchanting hospitality that made my task easy. Friendships resulted which I know will last throughout my life.

I was shown not only the present, but the past as well. I saw the landscape of the pioneers, saw that great valley between the Alleghanies and the Rockies that Daniel Drake explored. Studying the results of history, the marks and scars it had left everywhere, the historical process became alive to me.

I have been in Rome, in Greece, in most European countries, and have had a glimpse of the Orient. From all my travels I brought home strong impressions, but this journey across the American continent was the most stirring experience

I had ever had. Never before had I felt so clearly that I was
envisaging history in the making.

The science of medicine knows no political boundaries. Its
discoveries fly like sparks from land to land and over the ocean
itself. But the conditions for creative development, that great
sum of material and imponderable factors which bring the seed
to flower, are seldom found simultaneously in one country.
Padua brought forth Vesalius: witnessed the beginnings of
clinical instruction; gave the decisive stimulus to Harvey; and
finally became the working-place of Morgagni. After 1700,
Leyden, with its Hermann Boerhaave, was the post-graduate
school of European medicine. Scotland and England followed.
The center of gravity continued to shift: to Paris, to Vienna,
finally, about the middle of the last century, to Germany. Almost all the important European countries have in their time
been the leading voice in the concert of medicine. Whose turn
will it be next? To the historian it must seem that it will be
America's.

With this impression I went back to Leipzig. But there was
something else I carried with me. On my way to the West, in
Minneapolis, on a cold December morning, Dr. Welch had
knocked on my door, had come to ask me to join the Johns
Hopkins Medical School, to succeed him in the chair of the
History of Medicine, and to take charge of the new Institute
of the History of Medicine. I was entirely unprepared for such
an offer, and being on leave of absence from the University
of Leipzig, I could not decide while still away.

I was aware of what I would have to give up: Karl Sudhoff's
chair, the best-equipped Institute of Medical History in Europe,
a group of students to whom I was profoundly attached. I
would have to adopt another language, which to a writer is a
serious matter. Once before I had shifted from one language
to another, from French to German, so that I knew what it
meant.

On the other hand, I saw great possibilities for the development of my subject in America. Wherever I had been I had found a keen interest in the History of Medicine. I had further found great social problems in American medicine that had to be approached historically. Medical history in most countries was a purely antiquarian subject. My approach was somewhat different. Although I went through a strict philological school, and although I am still doing a good deal of philological work, I was always primarily interested in all the general problems of modern medicine; investigating the past in order to get to a clearer understanding of our own time, and to help in preparing the future; studying history in order to make unconscious trends conscious, so that we can face and discuss them openly. I felt that an Institute founded by Dr. Welch, backed by his authority, could not but be a vital Institute, an ideal place for such studies.

Personal considerations helped my decision—my attachment to Dr. Welch, the strong appeal the country had made to me, its dynamic vitality, its courage, its optimism in spite of depression, and last but not least, the fact that here one is constantly looking into the future, preparing for it rationally, while Europe is becoming more and more reactionary and mystical, losing that freedom of thought without which there can be no scientific research.

In April, 1932, I accepted the offer of the Hopkins, and was back in America a few months later.

Before I left Europe, however, and, as a matter of fact, the first day I landed in Europe from my American trip, I began writing this book. It was a bold undertaking, but I couldn't help it—I had to write this book. I was so overflowingly full of what I had experienced that I had to share my impressions, to trace a picture of American medicine, as it had become alive for me. An artist, after a great experience, a deep emotion, will be urged to put into tangible form what he has felt. In the same way, the historian who has felt the pulse of history will be bound to recreate the process he has witnessed. Ten years later I would undoubtedly have known much more about American medicine. But then, ten years later, I would be a part of American medicine myself, and it would be extremely difficult then to look at it detachedly, from the outside.

I began this book in Europe, continued and finished it in America in the winter of 1932–1933. It was the result of more than four years of intensive studies of which my journey across the continent was the final although decisive part.

When the question of an American edition arose I felt rather embarrassed. I knew what the book would mean to the European reader—an introduction into a world of which he has heard, but of which he can form only a vague idea; a world however to which he must pay more and more attention. But how would the American reader receive the book? I had endeavored to trace the development of American medicine in its setting—a setting obviously familiar to Americans.

And yet, with the exception of a few minor corrections, I have not changed the text. It could not be done without destroying the whole structure of the book. A book, after all, is an organic whole, built like a house, stone upon stone. You cannot remove a floor from a building without destroying the style—and the same is true of a book.

I therefore beg the American reader to accept this book for what it is, not as a textbook nor as a reference book, but as a picture of American medicine traced in its development and seen in its setting by a European physician who came unprejudiced, eager to learn and with a sympathetic understanding.

I could not translate the book myself as I was busily engaged in other studies. I am much indebted to Miss Hildegard Nagel for her excellent version, which renders the spirit and style of the book splendidly. I have read the manuscript and the proofs, and can readily assume full responsibility for the book. I also wish to thank Miss Helen C. Brooke, who read the manuscript as well as the proofs, and helped me before in preparing the original edition, for her valuable assistance.

Today as I write these lines, I no longer feel a stranger in America. The work of the Institute of the History of Medicine has developed in a very gratifying way, and the moral support it has gained all over the country has been extremely encouraging. For five years Dr. Welch was the guiding spirit of the place. He has left us today. Although physically absent, he is still with us, and will continue to guide and inspire our work as long as there is a Johns Hopkins Medical School, or any of the many institutions he founded, as long as there is—an American Medicine.

HENRY E. SIGERIST

The Johns Hopkins University
May, 1934

CHAPTER ONE

☆ ☆

THE SOIL

This country is immense; its size is prodigious. Two oceans wash its opposite shores; it reaches on the north as far as the polar ice-fields and on the south narrows to the edge of the Mexican plateau. It is drawn in a few broad definite strokes. A narrow mountain-range in the east, a wider range in the west, cross it from north to south. Lakes as large as salt seas divide their waters into a thousand smaller basins. Great rivers flow lazily through endless plains towards the Atlantic or rush head-long through rocky cañons down to the Pacific. In between lie the plains, once primeval forest as far as the eye could see; even today almost unbroken prairie or desert.

Immense, too, are the differences in climate. On the east coast a short spring, a sudden intense outburst of nature, fol-lowed by a long summer which persists far into the winter months. There is nothing more beautiful than a New England autumn, as the trees change color ever so slowly and for weeks hang on to their bright panoply of leaves. In California the climate is equable with slight changes in temperature, with much sunshine and light haze in the summer. The air in the mountain-plains of Arizona, New Mexico, and Colorado is sharp and tonic like Alpine air, and the wind can sting like a whip-lash. In the north the winters are long, with ice and snow; and the animals are fur-bearing. In the south there is tropical heat, with palms and a scorching sun and a deep-blue ocean.

Equally enormous are the climatic variations within many single localities. Red-hot summers alternate with ice-cold win-ters. It is possible to feel on some forenoon in November that summer is not yet over, and by evening to have the temperature fall to the freezing point. Storms of unheard-of velocity sweep over the great plains, leaving ruin and desolation in their wake. Almost everywhere a climate which never allows people to settle down, but forces them to be on their guard, ready to adapt themselves or to find new means of defense. A climate so capricious that each year in turn one feels that it was never like this before.

At the beginning of the sixteenth century this great continent was inhabited by a handful of men. From the northern boundary of Mexico to the ice-zone there were not more than a million, within the present territory of the United States not more than half a million, Indians, with sharply-cut features and skin ranging from pale yellow to deep copper.

Their origin is not certain, but it seems probable that they migrated from the north to the south, and that their home was once in Asia. They were divided into tribes scattered over the country—nomads in the north, who had their hunting-grounds and lived by the chase; but in the south, in Utah, Colorado, Arizona, and New Mexico, the tribes had made the great step from consumption to production. They had become domiciled. They lived in caves which they hollowed several stories high out of the soft volcanic tuff of the cliff. Houses grew up at their base, round like bee-hives, standing in the shelter of lonely valleys. The land was irrigated for cultivation and cattle-breeding. Long before the Spaniards came, the cliff-dwellings had been abandoned and more livable villages or pueblos had taken their place, with adobe huts built close together, again several stories high.

The northern Indians loved fighting. Unending feuds were waged between the tribes. If sustenance grew scarce at home, the neighbor's quarry would beckon. In their bright feather head-dresses, and terrifying war-paint, wrought to the peak of ecstasy by dancing to their beating drums, the warriors would fall on each other in mutual annihilation. In the south, on the other hand, where there were cornfields to take care of, the disposition of the people had become more peaceful. Women wove glowing textiles and painted their clay vessels with symbolic patterns, while the men carved utensils out of stone.

Old traditions, myths told in songs and dances, gave the story of the beginning of the world in which they had their being, recounted the events of a dim past which had determined the present appearance of this world. It was a world full of dangers. Danger threatened from fellow-men, from surrounding nature, and from the realm of spirits. Every object and every living thing had a soul. A tree might be cut down and burned or made into a canoe; a stone might be hewn into the shape of a tool. But both were bearers of a wonderful power—the Algonquins called it manitou—which had sometimes a kindly but often a baleful influence. Was it not likely that an animal slain for food would claim its revenge? And the spirits of the dead, hovering restlessly around the dwelling-places of the living, might now and then bring help, but more often threatened danger.

To propitiate this mysterious power, ward off its dangers, and get it under control, became the problem of a formal science. It was based on scrupulous obedience to certain prescribed laws or taboos, either prohibitions or commands. Every tribe knew that certain animals or parts of animals could not be eaten because they were sacred or accursed, bearers of manitou and therefore taboo. Certain occupations must be left undone at certain times and certain things must never be mentioned, being taboo.

By all possible means the Indians tried to participate in this magic force. When a boy grew to be a youth, he underwent severe castigations. Through fasting, ablutions, and purgations he purified his body to make it fit to receive the power of manitou. Those who came through the ordeal led fortunate lives. Their arrows missed neither animal nor enemy, and they escaped bad dreams and sickness.

By sacrifices and prayers, to which magic words gave the potency of conjurations, they sought to win manitou to their side, to hold it fast as a fetish in some object which would continue to radiate its power.

In every tribe there were particularly favored men who had unusual magic gifts. These were chosen people, who had known their vocation in their mother's womb or had learned it in a dream. On them were bestowed powerful runes and songs and the mightiest fetishes. They were honored and feared; for whoever disposed of such powers might easily use them for evil purposes. They formed their own guild within the tribe. We call them *medicine-men*, not because of their therapeutic function, but because the Indians gave their mysterious gift the name of *medicine*, when speaking to Europeans. The Siberian tribes called them *shamans*. All primitive peoples have these complex personalities: doctor, magician, and priest in one. (Fig. 2)

Men lived in constant dread of evil, of bad dreams which poisoned the day, of sickness and death. What should make a man sick? Something foreign in his system, which did not belong there. It could be seen only too often how sickness was caused by a thorn in the flesh, or a wound from an arrow. But there were other sicknesses that came swift as a shot, without any missile being seen. There must have been one, all the same, driven in by magic means; a ball of stone or hair, a splinter of bone or wood, a straw or almost anything. Or the foreign element might be an evil spirit, a demon or the ghost of a dead man, as the Dakotas and many other tribes believed.

In other cases the cause of sickness was not a too-much, but a too-little. The soul had been drawn by some inimical influence from the body, which was now ill and wasting away. Or the gall had emptied itself into the wrong place, as the Chippewas believed, and was now causing that part of the body to burn with pain.

2. MEDICINE MAN OF THE BLACKFOOT INDIANS

After a sketch by George Catlin (between 1832 and 1839)

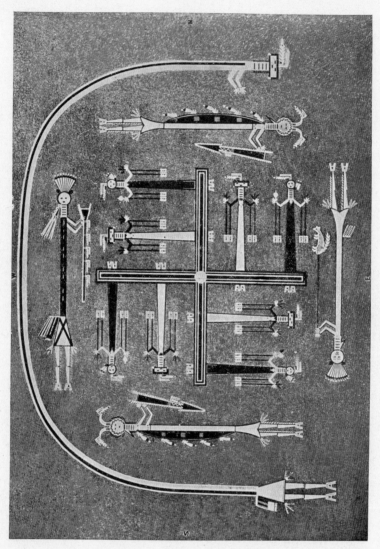

3. MAGIC SAND PAINTING OF THE NAVAJO INDIANS

In the Smithsonian Institution, Bureau of American Ethnology

And again a sickness would be regarded as the just punishment for a sin, perhaps the breaking of a taboo.

When a person fell ill, a medicine-man was sent for, and his first task was to make sure of the nature of the sickness the case presented. He asked about the dreams of his patient, about his enemies, if anything had happened recently, and if he were conscious of any sin. If this questioning led to no conclusion, more drastic methods were resorted to. The spirits were summoned. They had to investigate the sickness and give their testimony. Among the Sioux it was the custom to erect a hut of posts and hides. The medicine-man was laid down inside and sacrificial offerings were brought. Drums and rattles were sounded. A humming announced the approach of the spirits who, if favorably inclined, vouchsafed their diagnosis.

As soon as the nature of a disease was known, one could begin the treatment, which was determined strictly by the cause of the disease. Any foreign substance must be removed. The medicine-man came up with drum and rattle, with his medicine-bag containing the fetishes, sometimes with a mask on his face representing the guardian spirit which had entered into him and lent him its power. Murmuring prayers, he drew near to the patient and began to rub the painful spot, to knead and to suck it. He rubbed and kneaded and sucked for a long time, hours on end, at intervals repeating the words of the conjuration, which went like this among the Klamaths in Oregon:

> What do I remove out of my mouth?
> I draw the sickness out of my mouth.
> What is the thing which I take out?
> It is the sickness which I take out.

He rubbed and sucked and kneaded, over and over again, hour after hour. And all at once the thing was done. Jumping up, he spat out an object—it might be a stone, a ball of hair, a frog, a snake. The cure had succeeded, the strange thing was gotten rid of, and the sick man was released.

If it was a spirit which had taken possession of the patient, the ghost of an animal or a demon, a more complicated treatment was demanded. If it was an animal—a frog, for instance—an image of this animal was fashioned, as beautiful and alluring as possible; the body of wheat-meal, the eyes of charcoal, a red coral for its heart, and a string of turquoises for its windpipe. This was the Navajo method. The spirit left the sick man and took up its habitation in the image.

Or an effort would be made to make the demon's sojourn in the sick man untenable. He was frightened off with loud music and screaming. He was smoked out with burning wood, for which the Chippewas used sharp-needled cypress trees. The sick body was whipped so that the spirit might leave it for more comfortable quarters. And where men could not succeed by their own strength and guile, spirit must be cast out by spirit; good spirits were invoked to fight the evil ones, while the medicine-man directed the battle.

However, if the sickness had its origin in the loss of the soul, then it was the business of the medicine-man to bring it back. Where had it gone, if not to the land of spirits? There the shaman must look for it. The patient was put to sleep. The medicine-man summoned his guardian-spirit and sent him in pursuit of the lost soul. He searched for it, found it, and returned it to the patient, who was aroused with a cry and awoke recovered. The Twanas would wait till night for the hour of the spirits. The surface of the ground was stirred up and the medicine-man began to dance. As he danced, his movements grew wild. But only his body danced on earth; his soul was far off fighting the enemy spirits. He was contending for the stolen, captive soul. His gestures grew in violence. Excitement seized the onlookers. Loud cries arose which grew to a triumphant roar as the liberation was accomplished and the soul returned to the forsaken body and the sick man became well. Some tribes, like the Haidas, used special instruments, tastefully ornamented double-pronged forks made of bone, to catch the elusive soul.

If the patient had transgressed, then it was necessary to appease the angry deity. An interesting ceremony, still to be seen among the Navajos, had this object in view. Clean sand was spread on the ground and smoothed flat, whereupon the medicine-man covered it with a large allegorical painting, using pulverized colors prescribed by ritual. Attracted by the magic power of the painted symbols, the spirit would draw near. He inspected the picture, and if he found it in any way not right he would turn away unappeased. In that case, things would go badly with the sick man. But if the picture were as it should be, the spirit would give the spell a chance to work. He tarried and exposed himself to the charms of the magic songs. Graciously inclined, he forgave the sinner, whose sickness now attached itself to the painting. With a brush of eagle-feathers the medicine-man set himself to sweep away the picture, at the same time stroking the patient's body. As the picture was effaced, the sickness lifted. The sand was then carried to the east and scattered in a northerly direction. (Fig. 3)

Many tribes had several categories of medicine-men, whose functions had become partly specialized. Among the Hupas in California there were the dancing medicine-men, whose responsibility it was to determine the cause of an illness and to prescribe the right course of treatment. This was carried out by other medicine-men, who massaged the patient and sucked the disease out of him. Similarly, the Maidus, also in California, distinguished between the *dreamer* and the *healer*. The dreamer was a shaman in particularly close touch with the super-sensual world, having intimate association with spirits. On winter nights, these dreamers would assemble in their smoky huts and hold converse with the spirits who appeared in their midst. They could interpret the causes of disease. The second group were more than dreamers; they had the power to drive evil away. The office of shaman was hereditary among the Maidus. When a family was granted this terrible gift, all its children had to accept their destiny. Had any one of them tried to evade the intention of the spirits, he would have been annihilated by them.

As a rule there was one prerequisite to success; payment must be made in advance. The spirits would not answer if their gifts seemed insufficient. Unfortunate consequences might follow unsuccessful treatment. Indeed, when a shaman had bad luck and lost several patients in succession this was either malice aforethought, or he had forfeited his power. He was persecuted and often put to death. In some other tribes payment was not exacted until after treatment. The size of the gift varied with the result and the patient's rank, and might at times be quite considerable.

The art of healing among the Indian tribes is at the primitive stage of medicine. The ideas underlying it are found in all primitive peoples, though the forms of expression differ. Here, as in all parts of the world, we often find, along with the magical-religious elements, considerable practical knowledge and skill. As a rule the shamans are needed for only the most serious illnesses. The many little disorders of daily life—colds, indigestion, minor injuries—are treated with household remedies. They can be handled by the patient himself, his relatives, and also by members of the tribe who have special knowledge in these matters. At this stage of civilization it is the women who are acquainted with healing herbs. They, too, cultivate the fields and prepare the fruit of the harvest. They have besides a more soothing hand for the binding of wounds and the stilling of pain. In every tribe, we find these wise women. Though there have been now and then female shamans, for the most part the rôle of women in primitive medicine is found close to earth rather than in the realm of the supernatural.

The number of plants used for healing varied from tribe to

tribe. Some knew very few, others several dozen. They understood how they should be taken—usually as a drink—and how
to dry and preserve them. They were kept in the medicine bags
next to the fetishes. Drugs were specified as cathartics and emet-
ics. The beneficial effect of clearing out the system was well
known. They tried to accomplish this by other means as well;
by enemas, drinking salt water, and tickling the pharynx with
a feather.

Not only the intestines but the blood as well had to be kept
free from corruption; by means of cuppings, scarifications, and
venesections, for which special instruments such as a flint knife
with a wooden handle were often used. Attacks of rheumatism
were not rare and were combated by heat, by burning, by com-
presses, or the application of counter-irritants. The sweat-bath
is an ancient cultural heritage. It has been used extensively by
the Indians. The sick man was placed inside a low hut, usually
in a hammock, and water was poured over red-hot stones, causing a dense cloud of steam. Hot springs were also made use of.

It was easy to understand the uncomfortable effects of over-
eating. No medicine-man was required for explanation or advice.
One treated oneself, by fasting or keeping to a strict diet.

Surgical intervention was common. Wars and wounds provided plenty of opportunity. Foreign bodies such as arrow-heads
were removed. Flowing blood was stanched either by stuffing
the wound with eagle-down or by stanching powders which were
held pressed to the wound by a bandage. The wounds were
sometimes rinsed to stimulate healing or they were filled with
bark so that the pus would drain faster, or balsam was applied
to further granulation.

Bone-surgery was also rather highly developed in some tribes,
above all the Winnebagos in Wisconsin. One day a man falls
down a cliff and breaks his leg. He crawls back to his tent and
lies down by the fire. Weeks pass and the pain goes away, and
he can stand on his leg again; but it is shorter than the other,

he is a cripple. Some resourceful man must finally have conceived the idea of stretching a newly-broken leg. He gave it a tug, but the contraction of the muscles pulled it back again. Obviously the leg had somehow to be held in place. A lath, a piece of bark, anything that lay handy, was put next to the broken leg and bound tightly to it. Now the leg healed without getting shorter; the man could still work and fight. A great discovery had been made. It took place spontaneously in the most widely separated parts of the world, as like problems led to like solutions.

Trepanning, not infrequent among Peruvian and Mexican Indians, does not seem to have been practised north of Mexico; at least no trepanned skulls have so far been found. On the other hand, we read in the accounts of travellers of occasional laparotomies and even one Cæsarian operation.

As with all primitive people, confinements were in general easy. Certain rituals were followed. When her hour drew near, the woman went apart by herself or accompanied by other women to a stream in the forest, and came back with her child, purified. Many tribes, such as the Comanches, erected special confinement huts outside the encampment, to which the women retired. Taking the most varied positions, kneeling, sitting, crouching, or lying down, leaning against a post or another woman, they brought their children into the world. If the birth was slow, it was assisted by pressure or by massage. A Sioux woman, as soon as the navel cord was cut, put on a girdle which she drew in tight about her to hasten the afterbirth. Among other tribes, this was accomplished by a light pull on the navel cord. It is clear that women assisted each other, as they have everywhere else, and also that in every village there were individual older women who were believed to be especially experienced and adept.

At this stage of culture, obstetrics has nothing to do with medicine. Pregnancy, birth, and childbed are natural events.

They are the business of the family and relatives, and the help of the medicine-man is needed only in exceptional cases.

All the methods of treatment described in the last pages seem to us entirely rational. They may be from our point of view, but are only partly so to the Indian. The primitive man sees the world in a mystic light and all his cultural expressions conform to this general conception. A drug is dispensed, it is true, because experience has proved its beneficial action. But the source of its healing power is not considered to lie in any part of the plant itself, but in the blessing which is spoken over it. Here, as in all primitive medicine, empirical and magical religious elements are inextricably interwoven.

This is particularly evident in the case of tribal medicines, the preparation of which is essentially a religious rite. Such was a wound-panacea formerly made by the Iroquois; and so the Hopis still solemnly prepare an antidote or counter-poison to snake-bite, in preparation against their snake-dance, a ceremony of prayer for rain, held every two years in August. The dancers carry poisonous snakes in their mouths, and are frequently bitten. They fall sick but, thanks to the antidote, never die of the poison.

The medicine-man and the herb-doctor have been described. Many tribes have still a third kind of healer, whose origin is very interesting. Through the fact that a man had once been seriously ill, he entered a definite magical religious circle. He had been in close touch with the spirit world. He had been the subject of magical religious treatment. Was it not natural to expect that such a man, having survived the attack of spirits, would have won a certain power over them? Among the Zuñis there arose in this way associations of people who had recovered from an illness. They were still a long way from being medicine-men, but they had been through a certain initiation. They were considered to have special knowledge and were permitted to assist the medicine-men.

Of course, one tried to shield oneself against sickness as well as against all other misfortunes. The wrath of the spirits could be turned aside by a pure life and a scrupulous observance of taboos. Bad omens served as warnings that were never disregarded. If anyone had a bad dream or a relative dreamed evil things about him, a medicine-man was called, who tried by ceremonies to dispel the ill effect of the dream. For to the primitive man a dream has not only a prophetic but a causal importance. It does more than indicate a threatening misfortune; it brings it to pass. So much more necessary it is, then, to understand the omens, in order that their influence may be dispelled in time.

The evil spirits, who never ceased to lurk in ambush, and to whom one was especially exposed in situations where attention is necessarily relaxed, in sleep, at the toilet, during pregnancy, labor and childbed, were kept at a distance by magic amulets whose protective power was equally potent against human enemies. It was known that dangers sometimes emanated from a sick human being. He was shunned, driven into isolation, and his dwelling surrounded with vividly colored stakes, whose meaning was clear to all.

We naturally do not know what diseases most frequently afflicted the Indians in those far-off days. The bones which have been found, and many other signs point, on the whole, to a very healthy race of men. Many diseases had not yet appeared which in the old world have played havoc since ancient times. A healthy people, but emotional, psychically unstable, as is to be expected in this climate, and suggestible like all primitive races.

Years went by and became centuries. Men were born and died. Spring came and the tribes went hunting. Winter returned and they crawled into their tents. Fields were sown and the crop was harvested. Wars broke out and the peace-pipes smoked again. Life flowed on in one great, elemental, natural rhythm, for centuries on end.

Then one morning, on the 12th of October, 1492, the in-habitants of the little island of Guanahani beheld a miracle. Three ships came over the horizon's rim, and as they drew nearer, looked quite gigantic. Strange men with pale faces climbed out of them, fell on their knees and lifted their hands to heaven. One of them, with a shining sword in his hand, seemed to be their chief. A bright cloth fastened to a pole flut-tered in the wind. Christopher Columbus thought himself in India. Europe had discovered a new world.

Suddenly the fate of a continent was reversed. The old rhythm was abruptly broken. After a long overture, the curtain rises and the play begins.

CHAPTER TWO

COLONIAL TIMES

SLOWLY at first, but with ever-increasing swiftness, the action unfolds itself. The scene expands. Columbus goes and returns; hundreds, then thousands, follow in his wake. They find gold. Little enough, only what these savages wear in their noses. But they say that there is a great deal of the yellow metal to be found farther south. The white men search for it in island after island. They find a certain amount, but it does not suffice them. They pursue the trail and finally discover the mainland. Columbus himself lands on the continent which he still believes to be Asia. Then one day in the year 1513 Balboa stands on a peak and looks over the Pacific. A Florentine, Amerigo Vespucci, has in the meanwhile landed in Brazil, and an honest German cosmographer, Waldseemüller, who has never poked his head out from behind his own chimney corner, names the new world after him: America.

On the mainland, gold was found in unexpected quantities. In 1519, Hernando Cortez ran onto the Mexican coast with 600 men, burned his ships behind him, marched inland, and after two years of adventurous fighting conquered the Aztec Empire. The capital, with its incalculable treasures, fell into his hands. Here, not in the islands, were the sources of gold.

The march of conquest continues farther south, into Honduras, Nicaragua, Guatemala. In 1513 another great empire fell into Spanish hands, when Pizarro conquered the Incas of Peru.

The sun never set on the realm of Charles V. Terrible wars were waged to extend its boundaries. Any methods, even lies and treachery, were deemed justifiable. The natives were slaughtered or dragged away into bondage. But we must not forget that these conquerors as a rule were a mere handful of men, thousands of miles from home, in a country where nature itself was strange, in the midst of a hostile people with mysterious and disturbing customs. They knew that captives had their still-quivering hearts cut out from their living bodies. They had no choice; theirs was victory at any price or a painful death.

They won the victory. The great empire of New Spain was established and pacified. The banner of Castile was raised over vast territories that stretched from ocean to ocean. Then houses had to be built, fields plowed, and mines worked for gold. And, most important of all, the heathen had to be snatched from damnation and led into the arms of the only redeeming church. There were few white women in the new country, so the Spanish colonists married the daughters of natives. Was not this the most effective method of converting them to civilization and the true faith? A new race of mixed blood gradually evolved. The colonization was so thorough that the day was to come when the colonists should feel themselves a nation and break loose from their mother country.

Only fifteen years after the conquest of Mexico City, a school for *Indios* was established there, where Latin grammar, rhetoric, philosophy, music, and Mexican medicine were taught. Just imagine Aristotle and Cicero, where fifteen years before human sacrifices had been offered. After another fifteen years, on a petition of the inhabitants, the king granted them the privilege of erecting a university. It was solemnly inaugurated in 1553 as the *Daughter of Salamanca*, incorporated with the identical statutes as its venerable mother university. Still more remarkable, every chair could be filled with men from the colony. Spaniards and native-born were put on the same footing. In 1580 the first chair of medicine was established; the first medical book, the *Opera medicinalia* of Francisco Bravo, was published as early as 1570. Events moved still faster in Peru.

In 1551, eighteen years after the conquest, the capital already had its university. And there the degree of doctor of medicine was conferred for the first time on American soil.

The thirst for gold was not quenched. The coveted metal had been found in Central and South America. But to the north there lay a boundless and as yet unexplored continent. Why was this to prove poorer than the rest of the marvelous hemisphere? Conquistadors shot up over night. Why stay in restricted circumstances at home, when fortune beckoned with wealth and power across the sea? Whoever could scrape up the funds to fit out an expedition, would sail off into uncharted space, with the king's mandate in his pocket, to take possession of his share of the conquered territory.

As early as 1513 one of Columbus' companions, Ponce de Leon, had sailed north, discovered what he thought was an island, and, because of its luxuriant vegetation, christened it La Florida. He returned to Spain and came back in 1521 to look farther inland for gold, but the natives fell on his little band and Ponce himself was killed by an arrow.

Two years earlier Pineda, a Spanish pilot, had discovered the mouth of the Mississippi and had sailed westward along the coast of Texas. He was looking for the passage to India. He went on and on but found unbroken solid land; the coast line bent to the south, then to the east, till finally he reached Yucatan.

So it appeared that the passage must lie farther north and could be reached only by sailing northward. This route was the more tempting because captured Indios told wonderful tales of the northland, which they called Chicora and described as a region inhabited by giants and dwarfs, where there was gold in plenty. After various exploratory excursions which extended as far as the Chesapeake Bay, a great expeditionary force was got ready, equipped with everything necessary for the founding of a colony. With high hopes, Ayllon in 1526 set sail for the north. But he was not granted Cortez' success. The landing was made at a river's mouth in what is now the state of South Carolina. It was a cold winter; provisions gave out; many fell sick and the leader was among those who did not recover. Only a handful of broken men made the journey home.

In spite of these misfortunes, there was no lack of recruits to make a new trial; and there were always monks, Dominicans and Franciscans, burning with missionary zeal and eager to accompany the soldiers and colonists. Two years after the failure of Ayllon, in 1528, another imposing expedition, fitted out and commanded by Panfilo de Narvaez, disembarked on the west coast of Florida and went on by land. It was again the northern wonderland which lured them. And again hunger and sickness compelled the adventurers to turn back. They made their way to the coast but the fleet was no longer there. In canoes which they had put together themselves they set out for Mexico. But a storm arose and swamped their boats, and their leader was drowned. One of his officers, Cabeza de Vaca, managed to reach land with a few companions, where there awaited them a fabulous fate. The Indians received the shipwrecked men, who had escaped with their bare lives, in a friendly spirit, and offered them the best they had. Then suddenly an epidemic broke out among the natives. Whose fault could it be, if not the white man's? These pale people, who came out of the sunrise from over the sea, had peculiar powers. Thunder and lightning had been given into their hands. Faster than devils they rode on strange unknown beasts. However, he who sends sickness, can also take it away. So fate turned Cabeza de Vaca into a medicine-man *without examination and without any one inquiring about diplomas* as he puts it himself. What else could he do but play the rôle assigned him? He gave a clever performance, imitating the gestures of his dark colleagues, blessing the sick and blowing on them. Why not? He had powerful enough spells in the *Pater Noster* and the *Ave Maria*. He implored help of God the Almighty and made the sign of the cross over the patient. And he met with success. His life was granted him; he was fed when there was food to be had. But it was a miserable existence that he led for six long years for, after all, he was only a slave. He fled westward in what he thought was the direction of Mexico, on a long devious journey, through many changes of fortune—sometimes a starving prisoner treated as a slave, sometimes honored as a medicine-man with the whole tribe escorting him in ceremonial array. He crossed the Colorado and the Rio Grande and continued west almost to the Gulf of California; then turned south and reached Mexico eight years after the outset of his expedition. He returned to Spain and from there was sent as governor to South America. Few understood Indians as he did. He knew their good side. Indeed, his treatment of them was so humane that it aroused the enmity of his own countrymen. Like Columbus and many others after him, he was sent back in chains to Spain, dismissed from his offices, and banished to Africa. And the theologians argued without end as to whether a layman could perform miracles.

The south had produced its fruits. Peru had been conquered. It was unthinkable that the boundless northern continent should not hold its own share of treasure. In 1539 one of Pizarro's captains, Hernando de Soto, sets off with an armed force more impressive than any before. Again using Florida as the point of departure, they make their way inland, north and west, year after year. They cross the Mississippi at the point where Memphis now stands. Again misfortune assails the company; again hunger and disease instead of the looked-for gold. Again the leader is snatched away. De Soto dies, and is buried secretly by night, so that the Indians will not learn that the children of the sun are mortal. The fate of the expedition is sealed. And it is now certain that no gold exists in the eastern part of the northern continent.

But in the west, perhaps. One expedition after another sets off in that direction. While De Soto is exploring the Mississippi, Coronado is traversing the region of what is now Arizona and New Mexico, as far north as Kansas. He, too, is looking for a wonderland, the seven cities of Cibola, which, according to native descriptions, promise a second Mexico. He finds these cities, but they turn out to be miserable villages of clay, and there is no trace of the gold, jewels, fine garments, or any of the splendors of which he had dreamed. Another kind of marvel is discovered. One of Coronado's captains, Cardenas, finds the Grand Cañon of Arizona. But there were as yet no eyes to appreciate this miracle.

Still farther in the west, other explorers sailed northward along the coast of California. First Cabrillo, a Portuguese sealion, who lost his life on the voyage; then Vizcaino who in 1602 —so much time had gone by—discovered the lovely harbor of Monterey. But no gold had—so far—been found on these voyages.

Wealth and power, or destitution and ruin; such were the alternate destinies of the conquerors. Those who turned north had drawn the poorer lot. After a century of indescribably arduous voyages of exploration, abounding in losses and disappointments, the fact was incontestably established that there were no riches to be gleaned from the northern continent. The inhabitants were poor and the soil seemed equally so. In spite of this the north was systematically colonized. For one thing, it held people not yet converted to the blessed faith. Missionaries became pioneers. Everywhere, scattered over the whole country, the missions raised their protecting walls. The peal of bells rose to Heaven and called believers to prayer. The Indians in these districts were an agricultural people. They asked nothing better than to till their fields in peace. From the missionaries they learned many arts, from brick-making to music. They accepted the new faith, without surrendering the old one, it is true. A peculiar kind of amalgamation was consummated between the two religions and persists to this day. The Indians in the south of the United States are still Roman Catholics; but now, as of old, the medicine-man, himself a Catholic, calls on the ancient spirits.

There was another and very cogent reason for this colonization. The northern boundary of New Spain needed protection. The country had thrived. By 1574 there were already 200 Spanish settlements in the New World. The Indians had very soon dropped their opposition, and, by an adroit colonization policy, the process of assimilation was already far advanced. A stream of gold poured into the mother country. It is not surprising that other European powers turned envious eyes on New Spain. Many of them had by this time firmly established themselves in North America and were pushing south. It was urgently necessary to bar the door. Already the Spaniards had more than once come into unwelcome contact with these troublesome competitors.

In the year 1560 it was learned that a Frenchman, a certain Jean Ribaud, had founded a colony which he named Port Royal, and which lay within the boundaries of what is now South Carolina, which is on ground claimed by the Spaniards. The first colony came to nothing, but, only a few years later, more Frenchmen arrived, led by René de Laudonnière. This time they pushed still further south down to the mouth of St. John's River in Florida. This was going too far. It meant a constant threat to the Bahama route, along which the gold ships had to pass on their way to Spain. To make things worse these French were Huguenot heretics and their leaders creatures of the hated Admiral Coligny. It was only a year after the founding of Fort Caroline that Menendez, a competent seaman, landed close to the colony, at the place later to be called St. Augustine. He succeeded in taking the French by surprise, and a horrible massacre took place. Many were slain in their beds; others, who had surrendered under false promises, were slaughtered brutally to the last man. The colony was wiped out; however, many contemporaries praised Menendez for not burning the heretics to death as they deserved.

Revenge came quickly. It is true that the French government was not at the moment in a position to undertake any action against Spain; but a private gentleman, Dominique de Gourgues, who had learned to know the Spaniards as a prisoner of war, took the law into his own hands. He crossed the ocean with a band of resolute men, allied himself with the Indians, fell on the new Spanish colony, and paid back blood for blood.

As so often happened in the days to come, the Indians were not only shown the disgraceful spectacle of white men murdering each other in mutual hate, but were themselves asked to assist in the struggle.

The French had set foot in the new world as early as 1524, when a ship commanded by Verrazzano, an Italian sailor in French employ, entered the Hudson River. Ten years later a Breton seaman, Jacques Cartier, sailed up the St. Lawrence, and took possession of the country in the name of his king. Others followed. In 1608 a fort was erected at Quebec. They pushed westward as far as the Great Lakes; and during the course of the seventeenth century made their way southward down the Mississippi to its mouth, where Louisiana, the colony named after Louis XIV, still bears the impress of France.

The French, too, were looking for gold; and found, not the yellow metal itself, but costly furs which were readily exchanged for gold in the French markets. They trapped furbearing animals in the wilderness and on the lakes, and caught fish on the banks of Newfoundland. In the wake of the trappers came Jesuit missionaries, and exploring scientists, geographers, and botanists.

1588 was for Spain a year of misfortune. The war with England, which had been smouldering for some time, finally broke out. Philip II mobilized his fleet. It was ordered to proceed to the Netherlands for an attack on England. But its fate overtook it on its way through the English Channel. It was forced to accept the combat offered by the much more mobile English fleet. The battle lasted many days and ended with a Spanish defeat. A great storm finished what had been begun by English cannons. The proud fleet of Spain, the invincible armada, was annihilated, and with it Spanish preëminence at sea. It was clear to all the world that Spain had more than met its match in England. A new chapter of world history opens with the beginning of England's sea-power and her expansion into every corner of the globe. Elizabeth had been reigning thirty years. During this time her fleet had been very quietly built up; and now it had stood the test of fire.

These events must of necessity have their repercussions in the new world. Spain's rise as a world-power had passed its peak. It could do no more than attempt to hold on to what had already been won, and to expand in directions where England's interests were not involved, as for instance the coast of California.

England, on the contrary, now had a free field. From now on she is the deciding power in the history of the North American continent. For a hundred years English ships had sailed round the coasts of the new world without anywhere establishing a base. Giovanni Caboto—the English called him John Cabot—had sailed an English ship along the north coast in 1597, only a few years after the discovery of America. Others followed, reckless old sea-lions, free-booters, and adventurers, like Francis Drake who followed the west coast and sailed around the world, and John Hawkins who plied a lively slave-trade. They were looking for adventure and gold, and where could either be found more readily than on Spanish galleons steering home laden with riches? Spain was the Papist, the hereditary foe, to

molest whom was a meritorious deed. So they plundered ships
or pillaged the coast, whenever a chance offered. What was
more, these were enterprises entirely fit for gentlefolk. Drake
and Hawkins were knighted in appreciation of their exploits
and the court showed no compunction in giving financial support to these piratical raids.

However, a gradual interest was aroused in the establishment of a firmer footing on the new continent. Walter Raleigh,
Oxford student, soldier, sea-farer, and ardent enemy of Spain,
set forth on an expedition and in 1584 two of his ships landed
on a coast which seemed fabulously beautiful. The place was
named Virginia in honor of the virgin queen. But the colony
did not fulfill its promise. After two years it was given up. In
1587 a second set of colonists made a fresh attempt. A little girl
called Virginia Dare was born, the first child of Anglo-Saxon
blood to open its eyes on American soil. Again, fortune was un-
propitious. The time was not yet ripe. A few years later no
trace of the colonists could be found.

The century came to an end. Elizabeth died and Mary
Stuart's son, James I, ascended the throne. And now, colonization began to proceed more rapidly. Events followed each
other in quick succession. In little more than half a century the
east coast of North America had been settled and colonized;
and a new and larger England had sprung up beyond the
Atlantic.

Once more it was Virginia to which the colonists first turned,
undismayed by previous misadventures. A colonial company
had been founded in London; and in 1607 three ships bearing
105 colonists landed at the mouth of a river, which was named
the James River after the king and where the settlement of
Jamestown was built. The first years were difficult. Most of the
colonists were unused to manual labor. Many were mowed down
by disease. Dreams of gold were still cherished; and gold was
not to be found. In its stead they discovered a rich soil, suited

in particular for the cultivation of two plants which were to determine the colony's history.

One of them was tobacco. The smoking habit was common to natives all over the continent, and provided a constant source of astonishment to Europeans. Tobacco was brought over to Europe very early, though at first cultivated only as a decorative garden plant, until, about the middle of the sixteenth century, the French ambassador in Lisbon, Jean Nicot, drew attention to its reputed marvelous curative properties and promoted its medicinal use. The Indian way of smoking was introduced first into England, after the founding of Virginia. It was begun by sailors. Walter Raleigh became a smoker. The custom was taken up at court and soon came to be the fashion. To be sure, James I was a bitter enemy of smoking, going so far as to debate publicly against it at Oxford and compose a polemic denouncing its use. But all in vain. And when the plague broke out in London in 1614 and it was announced that smokers were less liable to be infected, the triumphant progress of tobacco could no longer be held in check. As a result the new colony was provided with an extremely valuable article of export. Indeed, tobacco leaves now and again took the place of gold as a medium of exchange. A colonist wanting to send for an English wife had first to get together her passage-money; this could, however, be paid in tobacco. In this way a wife could be obtained for 130 to 150 pounds of tobacco.

The other plant to thrive on Virginian soil was cotton. It was first brought over in 1621. So the direction in which the colony was to develop was already determined; no large, closely-settled cities, but great plantations stretching over the country. But plantations need labor. The white settlers were few in number. The Indians, unlike their South American brothers, were of no use in agriculture. Then in 1620 a Dutch ship arrived with a cargo of Negro slaves, and provided farm-hands which could very easily adapt themselves to the climate.

Similar climatic conditions prevailed to the south of Virginia; and in the ensuing period North and South Carolina were to develop along similar lines.

Turning to the north we find that, with Virginia as base, isolated trading-posts were built on the Chesapeake Bay for the exchange of merchandise for furs which the Indians brought from the northern forests. In 1632 this whole territory was bestowed by the king as a private and hereditary grant to an English nobleman, George Calvert, Lord Baltimore. Lord Baltimore had been converted to Catholicism and, in view of the intolerance met with by dissenters all over Europe, he had in mind the founding of a colony which should provide a refuge for Christians of every creed. He died without being able to carry out his purpose, but in the very next year, 1633, his son, Cecil Calvert, embarked with 200 colonists and accomplished what his father had planned. The colony was named Maryland, after Henrietta Maria, the wife of Charles I. There was, indeed, some disagreement with Virginia, which felt its interests endangered, but the difficulties were adroitly compromised. This domain of Lord Baltimore enjoyed a singularly fortunate development, thanks in part to its situation which combines the climatic advantages of north and south. While in Virginia the clergy belonged to the Episcopal church, Maryland naturally became the stronghold of Catholicism. But the tolerance and liberalism of the first Lord Baltimore continued to prevail.

Still more important to the future development of the country was the settlement of the coasts to the north of the Hudson. Their history is unusual.

During the sixteenth century a separate movement had started within English Protestantism, whose object it was to strip the Christian church of all outward forms, in order to lead it back to its original simplicity and purity. These Puritans, who attracted attention by their austere habits of living, formed their own religious communities, with every member participating in the government. After the death of Elizabeth, they became victims of persecution. The Stuart régime in any case made their life in England more difficult. Many of their number emigrated, moving in large numbers to Holland, the traditional country of religious freedom. But they did not feel at home there, either. It is not surprising that they longed to fare farther afield, to seek virgin ground where they could live unhindered according to their convictions and worship God in what seemed to them the right way. And, of course, America was the country which could best offer them this possibility.

On December 21, 1620, the Mayflower anchored off the American shore, bringing the one hundred and two pilgrim fathers. They had come from Holland and England, looking, not for gold, but for a new home which they could build up in the wilderness to the glory of God by the work of their hands. And even before they landed they had vowed to obey whatever man they themselves should choose as leader. The first settlement was called Plymouth in remembrance of their old home. Though they had come on their own initiative and in the beginning governed themselves without interference, they still remained English subjects. The new country became an English colony. More settlers followed; and in 1628 a royal charter was given to the Massachusetts Bay Company. It was granted far-reaching autonomy, with the proviso that its laws should not conflict with the laws of England.

In the old country, the Puritans continued to be the prey of religious persecution and economic stress. Those who wanted to escape emigrated, especially to America which offered them a life that was indeed hard, but independent and with un-dreamed-of opportunities. The northern coast was colonized within a few years. New Hampshire followed Massachusetts in 1633; Connecticut one year later, after hard fighting with the Indians; and in 1636 Rhode Island, a free state where state and church were separated, founded by Roger Williams, a young preacher who had freed himself from Puritan narrowness. These four colonies in 1643 formed New England.

But the English were not the only ones to seek their fortune on the east coast. An English captain in Dutch service, Henry Hudson, had in 1609 sailed up the river which was to be given his name in a Dutch ship called the *Halve Maene*. The remunerative fur-trade attracted the Hollanders also. For the protection of their traders they erected Fort Nassau on the Hudson in 1614; and, not far from it, nine years later Fort Orange, on the site of the present city of Albany. A trading association called the West Indian Company was founded in 1621. Two years later thirty families were sent over. The island of Manhattan was bought from the Indians and in 1626 New Amsterdam was founded.

The Swedes, too, established themselves in the new world. At the mouth and along the shores of the Delaware their forts had been built and a new Sweden had arisen.

But neither the Dutch nor the Swedish colonies endured for any length of time. There was no inherent reason for their existence. They were mere experiments and received inadequate support from home. The English took possession of them as early as 1664. New Amsterdam became New York. But the original settlers remained and gradually merged with the English.

In 1630, ten years after the landing of the Mayflower, the number of colonists had already increased to 7000. Ten years later there were three times as many; and a still larger number had by this time settled on the West Indian Islands. At the close of the century, around 1700, the number had grown to 260,000. Ninety percent were farmers and planters. Boston numbered 7000 inhabitants; New York 4000; Philadelphia also 4000, though not founded until 1683. Philadelphia, the city of brotherly love, was founded by the Quakers, whose religion was more radical than that of the Puritans; they recognized no differences of rank, had no use for clergy or prayer-books, rejected baptism and communion, oaths and war, and desired only to live a pure and simple life in love and peace. Such a doctrine would naturally lead to persecution; and the Quakers turned their eyes to America as the land of freedom. In 1674 a tract of land was bought on New Jersey territory. A year later came the first emigrants, founding Salem on the Delaware River. Additional land was granted later on. William Penn, son of the Admiral who had conquered Jamaica, came over in 1682. After him, the colony was called Pennsylvania. The city of Philadelphia was laid out according to a careful plan; and both it and the whole colony grew very fast.

During those first decades the colonists, especially in New England, led a very hard life. They had come meaning to build themselves homesteads, but the arable land was rocky and unyielding and had to be wrested from the forest by unremitting toil. There was no room for idlers. Masters and servants had to set their hands to the same tasks. In labor all were equal. Their houses were log-cabins. They kept their guns standing next to their spades. For the primeval forest, whose fringes were being gradually pushed westward, was not uninhabited.

The Spaniards fought the Indians till they had made themselves masters of the country, but later became interested in winning the souls and labor-power of the natives. A symbiosis occurred. In the beginning the master was white and the worker dark, until the two races gradually merged. But to the English colonist the Indians always remained savages with whom he could have nothing in common. What mattered their soul's salvation to him? One might as well go about converting raging beasts. There was no room for English and Indian on the same soil. The weaker must yield to the stronger. And though there was now and then a truce, and history can relate idylls of the red and white people, the fate of the Indians was nevertheless sealed. In this connection we must not forget that the Indians in Spanish America belonged to a much higher level of civilization and were therefore much more easily assimilated.

Life in New England was made still more somber by religious restrictions. Week-days demanded hard work. Sunday belonged to the Lord. They had left their homes, to live according to their belief. They were no longer exposed to persecution. Stern laws were promulgated, enforcing a simple, austere life, even after economic conditions had improved and the colonists found themselves in comfortable circumstances. Only too often the once persecuted became themselves persecutors who tolerated no dissenters. That the arts could not take root in such soil is sufficiently obvious.

In the southern colonies, on the other hand, where the sun shone warmer, and the earth was more fruitful, and where labor was provided by imported Negroes, the colonists naturally developed into a master-class. Their religion being the same as that in the mother country, there was more toleration. Life was easier. Charleston in South Carolina became famous as a city of good taste and gayety.

Life at that time was made even more difficult by the severe epidemics which ravaged the colonies over and over again. With them we arrive at last at the realm of medicine which is our more immediate concern. Having briefly studied the physical aspects of the country where American medicine was to take root, and having sketched the landing of the first settlers and the colonization of part of the country, we now come to the consideration of the kind of medicine that existed during the century and a half of the colonial period.

But first: what ought we to expect? The problem was gigantic. A group of people, after a sea-voyage which is an exploit in itself, finds itself transplanted into a completely strange environment, exposed to the inclemency of a freakish climate, and only too often without any defence against the pangs of hunger. Settlements were built in haste, to provide immediate shelter; and the sanitary arrangements were most primitive. To make things worse, many of the colonists were men who had spent their lives in work-shops or stores and who had no pioneer experience. Every one of them had been abruptly dislodged from the accustomed rhythm of his life. The imminent danger of disease hardly needs to be gone into.

The medical resources amounted to almost nothing. These expeditions landing in Virginia and New England were not expensively equipped. Most of the colonists were either originally poor or had become impoverished, and were escaping from destitution at home; and the emigrating religious communities had only moderate means at their disposal. Many things were missing at first; there were few medical necessities, and practically no physicians.

But that is only part of the story. We must remember that this is the seventeenth century, a period in which European medicine did not as yet command the knowledge enabling it to effect the sanitation of an unknown country. It was a century of great contrasts. The Thirty Years' War raged in Germany and quenched all intellectual life. The universities everywhere held fast to mediaeval forms and were incapable of perceiving the spirit of the new age. It is true that knowledge made tremendous strides. In Italy, Galileo was transforming the structure of science. In England, Harvey in 1628, eight years after the landing of the Mayflower, announced the theory of the circulation of the blood. All over Europe the iatrochemists and iatrophysicists were trying to solve the problems of normal and diseased life by concepts borrowed from the modern natural sciences. Supplementing the universities, academies of science sprang up as focal points for the new knowledge. Practical medicine was alone in being for a while untouched by the whole movement. It travelled for the most part in traditional ruts, and to a large extent based its procedures on Galenic principles. Practice was as reactionary as science was progressive, and a broad chasm yawned between treatment and theory. In the second half of the century Thomas Sydenham bridged the gap and enabled practical medical common-sense to win the victory over theoretic speculation. It was not till early in the eighteenth century that Hermann Boerhaave became the great clinical teacher for all Europe.

It would be unjust to expect very much from medicine in the American colonies at a time when there was so much left to be desired in Europe.

Europeans who resolved to emigrate to America met their first dangers on the voyage over, which often lasted several months. Not only storms, shipwreck, and fire; but also disease. The ships were small and usually over-crowded. The lack of fresh food made itself felt especially. Scurvy was common; but a means of prevention was discovered. Colonists going to New England were advised to bring lime-juice with them and use it as a relish for the meat. We can understand only too well that on such long voyages in small boats, many passengers were driven to the verge of despair by seasickness. But it was still more serious when a contagion broke out on board. How could the infected patients possibly be isolated in such close quarters?

As a result the chronicles have some terrible voyages to describe. The Puritans made their first attempt at colonization in 1618. A ship set out for Virginia. Their leader, Francis Blackwell, as well as the captain and 130 out of 180 passengers, died on the way over; so that disease brought about the failure of the enterprise. Smallpox broke out on the ship which was bringing William Penn to America in 1682, causing the death of thirty passengers. Any number of examples could be cited. Hardly a ship escaped without some form of sickness.

A successful landing meant deliverance from real dangers.

However, the end was not yet. Getting used to the climate was in itself a serious problem. Many who had managed to survive the voyage had nevertheless been ill, and the greater part of the company arrived in a weakened condition. And now they found themselves exposed to a foreign climate and forced to adapt themselves to new modes of life. No less than half of the passengers of the Mayflower died within three months. It was specially dangerous to land in Virginia at the beginning of summer heat. Of course the favorable seasons were gradually discovered; but for a long while the fact had to be reckoned with that 20 percent of the newcomers would within a short time succumb to the effects of hardship and climate.

The settlers carried with them the communicable diseases of their native country. In addition, they met with new ones indigenous to America. Measles, scarlet fever, and diphtheria never died out altogether, and from time to time flared up into violent epidemics. Just as in contemporary Europe, intestinal infections, such as typhoid and especially dysentery, found an ideal culture medium in the primitive water-supply. And, as in Europe, influenza appeared at regular intervals and subjected each generation in turn to its infection. ←

Smallpox was new to the continent, but was carried in very early by the Spaniards, inflicting heavy losses on the Indians and perhaps through them attaining a new virulence to which the northern colonists were subsequently exposed.

Yellow fever was entirely new to the European settlers. It was carried in from the West Indies in 1647 and cost many lives. Philadelphia lost 200 in 1699; that is, less than two decades after its founding; New York about 600 in 1702, or over 10 percent of its population.

If it is taken into account that sickness from other causes, all forms of rheumatism, diseases of the circulation, etc., were certainly not uncommon; that, in the beginning at least, the resistance of the people was lowered by hunger; and that, here as

in Europe, many children died in earliest infancy, the extraordinarily high mortality rate is only to be expected. Of the 1700
colonists who settled in Jamestown before 1618, 1100 died during the first few years. Up to 1700, 100,000 people had emigrated to Virginia, but its population at this time came to only
75,000 inhabitants.

What did they do, to combat disease? It must be first of all
noted that there were practically no physicians. It is true that
most ships had their surgeons, but at that time surgeons belonged to an inferior class of therapists who served an apprenticeship but received no academic training. Moreover, most
of them, like Giles Heale on the Mayflower, went back with
their ships. A few remained in the colonies. We are told that
there were two such surgeons among the early settlers of Virginia. History has retained their names. They were Will Wilkinson and Thomas Wotton. But what could they accomplish in
the face of the miseries which assailed the colonists and which
they themselves could not escape?

A few medical men came over to Virginia, some on their own
initiative, and others were sent by the London Company, which
was probably aware that the fate of the whole colony might
depend on medical aid. So, in 1608, came a certain Dr. Walter
Russel, who was very helpful indeed. Or they might come in
the company of great lords who did not want to undertake so
dangerous a journey without a physician. When Lord Delaware visited the colonies in 1610 he brought with him a
Dr. Lawrence Bohun who had studied in the Netherlands.
When his supply of drugs became low, he interested himself
in the herbs of the country and experimented with sassafras,
with a resin, and a kind of clay which he discovered.

But surgeons and physicians as a rule stayed only a year or
so. They returned to their homes, where an easier and safer
existence awaited them.

Before he could take permanent root, a physician had to have his share of the pioneer spirit and a dash of the love of adventure. Such a man was John Pott, sent over by the London Company in 1621, a pugnacious ruffian, constantly involved in litigation, who was for a time Governor of Virginia; a man who used his medical knowledge for all conceivable ends, even to poisoning Indians when the occasion demanded.

New England was even worse off as far as medical care was concerned. The people needed assistance in their trouble; and there were no physicians to be had. So they turned to the leaders, the clergy and the governors. These were not physicians, of course; they had no diplomas; but they were educated men, informed on many subjects and prepared for any act of self-sacrifice.

With the Mayflower had come over a deacon called Samuel Fuller who, though he had no doctor's degree, acted as physician for the young colony for thirteen years until his death. He had been with the Puritans in Leyden, and it is not unlikely that he availed himself of the opportunity to gain some knowledge of medicine. We know that the Leyden anatomy classes were very generally visited, and that the clergy often interested themselves in medicine on the chance that they might later be working in an isolated district. However that may be, Fuller's help was much in demand. His home was in Plymouth, but he was often called to neighboring communities. He was always ready to give his services, even to the Indians; and combined medical aid with spiritual consolation. His wife acted as midwife. When Fuller died of smallpox in 1633, he left a gap which was hard to fill.

Fuller was not the only cleric to carry on medical practice. We will meet with others who distinguished themselves in that way. After the clergy it was the governors to whom the people turned for counsel in sickness. A governor was considered the father of his colony. So we find John Endicott in Salem giving medical advice. He showed his recognition of the importance of medicine to the colony by allowing his son to become a physician. John Winthrop, the founder of Boston, was even more enterprising. Naturally medical books for reference were as yet very rare in the colonies. Winthrop sought advice of a friend in England; and a very interesting document of the year 1643 is still extant: a long letter addressed to him by a Dr. Stafford in London containing a collection of prescriptions and therapeutic directions. For that is just what is wanted in primitive circumstances—succinct and clear directions for the treatment of definite diseases. The letter is worth reading for the last paragraph alone, which is the earliest document of American medical ethics: "No man can with a good Conscience take a fee or reward before ye partie receive benefit apparent: and then he is not to demand any thing, that shall be so given him, for it commes from God.

"A man is not to neglect that partie, to whom he hath once administered, but to visit him at least once a day, and to medle with no more, then he can well attend. In so doeing he shall discharge a good Conscience before God and Man."

Winthrop's son, John Winthrop, Jr., who became Governor of Connecticut, surpassed his father in the extent of his medical activities. On account of his official burdens, his advice was given for the most part in writing: and his medical correspondence, some of which has been preserved, reached all New England. The letters are touching. "Our youngest childe," writes a father, "about 9 weeks old, ever since it was 3 or 4 days old, hath appeared full of red spots or pimples, somewhat like to measles, and seemed allways to be bigg, and to hang ouer on the eyebrowes and lidds; but now of late the eye lidds have swelled and looked very red, burneing exceedingly, and now at last they are swelled up that the sight is vtterly closed in, . . . it is somewhat extraordinary such as none of our women can tell that they have never seen the like."

Another writes: "Sir, you were pleased to furnish my wife with more cordiall powders for Graciana (his daughter) but no directions within or amongst them can we find; but truly one of the most needful directions is how to make her willing and apt to take it, for though it seemes very pleasant of itself yet is she grown so marvelous aukward and averse from takeing it in beer. Wherefore I would entreat you to prescribe to vs the varyety of wayes in which it may be given so effectually; wee doubt els it may do much less good, being given by force only."

And again another: "My wife with thankfulness acknowledges the good she hath found by following your directions, but doth much desire your presence here, as soone as the season, and your occasions will permit, both in reference to my daughter Hopkins, and my daughter Hannah, who hath bin exercised these 4 or 5 days with vapours rising (as we conceive) out of her stomach into her head, hindering both her sleepe and appetite to meate, and apt to putt her into fainting fits, whether from winde, or the mother, or from what other cause I cannot informe."

Through these few morsels of correspondence we obtain a very illuminating glimpse of the medical activities of these governors, and can see how all manner of things were demanded of them. Young Winthrop was moreover an unusually well-educated man, who had studied in Dublin and travelled extensively in Europe. He had a special interest in chemistry and astronomy. When the Royal Society was founded in London in 1661, he was proposed as a member and was admitted in the following year. At his death he left behind him a library of a thousand books.

Still other professions were called upon for medical service; especially, for instance, the school-masters. In Dutch New Amsterdam, nursing and other assistance were part of their official function. And, of course, in New England as elsewhere in the colonies were found occasional surgeons.

Obviously this clerical and lay medicine would have to be very primitive. It was a peculiar mixture of religious medicine, folk-medicine, and scientific principle. One invoked the word of God, let blood, or prescribed drugs, to the best of one's understanding. We must not forget that at this period European medicine, even when practised by physicians, was effective only in exceptional cases. This is the time of Molière's bitter satires. The physicians he describes can, of course, speak Latin, but their treatment confines itself to *seignare deinde purgare*.

The best that could be done was done, and every effort was concentrated on holding in check the great epidemics by means of government regulation. When in 1647 news of a contagious disease in the Barbados was received in Boston, strict quarantine measures were enforced for all ships arriving from the West Indies. Similar measures were taken two years later in regard to ships from England, because of the plague in London at that time.

Smallpox was a constant source of trouble. For this reason a minister called Thomas Thacher, equally famous as preacher and physician, and who died of an infection as a sacrifice to his double calling, wrote a leaflet in 1677, explaining the nature of smallpox to the people, and giving directions for its control. "These things I have written, Candid Reader, not to inform the Learned Physitian that hath much more cause to understand what pertains to this disease than I, but to give some light to those that have not such advantages . . . I am, though no Physitian, yet a well-wisher to the sick."

The leaflet was printed, appearing under the title *A Brief Rule to Guide the Common People of New-England how to order themselves and theirs in the Small Pocks, or Measles,* and is the first American medical publication to be printed. Just as in Europe the first medical incunabulum in 1456 was no learned book, but a single sheet describing the procedure of blood-letting, so the first medical incunabulum of America is also a

single printed page of practical directions. It is the only medical
work of the century to appear in print.

We are beginning to comprehend that American medicine has
travelled at furious speed through all the successive stages of
world-medicine, until, keeping up the same pace, it has at-
tained a form towards which Europe is progressing more
slowly. Europe, too, had its period of clerical medicine, lasting,
however, for hundreds of years.

Smallpox came back again and again. But finally an effective
means of prevention was discovered. Early in the eighteenth
century, the knowledge of smallpox inoculation or variolation,
began to spread into Europe from the East. In 1717 there appeared in the Philosophical Transactions of the Royal Society
two communications which described the methods used by the
Turks. In 1721 Lady Mary Wortley Montagu, wife of the
British ambassador in Constantinople, returned to England and
became the propagandist of variolation. Cotton Mather in
Boston—again a clergyman—read the reports of the Royal
Society, and immediately understood that this new method
could be of the utmost importance to his afflicted colony. He
persuaded a friend, Zabdiel Boylston, to test the method; and
the latter had the courage to do so. In June, 1721, at a time
when not a soul on the continent of western Europe knew anything of variolation, Boylston inoculated his own son, another
boy, and two colored servants. With complete success. After this
several hundred people were inoculated. Six of them were
taken sick and died. Probably these had been ill before their
inoculation. Of those not inoculated about 6000 were taken sick
and 844 died.

Even today, though variolation has been replaced by the
harmless method of vaccination, there are still many bitter opponents of inoculation. The idea of being made artificially ill
in order to be protected against illness is repugnant to many
people. Certain religious sects believe inoculation a sinful inter-

ference with nature. It is not surprising that Puritan Boston was of the same opinion, and that the early defenders of inoculation were persecuted. In Europe the Enlightenment paved the way for variolation. It had no less important a champion than Voltaire. Conditions were different in Boston. A storm arose against Mather and Boylston; and their lives were no longer safe, since the war was not confined to polemics. One day a bomb was thrown into Mather's house, fortunately without exploding. However, after a few years the excitement died down. When smallpox broke out once more in 1752, there was very little opposition. Physicians formerly bitterly opposed to Boylston's method now openly testified to their approval, and in consequence 2000 people were inoculated. Benjamin Franklin was among the partisans of the treatment. Washington and Jefferson arranged for the inoculation of their slaves, and the soldiers were inoculated during the Revolutionary War.

During the eighteenth century life in the colonies took on a more stable form. People had moved into new houses, in which they felt warm, comfortable, and at home. They barred their gates nervously against interlopers. In fact, immigration stopped almost entirely for a hundred years beginning with the middle of the seventeenth century. A life grew up, of which the architectural monuments are found along the whole eastern coast; great manor-houses in the south, handsome town and country houses in the north, all with many rooms and huge kitchens where whole oxen could be roasted, and with outbuildings for the colored helpers. Today we make pious pilgrimages to these memorials of the golden age of the colonial period.

New generations were born in this distant country. It is true that they spoke the language of England, shared its political forms, and had in their midst the representatives of the king. But the ties grew looser, more so in New England than in the south. The Atlantic crossing was tiresome and expensive. The

new world became their real home. There was no need to go
to Oxford or Cambridge for a higher education. They had their
own Cambridge with its Harvard College, founded as early as
1636. It was followed by Yale College in New Haven in 1701.
Both antedate by far the universities of Göttingen and Berlin.

The changed conditions would naturally have their effect on
medicine. The period of clerical medicine was over. No matter
how primitive the therapeutic methods of the clergy had been,
their work had been a blessing, giving help and comfort to
many. Above all, they had stuck to their guns. Their fate was
inextricably bound up with the fate of the colonies, while the
academic physician was constantly tempted by the easier life he
had left behind him.

Though for that matter, medical education even in the
eighteenth century was not much to boast of. Harvard had no
medical school until 1781; Yale not till 1810. Before the outbreak of the Revolution there was no academic medical instruction outside Philadelphia and New York. So one had to find
another way out. After the era of church medicine a period
ensued in which therapy was taught and learned by the apprentice method. As in the days of Hippocrates, a student
would choose a master, go with him on his rounds, listen to
every word he said, and compound his salves at home. Zabdiel
Boylston, who showed such intelligence and courage in the matter of smallpox, and who was without doubt the most prominent physician in the Boston of his time, never went to a medical
school, but had studied at home with his father. In many families, like the Clarks in Massachusetts, the art of medicine was
handed down from father to son, generation after generation.
A youth would go to college to get his bachelor's degree, and
afterwards study with a physician. Of the ten practitioners in
Boston in 1721, only one had a doctor's degree. It is calculated
that at the outbreak of the Revolution there were about 3500

practitioners in the colonies, of whom not more than 400 were doctors of medicine.

This apprentice method brought with it many advantages. At a time when in Paris and most European universities medicine was taught purely theoretically, without any concrete bedside illustration, in America it was learned in daily practical contact with patients. Whenever there was an opportunity—which was seldom enough—a cadaver would be dissected.

This practical training had a further advantage. In Europe at that time a sharp line was drawn between surgery and medicine. The physician was a university man; the surgeon only a skilled craftsman. Physicians and surgeons were recruited from different social classes, and jealousies only too frequently poisoned their inevitable collaboration. Not till the nineteenth century was the equalization of the two professions brought about in Europe. In America, on the other hand, where the physician shared the apprentice training, there could be no sharp distinction between medicine and surgery. So this particular danger was obviated by pressure of circumstance.

It was granted a few individuals to finish their education abroad. After going through college and a time of practical training, they would cross the ocean, to England as a rule, but also to Scotland, where Edinburgh was carrying on the teachings of Leyden. Some went as far as the Continent, particularly to Holland. They took their doctor's degree in Europe. They learned pathology from John Hunter and obstetrics from Smellie. In Edinburgh they could feel a breath of the inspiration of Boerhaave's clinic. Laden with the latest knowledge, they returned home. Every one wanted to learn from them, and was eager to hear what they had seen and heard. In 1735 a medical society was founded in Boston, which remained active until 1741, and was succeeded in 1781 by the still existing Massachusetts Medical Society. It is easy to see that these physicians returning from Europe would draw to them many young men, and would become popular teachers. This was true of Dr. William Shippen, Jr., of Philadelphia. He had been taught by his father, and afterwards studied five years in England and Scotland. He came home in 1762 and began to teach obstetrics. With the help of models and drawings he demonstrated the anatomy of pregnant women. A small private clinic for poor women served for the practical instruction given to medical students and midwives. Shippen gave similar instruction in anatomy and surgery, not only with models, but also by using cadavers. We will come across him again as one of the first to hold a chair in an American medical school.

So in the course of the eighteenth century a few medical personalities began one by one to stand out; no great scientists, but competent practitioners, with sound judgment and many-sided interests in botany, astronomy, and much besides. Practitioners who knew how to interpret their experience and pass their knowledge on to younger men; like James Lloyd of Boston, a pupil of Hunter and Smellie, and a very popular teacher. Practitioners who could use a pen on occasion, like William Douglas, likewise from Boston. Is he subject to criticism because of his violent opposition to Boylston and smallpox inoculation? It is easy to pass judgment from the perspective of history. But, after all, to a careful physician these new methods might easily have appeared a reckless gambling with human lives. When in 1735–36 Boston was visited by a severe scarlet fever epidemic, Douglas showed much energy and clinical insight. He described the course of the epidemic in an excellent monograph, *The Practical History of a New Epidemical Eruptive Miliary Fever, with an Angina Ulcusculosa which prevailed in Boston, New England, in the years 1735 and 1736*, which appeared twelve years before John Fothergill's classic dissertation.

The American colonies, like the rest of the world, were bound sooner or later to come up against the burning question: what constitutes a physician? Frederick II of the Holy Roman Empire, as early as the thirteenth century, issued an edict which made the privilege of practising medicine dependent on a required course of study and a license given at Salerno. In the ensuing period universities sprang up all over Europe, whose diplomas vouched for a definite sum of knowledge. Many of the little kingdoms and duchies of the baroque period created within their own boundaries medical boards which controlled licenses. Surgeons were originally organized in exclusive guilds, and later came in many places to maintain special schools or academies. Almost all governments had strict medical laws for the control of charlatanism and the protection of society from abuses on the part of physicians.

The American colonies, however, were at first without either medical schools or any sort of government health department. Practice was as free as in the ancient world; any one could call himself a physician and carry on any method of healing he pleased. Medical advice was badly needed, and whoever knew anything about it and could help in an emergency, was necessarily welcome. The dangers of such a situation are obvious. There was no clear line drawn around quackery. But we hear little of quacks, probably because the New England communities were small, every one knew every one else, and the good or bad results of treatment could not long be hidden. Nevertheless, it stands to reason that many abuses went on; and public intervention became necessary. So we are told that, as early as 1631, a certain Nicholas Knopp was flogged and made to do penance, for selling worthless remedies. A Massachusetts law of 1649 prohibits all but recognized and tried methods of treatment. What court was there to sit on matters of this sort? The same law decrees that no severe and violent treatment shall be inflicted on the body of any person without the advice and consent of people who have a knowledge of the medical arts, if such are within reach. In any case, the wisest and most responsible men present must be consulted; and the patient's consent is essential, providing he is conscious at the time. Non-observance is to be severely punished. Interesting and significant is the added comment that this law is not intended to deter any one from the legitimate practice of his art; on the contrary, it seeks to make more evident the fitness and superiority of such persons.

Interesting from the standpoint of criminal law is a New Amsterdam ordinance of 1657, according to which the surgeon called in to treat a wound is obliged to inquire after and report the culprit; a law inconceivable in a country with an established medical profession.

There was evidently fear of competition from ship-surgeons. Most of the ships that made port had their own surgeons on board, and since what comes from a distance has always a special attraction, they were sure to be popular. At the same time, no one really knew what kind of people they were. In Boston and New Amsterdam the law required that foreign surgeons could practise on land only after having been approved and licensed by the local physicians and surgeons.

These ordinances had their amusing side. In 1652 the surgeons of New Amsterdam had demanded the exclusive right of shaving. The government vouchsafed the wise reply that: ". . . Shaving alone doth not appertain exclusively to chirurgery, but is an appendix thereunto; that no man can be prevented operating on himself; nor to do to another the friendly act provided it be through courtesy, and not for gain which is hereby forbidden."

Many ordinances, especially in Virginia, had to do with medical fees. Maximum tariffs were established to protect patients from exploitation. In a Virginia statute of 1736 it is pointed out that medical treatment in the colonies is for the most part in the hands of apothecaries, surgeons, or people who have only just finished a medical course; many of them having shown themselves quite unskilled in the healing art, but nevertheless demanding exorbitant fees and unreasonable prices for their medicine.

Another very early law prescribes that physicians in possession of a doctor's degree may charge higher fees.

Not till towards the end of the colonial period was an attempt made to establish some system by requiring licenses. New York, where quackery especially prospered, led the way. In 1760 a law was enacted that no one should practise medicine or surgery or both, who had not previously been examined and licensed. The government appointed the board of examiners and moreover determined the license requirements.

The Revolution intervened; and it seems that this law could not be adequately enforced during those troubled times. At any rate, a new law was enacted for the State and County of New York in 1792, which is interesting because it mentions the requirements for a medical training. To obtain a license, it was not only necessary to pass an examination but the candidate had to show that he had completed a two-year course of study under a recognized physician, if he had a college education; otherwise a three-year course. Persons with a medical degree from an American college or university did not need a license. New Jersey enacted similar laws in 1772.

It was a promising beginning for the state regulation of medical affairs. But we will see in a later chapter that the goal was still a long way off.

All other health regulation in colonial times had to do with measures of protection against communicable diseases, as for instance the many quarantine regulations that had to be enacted from time to time, and which have already been mentioned. It was well understood that contagions usually enter a country through its sea-ports. This was of special importance here, where the settled territory consisted of a narrow stretch of sea-coast and all the larger cities were harbor-towns. Any incoming ship might carry deadly germs. Europe was infected through and through with disease, and the West Indies provided a never-failing source of contagion. No wonder that an unending succession of ordinances was passed in an effort to ensure protection. Smallpox, especially, caused a great deal of trouble through the whole of the eighteenth century, and was the occasion of many laws. In Massachusetts, a severe epidemic in a city was sufficient reason for the court to adjourn or move its seat. Keeping an illness secret was considered particularly reprehensible and dangerous; and a decree of 1731 requires that every house with a case of smallpox be distinguished by hanging out a red handkerchief.

An account of colonial medicine must include a brief discussion of hospitals. Here, too, the development is a condensed replica of general medical history. Ancient Greece had no hospitals, but a physician would on occasion take into his house, or iatreion, patients who needed special care or prolonged nursing after an operation. The same sort of thing happened in the early days of Virginia. In the difficulties of the first years the colonists had to give each other mutual assistance. Women were scarce. Who was to nurse and take charge of a patient? A neighbor if he was in a position to do so. Or perhaps the physician. Often he lived miles away and could not make the patient daily visits. So the invalid was sometimes brought to his house. It happened too often to please the physician, as we can read in a variety of sources.

The first hospitals of western people sprang up in the Middle Ages, as an expression of Christian charity. They were something very different from what is now understood by the term. They were not primarily places for medical treatment, but nursing homes, poor-houses, hostelries, and inns. They were houses where a homeless man could find a roof for his head. They were called xenodochia.

The same phenomenon appears again in Virginia. In 1612, only a few years after the founding of the colony, such a house was erected at Henricopolis on the James River; a wooden house surrounded by stockades and protected by block-houses, containing 80 beds for the care of those needing assistance. Ten years later the Indians attacked the settlement and it was destroyed by flames.

But new houses of the same sort were planned by the Colonial Company "for the better preserving and nourishing of the emigrants"; guest-houses they were called, or literally xenodochia. They were built in cities or on plantations, and contained a proportion of 25 beds to every 50 people who applied for help. When the company dissolved these refuges were closed.

During the course of the eighteenth century, poor-houses that would also take charge of the indigent sick were founded in most of the colonies; as for instance in Philadelphia in 1732, a little later in New York, and in 1736 in New Orleans, where *l'Hôpital des Pauvres de la Charité* was established by means of an endowment given by a citizen named Jean Louis.

The first hospital, however, to serve exclusively for the care and medical treatment of sick people was the Pennsylvania Hospital in Philadelphia. It was founded at the instigation of a physician called Thomas Bond. The funds were raised by subscription. Three physicians, among them Bond himself, declared themselves prepared to take charge of the patients for the first three years without compensation. A rented building was occupied in 1752. A new building was erected and opened in 1756. (Fig. 4.) The ground-floor accommodated the mental patients;

the second story contained the men's division; and the third the women's. The new hospital won the admiration of visitors from at home and abroad.

Twenty years passed, before Philadelphia's example was imitated. New York followed with the New York Hospital. The charter was granted in 1771, and the hospital opened in 1776.

While Thomas Bond was making his plans for the Philadelphia hospital and knocking at door after door for subscriptions, he was often met with the question: "Have you been to Franklin about it? What does he say?" And not till Franklin had been won over to the cause and had begun to beat the drum for the roll-call, did the plan approach completion. Franklin was indeed one of the greatest Americans. He embodies the most admirable national type. What is more, his significance transcends local limitations. He is one of the few Americans ever heard of by European children, though known perhaps only as the inventor of the lightning-rod. With Voltaire, Rousseau, and the Encyclopedists, he belongs to the history of the eighteenth century. We cannot close this chapter in any better way than by a brief sketch of his life, and the attempt to evaluate his services to science and medicine, and to American intellectual life as a whole.

He was the youngest of seventeen children; a true Benjamin. He was born in Boston in 1706, the son of a soap- and candle-maker. His father died at 87, his mother at 85, and he himself was to reach the age of 84. They thought of educating him for the ministry, but it was too expensive; and so at the age of ten years he was apprenticed to his father and helped manufacture soap and candles. He read whatever he could get hold of. His favorite book was Plutarch, which he read surrounded by soap-basins, as another boy, Napoleon, was later to read the same book in the midst of wicker baskets. Both were intoxicated with the deeds of the ancients.

4. PENNSYLVANIA HOSPITAL IN PHILADELPHIA

Benjamin wanted to go to sea, but his father objected. An older brother ran a printing-press, and the boy was sent to him to learn the trade. This was an improvement on soap-making. For one thing, there was more to read. He read; carried on long arguments with his friends; and wrote very bad ballads. He also wrote anonymous newspaper articles for a paper printed by his brother. These were much better. His brother was a rough bully who used his fists very freely; and something innate in the boy rose up in instinctive protest against repression and tyranny. It ended in a break; and at the age of seventeen Franklin left Boston. He went first to New York but, finding no work, proceeded to Philadelphia. He had not a penny. Armed with nothing but the historic three rolls, he trudged the streets of the city which was to be the scene of his future activity. But he had his trade. He found a patron in the Governor, who wanted to make him manager of a new printing house, and sent him to England to buy the machines.

Franklin was not yet nineteen when he visited Europe for the first time. Unfortunately a disappointment awaited him. It turned out that the Governor had no credit. The printing enterprise came to nothing and Franklin had to earn his living in London by working in a printing shop. However, the eighteen months in the metropolis were not wasted. He saw, read, and heard many things; and returned to Philadelphia a full-grown man, able to set himself up as an independent printer.

He was above all a representative of the civic virtues, the enlightened citizen of a democratic community. His every activity was dedicated to the interest of the public. His printing-press, which from 1732 on published Poor Richard's Almanac, disseminated wise counsels among the people. He was always trying to make good deficiencies. Fires were frequent; so he founded a fire insurance company. The stoves used at that time were impractical, so he invented a new and less wasteful model. The schools were inferior. Franklin started a collection to estab-

lish a new and better school. His library was an encouragement
to adult education. When the Indians became once more dangerous, Franklin formed a voluntary company of militia, which was
joined on the spot by 100,000 men. One can see that the idea of
a hospital would appeal to him. Such a project was entirely in his
line; and he would naturally play an active part in its realization.

It was in ways of this sort that the ideals of the Enlightenment most frequently found expression. The lot of individual
men was to be improved and their lives made more comfortable
and happy. This was to be accomplished by reason, by the reasonable enlightenment of each individual. Reason in Franklin,
however, never led to Atheism, but remained in complete accord
with his faith. His common-sense attitude comes strikingly to
the surface in a letter. On his second trip to Europe he nar-
rowly escaped shipwreck and writes: "Perhaps I should on this
occasion vow to build a chapel to some saint; but . . . if I were
to vow at all, it should be to build a lighthouse."

Franklin had the genuine scientific curiosity of the investigator. He was a member of the Royal Society and numerous
other scientific associations and himself founded an academy of
the sciences in Philadelphia. From 1727 on, a group of men
with scientific interests met regularly at his house for evenings
of discussion. This club in 1769 became the American Philosophical Society, still one of the most distinguished organizations in the country.

But it was not so much pure science for its own sake, as its
application to problems of daily living that fascinated Franklin.
He looked at natural sciences primarily as means of effecting
improvements in living conditions. He followed with intense
interest every new scientific discovery, and kept in constant
touch with European students. He never stopped experimenting, fussing about with all kinds of trifles, and making discov-

eries very like Edison's a century later. During the eighteenth century electricity held the foreground of interest. Franklin had a Leyden jar with which to experiment, and invented the lightning conductor. He tried to find a way to use electricity for the medical treatment of paralysis. The enormous potentialities of electricity were quite clear to him, and he was a constant experimenter in all other directions. As he grew older, he needed two pairs of glasses; one for reading and one for distance. That is always a nuisance. Why not combine them both? So he ground himself bifocal spectacles, with the upper half less convex than the lower, and achieved his object.

After 1757, Franklin's life belongs mainly to political history. Still, he never lost his interest in science. When after the Revolution he was living as Ambassador in Paris, he was an active member of the Académie des Sciences and the Société Royale de Médecine. He writes home long accounts of Mongolfier's first attempts at flying, and here, too, he envisages possibilities. A young physician, who was soon to achieve renown, Marat by name, dedicated to him his work on physics.

However, political events were under way that were to determine the future fate of America. Events calling for the services of the best men, and in which Philadelphia's first citizen must play his part. Events to which we must now turn our attention.

CHAPTER THREE

THE UNITED STATES

DURING the course of the eighteenth century the thirteen colonies had gained in strength. The population had grown in number, partly by an increase in the original elements and partly by renewed immigration. Many of the newcomers were Germans, who for the most part settled in Pennsylvania. First to come were the Mennonites, shortly after the colony was founded; then followed Rhinelanders from the Palatinate whose homes had been laid waste by Louis XIV, and a little later Rhinelanders from the lower Rhine; political and religious refugees of every shade of opinion. The coast was already well settled; so they proceeded farther inland, to become farmers and very good farmers, too. In 1776 the colonies numbered two million inhabitants, of whom two-thirds were English, one-sixth Scotch and Irish, and one-tenth German.

The colonies were naturally drawn into the conflicts at that time taking place in Europe. The Seven Years' War was fought by the English and French not only at sea and on the mainland of Europe, but on American soil. Assisted by allied Indians, the French advanced against the colonies from Canada and the Mississippi Valley; and England, to protect her territories, was forced to send over a considerable section of her army. The war ended in 1763 with the Peace of Paris, by the terms of which France renounced her North American possessions. Canada and the region east of the Mississippi were ceded to England, and Louisiana to Spain, who in turn ceded Florida to England. The northern continent was now divided between only two powers: England in the east and north, and Spain in the south, the latter, however, immediately beginning to expand the sphere of her influence by erecting a succession of missions and military posts along the coast of California.

No sooner had England brought this profitable war to a successful conclusion, than she was faced with difficulties arising in the colonies. Hoping to placate the Indians by reserving for their use the territory between the Alleghanies and the Mississippi, England forbade the colonization of this district. But that was just what the colonies would not agree to. Large numbers of the population had been impoverished by the war; and their one chance of recovery was to begin life over again on new soil. The decree was disregarded. The people's self-confidence had been strengthened. Now that there was no longer any danger of a French attack, the troops from England, maintained in part by colonial taxes, were felt to be a nuisance. The atmosphere was heavily charged, and little was needed to bring about an explosion.

England had incurred heavy expenses through the war and considered it only just that the colonies should pay a part of the cost. New import taxes which specially concerned New England were decided upon in 1764. In 1765 a stamp-tax was enacted, directed against all the colonies alike. Every one of them rebelled, contesting the right of the English Parliament to tax the colonies without their consent. Feeling ran very high. Clever demagogues like Samuel Adams fanned the flames. A clash in Boston—troops provoked by the mob had fired off their guns—was magnified into a massacre. Thoughtful men tried to mediate between the factions; among them Franklin, who was at that time in London. The English government gave in and repealed the taxes, to be sure without surrendering the fundamental right to impose them. The conservative element in America was reassured, but the populace remained agitated.

An incident unimportant in itself finally precipitated the avalanche. The East India Company had piled up a huge supply of tea which it did not know how to get rid of. The mon-

opoly of selling tea in the colonies was granted it by the government without any consideration for the interests of the American
middleman. A cargo reached Boston in December, 1773. A crowd
of citizens got together, took possession of the shipload of tea
worth $50,000, and dumped it into the sea. This constituted
open rebellion. The government was forced into action. It blockaded Boston Harbor, annulled the charter of Massachusetts,
and proclaimed a military dictatorship of the colony. The
Continental Congress representing all the colonies assembled at
Philadelphia in September, 1774. Trade with England was completely broken off, and militia were put in training. As early
as April of the following year the two sides met in armed conflict at Lexington and Concord, and a battle involving serious
losses was fought at Bunker Hill on June 17th. There was
now no turning back. Revolutionary governments were appointed in all the colonies which recognized the Congress as
supreme authority. Washington, a gentleman land-owner from
Virginia (his estate is now a national shrine) who had already
distinguished himself as a soldier, was made commander-in-
chief. Under his leadership the untrained and poorly-equipped
troops fought the enemy with varying fortune. In March, 1776,
he succeeded in driving the English out of Boston. The country was now free of enemy troops, and on July 4, 1776, Congress
approved the Declaration of Independence. The thirteen states
had become the United States of America. The Declaration
enumerates the shortcomings of England and closes with the
words:

*We, therefore, the representatives of the United States of
America, in General Congress, Assembled, appealing to the
Supreme Judge of the world for the rectitude of our intentions,
do, in the Name, and by authority of the good People of these
Colonies, solemnly publish and declare, That these United
Colonies are, and of Right ought to be Free and Independent
States; that they are Absolved from all Allegiance to the*

British Crown, and that all political connection between them and the State of Great Britain is and ought to be totally dissolved; and that as Free and Independent States, they have full Power to levy War, conclude Peace, contract Alliances, establish Commerce, and to do all other Acts and Things which Independent States may of right do. And for the support of this Declaration, with a firm reliance on the protection of Divine Providence, we mutually pledge to each other our Lives, our Fortunes, and our sacred Honor.

It was more than a secession from the Empire. A revolution had taken place. The Declaration of Independence opens with the assertion: *We hold these truths to be self-evident: that all men are created equal; that they are endowed by their Creator with certain unalienable rights; that among these are life, liberty, and the pursuit of happiness.* The philosophy of the Enlightenment had borne fruit. The radical elements had triumphed over the conservative. The Rights of Man were for the first time proclaimed in an official document. It was only fourteen years before that a shy little man called Jean Jacques Rousseau had written his *Contrat Social*.

Independence had been declared, but was not yet won. Instead of giving in, England sent over fresh troops which inflicted a severe defeat on Washington's army at Brooklyn and forced it to retreat. The situation was most critical; and it may be doubted whether without outside help the American army could in the long run have succeeded in keeping at bay the well-trained English troops, reinforced as they were by German mercenaries; especially as among the colonists were found many people who remained loyal to the British crown and would have welcomed the return to former conditions. But England had in Europe her traditional opponents, only too glad to seize the opportunity to injure her. When on October 16, 1777, the little army compelled an English force to surrender at Saratoga, the gallantry of its fight for freedom aroused sympathy and admiration. France, Spain, and Holland recognized the United States government. Franklin, who was living in Paris as envoy, was successful in concluding in 1778 a treaty of trade and alliance with France. England retorted with a declaration of war, which soon came to include Spain and Holland. But now France sent over money, ammunition, troops, and the Marquis de Lafayette. England could not withstand the united forces. A part of her army withdrew to New York; another fought on in the south, until it was surrounded by Washington and Lafayette and compelled to capitulate on October 19, 1781.

This battle decided the outcome of the war. Peace negotiations were initiated; and in the Treaty of Versailles England recognized the independence of the thirteen united states and was obliged to cede to America the western territory lying between the Alleghanies and the Mississippi.

Liberty was an accomplished fact. But the country was in a miserable condition. Congress had issued paper money and finances had been disorganized by inflation. The once thriving trade was at a standstill. The common struggle had united the colonies; but, now that war was over, it became apparent that the thirteen states had each their separate interests. Each drew up its own constitution. Congress had very little authority. Two contrary political tendencies developed. The Federalists contended for a strong central government, while the Antifederalists had in mind a loose confederation of states with as little federal interference as possible.

America was guided through those years of confusion by a group of extraordinary men. Early in the year 1787 they met in Philadelphia for a constitutional assembly. After three months of debate a constitution was established which represented a compromise between the conflicting tendencies. The constitution was sent for ratification to the individual states; and was eventually accepted, though not without a struggle. Writs were issued for election of Congress and President, and on

March 4, 1789, in New York City, Washington assumed office as first President of the United States. A month later revolution broke out in France.

It is altogether fitting that Washington should be honored as the greatest national hero and that his strong features should be seen on the walls of every government office. Though he was neither a great general nor a great statesman, he was a great man. Just as during the disheartening years of the war he had held his troops together till victory was won, in the same way when President he succeeded by the power of his personality in creating out of the thirteen states the miracle of a nation. He was a man of the utmost probity and disinterestedness, never accepting the slightest payment for his services.

He died, his task accomplished, in 1799, and a year later the federal government moved to a newly-founded city named in his honor. Situated on the shores of the Potomac, not far from his home at Mt. Vernon, on ground surrendered by Maryland to form the United States District of Columbia, the city is one of the most beautiful capitals of the world. The white marble of the office-buildings gleams in the southern sun above the dark green box hedges. The great monumental avenues converge in the shape of a star at whose central point rises the Capitol. High on its superb dome a statue of Liberty stands luminous against the clear blue sky. A splendid and beautiful city, Washington is a fitting symbol of a great and powerful nation.

But in 1800 all this was still in the future. War with England broke out once more in 1812—as Napoleon was marching on Russia—and was fought with intense bitterness on both sides. The nation's economic equilibrium was again shaken, but its sense of unity was reinforced.

The treaty of Ghent in 1814, which brought the hostilities to an end, marks an important turning-point in American history. Till now the fate of the Union had been closely bound up with events in Europe; but from this time on ensues a period of independence and detachment. America withdraws into herself, and for a hundred years, till the outbreak of the World War, turns her attention westward rather than across the Atlantic. A tremendous drama, an epic event of unheard-of magnitude, begins to unfold: the conquest, settlement, and cultivation of one great section of the globe, all within a dizzyingly short space of time.

West of the Alleghanies, where only a short time ago Indians still had their hunting-grounds, there were estimated in 1800 to be a million inhabitants. Ten years later the number had risen to two and a half million; and in 1830 to three and a half million. Slowly but steadily the frontier was pushed westward. This frontier was not so much a geographical boundary-line as a *state of mind*. When the boundary shifted, the situation would repeat itself. Always the first to make their way into the untrodden forest would be hunters and trappers, fearing neither God nor Devil, equally ready to fight Indians or trade them whiskey for fur—often a very good business, the foundation for huge estates like those of Astor and Girard.

In the footsteps of the trappers followed a second army of pioneers, settlers who brought their families and built themselves cabins to shelter them while they dug up the earth of the virgin forest to plant their crops. They sold the land as fast as it had been wrested from the forest, and followed the trappers westward. The land was bought by the third army of pioneers, farmers who settled permanently and formed stable communities. One building would be used as a church, another as a store for the exchange of goods. The store-keeper and the preacher would be followed by the doctor, who would have an enormous district under his charge; and after him in due time would come lawyers and bankers.

Carrying their flint-locks, a few tools, and a Bible, the pioneers passed westward in an endless stream. All day long they drove along rough, uneven roads that followed old Indian trails, and at night they backed their covered wagons in a protective circle and listened anxiously for distant drums. For the Indians had not yet given up the fight. Grimly they contested their hunting-grounds in the face of the flood sweeping in from the East. The struggle was bitter, and whole settlements and whole tribes were annihilated. Just as in the eighteenth century a group of Indian tribes had been united against the white man by the great chief Pontiac, so it happened again under the leadership of Tecumseh. But all in vain. In 1825 Congress set apart an Indian reservation west of the Mississippi and resolved that all Indians remaining in the lands east of the river should be removed to the other side. The plan was carried out but the fighting continued; for there was no stopping the westward march of the pioneers. They continued to press on till one day they stood on the edge of the prairie.

It had needed pluck to cross the ocean. But, after all, the ship was arranged very like a house and was a product of civilization. The only dangers derived from the natural and familiar elements of wind and water. But here lay the prairie. It begins near the southern boundary of Omaha, by the Missouri. Today, travelling through its expanse for hours and days and nights we no longer see on each side prairie wastes, but the vast, billowing wheat-fields of Kansas. Nevertheless there still comes over us something of the same strange dread which was felt by the travellers in the old days. Nowhere else are the days so long and monotonous and the nights of such endless, unbroken darkness. In the woods the pioneers were at home; but here they left the woods behind them. To set out in a wagon, alone or with a small company, into this wide expanse, was a daring undertaking, and meant a hard struggle, with men as well as with the elements. For the prairie was not uninhabited. Indians roamed to and fro across it, Sioux, Blackfeet, Pawnees, Comanches, and Apaches, hunting buffalo on horseback and knowing by heart every curve of the rolling country. They were not entirely subjugated until the end of the century. The last Apache uprising was in 1900.

The life of the pioneers was hard. They had no weapons but their youth and their iron will with which to win for themselves wealth and position. They had only their own capacities to draw upon. The original thirteen states, and also Vermont, which joined the Union in 1791, had already a history, traditions, and an active cultural life. But the West had to begin at the beginning all over again. There was as yet no energy free for the creation of intellectual goods. The demands of the spirit could be satisfied only in the church; and sometimes found release in veritable religious explosions. Sectarianism flourished. Baptists and Methodists won countless adherents. Joe Smith founded the singular community of Mormons in 1833. Driven from one place to another, they made their way westward till, after indescribable hardships, they finally, around the middle of the century, found near the Great Salt Lake, on what was then Mexican soil, a permanent home where they were able to live according to their own ideas and by their great industry soon to attain to affluence.

The western pioneers were native-born Americans; men, or descendants of men, who had fought in the War of Independence. European immigration sufficed only to fill the gaps which they had left behind them in the East, and remained negligible until 1825. While the east coast naturally never lost touch with Europe, the West grew to be the breeding-ground of unadulterated Americanism.

The settlement of the West led to the formation of new states. The mountainous region of Kentucky, largely peopled by men from Virginia, joined the Union in 1792. Tennessee, the offspring of North Carolina, followed in 1796; Ohio in 1802. With the transportation facilities of that time, the Alleghanies formed an almost impassable barrier between East and

West. In consequence the Mississippi became the main artery of western life, as the natural trade-route to the outside world, with New Orleans as the port of exit. Whoever controlled Louisiana, held the key to the West. When Spain ceded the colony to France, and the French fleet blockaded the mouth of the river, there was great consternation. Negotiations were at once initiated. Napoleon needed money and sold Louisiana to the Union for 15 million dollars. Ol' Man River was free again. Again ships passed busily up and down, and the old songs were heard along the shore. St. Louis developed into the most important port on the route north, and as a result became the gateway to the West. In 1807 Robert Fulton's first steamboat went up the Hudson, and in 1811 the great paddle-wheels were seen for the first time on the Mississippi.

Louisiana was admitted as a state in 1812. It was soon followed by others: slave-states in the South, free states in the North. In order to maintain the balance between North and South it was always carefully arranged that a new northern state should be matched by a new southern one. So Indiana in 1816 was followed the next year by Mississippi; Illinois in 1818 by Alabama the year following; and Maine in 1820 by Missouri in 1821.

The movement for independence had spread to South and Central America. In 1821 Mexico drove out the Spanish rulers and declared itself independent. Its territory extended far into the north but it lacked men to people this expanse of country. As a result it was North Americans who came to settle on the Texas plains. They soon surpassed the natives in number, and inevitably began to clamor for annexation. The admission of Texas as a state of the Union in 1845 naturally led to war with Mexico which, as was to be expected, ended with a victory for the United States. Mexico City was seized; and the defeated country was obliged to give up all its North American possessions: Texas, California, Arizona, New Mexico, Nevada, Utah, and Colorado. Since Florida had already been ceded by Spain in 1819, the Union found itself, by the middle of the nineteenth century, in possession of an unbroken stretch of continent, reaching from ocean to ocean and from the Gulf of Mexico to the Canadian border.

The year 1817 is a mile-stone in the economic development of the Union. In that year was begun the building of the Erie Canal, a gigantic project designed to connect Lake Erie with the Hudson and provide the long-wanted water-way between East and West. By this route the West could ship its products in a direct line to the East; and the East had the whole wide West opened as a market for its manufactures.

For important events were occurring also in the East. Eli Whitney had invented his cotton gin as early as 1793. Almost simultaneously spinning and weaving machines were introduced in England. The consequence of these innovations was an unprecedented boom in cotton-growing and the manufacture of textiles. The whole South was covered with cotton fields. While in 1791 American production accounted for only 0.4 percent of world production, it increased steadily from year to year, till around 1860 it had risen to 66 percent. The cotton was sent north for manufacture, and the textile industry, under a protective tariff, developed rapidly.

The factories needed labor. At first this was provided by women and children; but with the progress of industrialization came an increasing demand. Americans did not find factory-work congenial. The poor preferred going west, where they could begin over again as free men. The problem was solved by renewed European immigration, which furnished a plentiful supply of cheap labor.

We have mentioned that there was little immigration before 1825. Conditions were now changed. The European proletariat poured into America in an ever-widening stream, drawn by the prospect of work and money. The West lay open to the more adventurous. Political refugees found a new home. Valuable men like Carl Schurz and the physician Abraham Jacobi who came over after the Revolution of 1848 were to play an important part in the intellectual life of America. One hundred and fifty-two thousand people immigrated between 1821 and 1830; between 1831–1840 the number rose to 600,000; 1841–1850 it reached 1,700,000; and in the following decade 2,600,000.

By 1860 the population had risen to 31.4 million. And all these people toiled at a feverish rate. The country was flooded with gold. In 1850 the merchant ships outnumbered the English navy. It was true here, if anywhere, that every private carried a marshal's baton in his knapsack. There were no classes and no differences of station. A newsboy could become President. The first Presidents had come from the upper class; they had been in reality aristocrats. But with Andrew Jackson, a man of the people took the wheel. To be sure, he brought with him a political corruption which has never ceased poisoning public life.

The nation was intoxicated with its own activity. Work seemed a moral obligation. But work and making money were synonymous. Getting rich was a patriotic achievement. Money was not only acquired, but, just as now, was most generously given away. The possessor of wealth felt it his bounden duty to expend a large part of it for the public benefit. The contrast to Europe is interesting. The ideal of European capitalism is by toil and economy to build up a fortune which shall make life more comfortable for one's heirs. The care of the poor and the cultivation of art and science are the affair of the state. In America it is believed that the less the state has to say the better. Nowhere in the world has private initiative supported by private endowments solved so many problems which in Europe would be laid at the door of an unavoidably bureaucratic government. What this has meant for medicine, the following chapters will show.

During the middle of the century a wave of optimism swept over the country, finding philosophic expression in the writings of Emerson. Though Emerson is not much read nowadays, his optimistic and fundamentally youthful approach still prevails, in spite of many subsequent bitter experiences. And this, as we shall see, is not without significance for science.

A further characteristic became noticeable at this time. A growing child is stood up periodically against a closet door, and the marks show how much he has grown. In America everything was in a state of growth. No wonder that there was an effort to compute progress by numbers, and that mere size became an object of worship. Great fortunes were made, lost, and remade over night. A tract of land on the periphery of a city might increase in value a hundredfold in the course of a few years. Cities grew at a dizzy rate. In 1804 Fort Dearborn was erected by the government at the edge of a swamp on the south shore of Lake Michigan. The garrison was massacred by the Indians in 1812. The fort was rebuilt and by 1831 a village of 100 inhabitants, called Chicago, had grown up in its shelter. In 1837 the village had grown to a town of 4170 inhabitants. In 1870 the population had risen to 30,000. Ten years later it had quadrupled, and in ten more years it had increased tenfold. In 1900 there were 1.7 million people in Chicago; today there are about 3.5 million. Most of the cities of the West and Middle West developed in a similar way, though on a smaller scale. For a city an increase in population means increase in consumption and production; it means new industries and a rise in the standard of living. The number of the population was made the index of progress; "bigger" and "better" became synonymous. Statistics came to be a popular science. But numbers are also important in the affairs of an individual. For the business man a definite figure, or his balance at hand, measures the success or failure of his year's work. In a society almost entirely made up of business men, and in which the salaried worker played no great part, there would naturally be a tendency to evaluate everything in terms of figures, including things of the mind and the capacities and usefulness of men. This is another problem to which we must return later.

Fortune favored the economic development of America as if it were its guardian angel. Mexico ceded California in 1848, and before the year was up gold was found not far from Sacramento, on the estate of General Sutter, a Swiss by birth. Here was suddenly a new and even swifter source of wealth. A race for the far West started in 1849. The journey was long and dangerous. The gold lay beyond deserts and mountains, or else at the end of an interminable sea-voyage, but the lure of gold could not be resisted. The dreamy land of California, with its blue skies and tropical palms, its Spanish houses and baroque churches—a land whose fruitfulness had only just been discovered—was changed in an instant to a battleground of unleashed passions. Adventurers from all over the world, proscribed criminals, and every sort of derelict crowded together in this new Eldorado. No law was heeded; no life was counted of any consequence; gold was all that mattered. The city of St. Francis was swollen to bursting. By the time the gold rush was over, the last kernel had been picked up. Peace returned and the country became a garden. The only gold remaining was the Golden Gate, the harbor of San Francisco, shining every evening in the light of the setting sun. And the golden oranges. But in the meanwhile the national wealth had been increased by countless millions.

Such unorganized progress could not proceed without reverses. Economic crises occurred again and again. But America was in a more fortunate situation than other countries. During the business depression of 1837, those thrown out of work could be absorbed by the great West. When, after a period of soaring prosperity during the Crimean War, another depression came in 1857, gold was quite unexpectedly found in Colorado.

The country was limitless and the treasures of its soil were beyond measure.

Nevertheless, the nation had severe trials before it; a very different sort of crisis had to be met. North and South had grown away from each other. From the very beginning, conditions had differed in the northern and southern colonies. Climate, economic conditions, and the whole manner of life were dissimilar. While the influx of immigration turned New York more and more into an international metropolis, and the North as a whole became more and more industrialized, the South adhered to its old habits, remaining an agricultural country of enormous cotton-plantations, with Negro slaves as working capital. Northern industry was protected by tariffs considered by the South injurious to its own interests. The two groups were held together in a Union in the founding and building-up of which southerners and slave-holders had taken a prominent part. Time widened the breach. Slavery was naturally an inconsistency in a state founded on the proposition that "all men are created equal" and that "life, liberty, and the pursuit of happiness" belong to the inalienable rights of man. The abolition of slavery became a slogan which cost the North nothing and meant ruin to the South.

The idea of secession had been played with before this and sometimes used as a threat by the South. The threat became earnest when on December 20, 1860, South Carolina withdrew from the Union, and within a few months fourteen other states followed her example, formed a federation, and elected Jefferson Davis as President. The great, prosperous, ambitious country had suddenly fallen apart. Fifteen slave states opposed eighteen free states. What was to happen? New England was not altogether reluctant to part with the South. It was the intervention of the West that saved the Union—that West which had no colonial history, which was purely American, a creation of the federal government which it now hoped to preserve. The West and the men of the common people. Lincoln and Grant, the two men who guided the country through those desperate years, were both westerners and both close to the soil.

War was unavoidable. In April, 1861, the first shots were fired. The Civil War lasted four years and was fought on a huge front with fearful losses. Lincoln, who was inaugurated in March, 1861, fought to preserve the Union rather than liberate the slaves. The slave question at first fell into the background; and only later in the war, under pressure of public opinion, was emancipation proclaimed.

The North had the greater man-power, and controlled industry and the fleet, so that it was able to blockade its opponent. The South had better disciplined troops and more competent officers, among them the most competent of all, Robert E. Lee. The war was fought chiefly on southern ground and became for the South a struggle for freedom and independence, carried on by the entire population with magnificent heroism. The South, closely connected by its cotton interests with France and more especially with England, had counted on their assistance. But though a war of independence was sure to rouse the sympathies of Europe, the idea of slavery was very unpopular. As no help came (Napoleon III, on the contrary, using the opportunity to play his own game in Mexico) the victory could not long remain in doubt. Lee was forced to surrender in April, 1865.

The South was defeated, and the Union was saved. The war was over. With wise prevision Lincoln recognized that it was now a matter of rebuilding and conciliating the South, and making it again a willing part of the Union. Then, five days after the signing of peace, Lincoln was assassinated.

Now came ten bad years. The North had done good business during the war; and the battle losses had been made good by immigration. The South was laid waste. Its whole economic structure was destroyed. And to crown everything, the North proceeded to revenge itself for the South's disloyalty. The struggle for independence was termed a rebellion which called for punishment. The country was subjected to military occupation and sucked dry by corrupt officials. The Negroes were incited to violence against their former masters. In some states they were in the majority. It was true that they had their freedom, but this gave them no understanding of politics. The ensuing chaos may be readily imagined. And the South had not yet recovered from the blows of war.

The ten years went by. In 1876 the Union could look back on a hundred years of existence. A World's Fair was held in Philadelphia, where could be seen the latest technical inventions. It had been a stormy century. But the nation was once more united, and peace restored. The country could begin to grow again.

One vast stretch of territory still remained to be conquered. The great waste of prairie between the Middle West and the Rocky Mountains had till now seemed worthless and formidable. This time the railroad turned pioneer. The first railroad connection between the two oceans was completed in 1869. This powerful line, a private undertaking, of course, though receiving support from the federal government, took only a few years to build. Starting from Omaha it ran across the prairie, over the Rockies, and past the Great Salt Lake into California. The Union Pacific and the Central Pacific were only the beginning. Many more transcontinental roads followed to the north and south, opening up the country in every direction. The Indians, whose last domains were now encroached upon, resisted and had to be put down; and were eventually provided for in special reservations.

The railroad made possible the shipment of cattle to Chicago slaughter-houses; and great herds were driven by cow-

boys from the Texas plains to the freight-stations farther
north. Then the day came when it was discovered that the
prairie was not a desert and that its soil could bear fruit. The
pasture-land became farming-country.

From this discovery in the year 1890 dates the end of the
frontier period. The continent was now parcelled out, settled,
and put in order. The romantic Wild West was a thing of the
past. Gone were the days of the trappers, the Gold Rush, Buffalo Bill, and the cowboys. The world had become more sober
and more objective. But, though on a different plane, there
was, and still is, plenty of romance to be found. America is still
a pioneer country, though there are no longer virgin forests to
chop down nor Indians to subdue. In other spheres there are
wide stretches of territory that have not yet been conquered.

The immediate developments of the next period were vertical
rather than horizontal. Powerful business organizations were
built up. Financial, industrial, and transportation enterprises
formed groups that dominated trade and politics. The trusts
rose to power, little by little acquiring entire control of a
product, from raw material to finished article. They were opposed, but their strength was unbroken. The soil brought forth
its immeasurable riches. A hole was bored, and oil gushed from
the ground. The automobile began its triumphant progress. The
factory belt was set running. Control remained in the hands of
a few men, not in Washington, but in New York. Gigantic
fortunes were made. This stupendous development found a
visual symbol in the tall buildings which make a fairyland of
New York, and lend every big city at moments—Philadelphia
seen at evening from the new Art Museum, Chicago on the
Lake Shore, San Francisco from the Berkeley ferry—the aspect
of a Fata Morgana.

Production and sale continued, and the population multiplied
and bought more and more goods. Millions of people poured

from Europe in steadily increasing numbers. From 1871–80 there were 2.8 million; in 1881–90, 5.2 million; 1891–1900, 3.6 million; 1901–10, as much as 8.7 million; 1911–20, 5.7 million. But a singular shift took place in the composition of the immigrant group. Up to 1890, the overwhelming majority of immigrants had been English or, if not, Irish, Scotch, Germans, Scandinavians, or Swiss. Missouri had been largely settled by Germans; cities like St. Louis and, even more, Cincinnati and Milwaukee had a definitely German character. Scandinavians left their mark on Minnesota and the Dakotas. But after 1890 the situation was completely changed. From now on the preponderant number of immigrants come from Slavic or Latin countries: South Italians, Greeks, Poles, and Jews from Eastern Europe. Of the immigrants entering the United States from 1861–70, 98.4 percent belonged to Nordic and only 1.6 percent to Slavic or Latin peoples. From 1911–20 the proportion is reversed. During this period 22.8 percent belonged to Nordic and 77.2 percent to Slavic and Mediterranean races. And whereas the English and Germans had come over with the intention of settling and building for themselves a new existence, these newcomers were for the most part illiterate proletarians who entered the country with the hope of earning a little money to take back with them to their native land. These are the people one sometimes comes across in lonely huts perched in a niche of the Peloponnesian hills, who tell one in English how they once polished shoes in New York. Most of them, it is true, remain in the New World, finding work in the factories of Michigan, taking up all sorts of small trades, or adding to the proletariat of the big cities. They form national groups with their own churches and their own segregated streets. We see something new in American history. The early immigrants were assimilated without any trouble and very shortly turned into good Americans, but this later wave of immigration was difficult to assimilate and threatened to transform the whole character of the nation. The well-known immigration laws determining a fixed quota for every country were for this reason an absolutely essential measure of defence.

The nation continued to grow. Even the South participated in the development of industry. Conflicts arose between employers and employees, not in regard to the system, since all were equally convinced adherents of capitalism, but in regard to wages, the division of profits, the opportunities for gain. The capitalistic system reached its highest peak. Whether it can ever maintain itself at that point for any length of time, the future will show. To a pronounced individualism inherited from pioneer days was added, through the agency of industrial mass production and the standardization of ideas and things, a special form of collectivism. No country is less receptive to Marxism, but none is essentially nearer to Russia. It is only the symptoms which differ.

So tremendous a country presupposes a tremendous home market. But by efficient management and steady improvement in machinery, production capacity was heightened to such an extent that winning new markets by means of imperialistic expansion seemed the only solution. The nearest vulnerable territory lay in Central and South America and in Eastern Asia. In 1898 a more or less forced conflict with Spain provided the excuse for annexing Porto Rico and the Philippines, and making Cuba nominally free but economically dependent on America. In the same year the Hawaiian Islands were brought by peaceful means under American domination. Hawaii and the Philippines, it should be noted, are navy stations of the first rank.

Now that America owned islands in the eastern and western oceans, a water-route connecting her possessions became an immediate problem. The Panama Canal was built (1906–1914) after local unrest had been adroitly fanned and exploited in order to get possession of the needed territory, and after, as we shall see, physicians had accomplished the great work which made it possible to succeed where the French had failed.

Then one day an Austrian archduke was murdered in Eastern Europe, and the World War broke out. True to its principle of non-interference in European affairs, America declared her neutrality. The demand for American goods was enormous; export trade assumed gigantic proportions, and industry worked at a feverish pace. But it was difficult to do business in a warring world without giving offense. Conflicts multiplied; and we all remember how in the Spring of 1917 America declared war on Germany and, with all the energy with which she had brought so many great questions to a successful solution, now met this problem also, putting a million men under arms and by this influx of fresh troops finally deciding the war in favor of the Allies.

For the first time in over a hundred years the United States became involved in European politics. Behind its actions lay a great deal of idealism and romance, some sentimentality and a touch of war psychosis. But what country was free of these manifestations? The ordinary enlisted man believed that this was a war for democracy and liberty and against tyranny. There was much talk of Lafayette and the debt of gratitude to France. It must not be forgotten that America, on first entering the war, formally relinquished all war-profits in the ordinary sense. Economic gains were hers in plenty without active military participation.

The reaction came very soon. The crowds of returning troops were obviously not very enthusiastic about their visit to the old world. Interest again centered at home; the traditional Monroe Doctrine resumed its old power. Now that every one had sobered down, Wilson's high-sounding ideology found little response. Europe was a mass of ruins, torn by conflicting passions. Why have anything more to do with it? The victory was won. Back to normalcy. Wilson's peace-treaty, which would have permanently bound the United States to Europe through adherence to the League of Nations, was voted down.

America's industrial organization was intact. Her war-losses were small, less than the country's annual loss by accident. After an unavoidable crisis, brought about by the liquidation of the war, and the presence of a surplus of supplies, came a period of unprecedented prosperity. Gold poured into the country, and in 1928 it was possible for a President to believe that poverty was about to be abolished. But we must always bear in mind that these years that were only yesterday were not only the era of jazz, radio, short skirts, crime waves, and all sorts of record-breaking activities, not only the age of exaggerated materialism; no, much of the money made in those years was turned to great, constructive tasks. It went to the founding of museums, concert-halls and schools; and we shall come to see how just at this time medical institutions such as hospitals and schools underwent a complete reorganization.

Then in the fall of 1929 came the crash. A dream was over; an illusion had been dispelled. America was brutally reminded that she did not stand alone in the world, but was a part of the general economic life. The depression followed, in the midst of which we still live. For America, it has been a fortunate thing. Perhaps in the perspective of future centuries the year 1929 will appear as the beginning of a new era.

Looking back on the history of these three hundred years, we are aware of a never ceasing struggle, with the elements, with the Indians, and with the soil itself; a struggle for necessities, for comfort, and for wealth. Culture and the things of the spirit came out the little end of the horn. The promising beginnings of the colonial period were nipped in the bud by the sudden rise of industrialism. It is true that America has produced great writers like Longfellow, Edgar Allan Poe, Mark Twain, and above all, Walt Whitman; and a painter and etcher of the calibre of Whistler. But many of these men, like Poe and Whistler, though American by birth, really belonged to the cultural life of Europe. In their own country their influence usually amounted to little. It is also true that in the Negro spirituals and the songs made by cowboys and the men who built the great railroads America has the beginnings of native poetry. Still, there can be no doubt that during the nineteenth and early twentieth centuries thought and imagination played a very subordinate rôle in the national life.

Today, on the contrary, we can perceive a marked change; a return to the spirit. The opportunities for sudden wealth are at an end. The material living standard has had to be lowered, but the standard for schools and colleges has been raised. After the headlong *fugato* comes a *fermata*. The pioneer spirit is still with us, and there are still virgin forests and broad wastes of prairie to subdue; but these lie within the domain of intellectual life. And the fight has already begun.

CHAPTER FOUR

PIONEERS

BEFORE we begin the systematic discussion of American medicine we must make the acquaintance of individual men. Here as everywhere there were, first of all, men; institutions came later. At the present moment this sequence is occasionally reversed, to the general disadvantage.

We have seen that medical conditions during colonial times were of necessity primitive. To bring about changes, to approximate European standards, to keep in step with progress abroad—this was the task of individual men, leaders who cleared the way. Their difficulties were the greater since the situation in the western frontier-country was altogether different from that in Europe. Here the physician was confronted with problems whose solution could not be learned by heart in the old world and quite simply carried over into the new. Here he became a pioneer, in the literal meaning of the word.

We can single out only a few of these path-finders. Their number is large. Many are still living among us, for in the science of medicine as elsewhere, the age of pioneers has not yet come to an end. There are still certain recalcitrant territories, waiting for the man who is to bring them under control.

John Morgan (1735–1789) and Benjamin Rush (1745–1813)

Their field of action was Philadelphia. There was only ten years' difference in their ages and their careers were nearly identical. They studied under similar conditions, and both served as physicians in the Revolutionary army, both holding positions of rank. They worked in the same hospital. They were both aggressive, though very different in character.

John Morgan's father was a Welsh immigrant. The son wanted to be a physician. The customary method was to become the pupil of a physician. Dr. John Redman was at that time a distinguished practitioner in Philadelphia, who attracted many students; and so we find Morgan under his tutelage for the six years which were the usual period of study. At the same time he was attending the college founded by Franklin and, in 1757, was among the first to receive the bachelor's degree. After that he went to war. War had broken out between England and France. Pennsylvania raised troops, and Morgan went along as surgeon. What better chance for practice in surgery could have been given him?

However, he did not wait for peace to be declared. Bent on further study, he sailed for Europe in 1760. First to London, where he studied anatomy under William Hunter. This more than anything he had missed at home. And how necessary the knowledge of anatomy is had been shown him during his service as an army surgeon. In William Hunter, who was equally remarkable as anatomist, surgeon, and obstetrician, he found a splendid teacher. He also met William's younger brother, John Hunter, who was on the point of embarking as navy-surgeon in that same war against France in which Morgan himself had taken part.

William Hunter was from Edinburgh, where he had studied with Cullen; and now Edinburgh became Morgan's goal also. The Edinburgh faculty, with the two Alexander Monroe's, father and son, Cullen as clinician, as well as Whytt, Rutherford, and Hope, was then at its highest point; and whenever in those days American physicians came to Europe, Edinburgh was their first objective.

Morgan remained two years. He learned a great deal, and eventually obtained his degree in 1763, on the occasion of his presenting a dissertation on the *Formation of Pus*. But his student period was not yet finished. He went to Paris and spent a winter there, mostly in the study of chemistry; and won his first laurels. Coming from Hunter, he was past master in anatomical technique. He devised an apparatus for kidney-injections which was so superlative that the doors of the Académie de Chirurgie were opened to him as a member.

He continued his travels as far as Italy. Americans had already a predilection for celebrities; and so on his way through Geneva Morgan did not neglect to call on Voltaire. He then went over the Alps to Padua, where he was pleasantly received by old Morgagni, who had just published his great work *De sedibus et causis morborum*, which laid the foundation of pathological anatomy.

It is delightful to picture this young American in Padua. We see the venerable university, where Pietro d'Abano taught, where Fracastoro studied, where Vesalius spent the decisive years of his life, where Harvey received such deep impressions, where now Morgagni has been working for half a century. Along comes a young man from a distant colony, from an unknown world, greedy to see and to learn. Morgagni rejoiced in the young man and presented him with his works inscribed in the author's handwriting. They are still to be seen in Philadelphia.

Morgan went on his way; he returned to England, was given the licentiate of the Royal College of Physicians, became a member of the Royal Society. He was no longer a beginner. He was known, appreciated, well spoken of; and much was expected of him.

He had now been in Europe for five years, and had absorbed much learning. Above all, he had seen how medicine was studied in the old world, he had observed old and modern universities. He recalled the conditions at home, his own student years with Dr. Redman. There was much one could learn, even by these methods, but was not a sound theoretical basis absolutely essential? Medicine was no longer a craft but a science, the employment and advancement of which was urgent. Medicine was a branch of the Universitas litterarum.

Gradually an idea evolves and takes form. Might it not be possible, even over there in the new world, to raise medicine to the level of a university subject? Very few can afford the luxury of a trip to Europe. It is high time that the colonies offer their sons a possibility of the very best education. The facilities exist. Philadelphia has its high schools, its colleges. These can be expanded. A hospital lies available, adequate to meet all demands. He sits down in Paris, where he happens to be, and begins to work out a project for the institution of medical schools in America. He is full of the plan; talks it over with his friends, his teachers; and gives them his manuscript to read.

In April, 1765, he returns to Philadelphia. He brings with him a fund of knowledge, his manuscript—and a silk umbrella which causes a tremendous sensation. People rush to the window to see him pass. Europe has certainly affected him in many ways! Above all, he brings a letter from Thomas Penn to the Trustees of the College, warmly recommending his plan. So no time is lost. He comes back in April. Already, on May 3rd, the Board of Trustees has held a meeting, at which they accept the plan and appoint Morgan Professor of Theoretic and Practical Medicine at the College. On the 30th and 31st of May, on the occasion of the close of the semester and the graduating of students, Morgan in his ceremonial gown made his great speech, "Discourse upon the Institution of Medical Schools in America." He had a great deal to say and spoke on two consecutive days.

The idea had become actuality. We have seen how William Shippen, another Philadelphia physician, who had pursued a similar course of study abroad, and had returned in 1762, three years before Morgan, had begun to give instruction in anatomy, surgery, and obstetrics. This was carried on entirely as a private matter, but the thought of a school had lately come into his mind.

Morgan, on the other hand, knew exactly what he was driving at. He saw and had no hesitation in stating that private organizations depending on individuals are never stable, that nothing but a connection with a university can offer assurance of stability. Shippen's valuable qualifications as a teacher were soon recognized and as early as September, 1765, he was appointed Professor of Anatomy and Surgery.

The courses began in November. The faculty was still very small, but the gaps were gradually filled out. A pupil of Linné's, Adam Kuhn, was made Professor of Materia Medica and of Botany. In 1769 Benjamin Rush became Professor of Chemistry. Clinical instruction was given at the hospital by one of its physicians, Thomas Bond, and the Provost of the College, Smith, gave lectures on natural science.

In this way Philadelphia, in the year 1769, possessed a faculty of medicine which was the peer of European institutions, indeed superior to many because of its up-to-date curriculum. In 1768 ten students were for the first time given the degree of Bachelor of Medicine; the first degrees of Doctor of Medicine followed three years later.

It was a great step forward. A model had been created. It had been shown how, without great ostentation or expense, and using existing equipment, it was possible to give medical instruction an academic form. And this was without doubt Morgan's greatest contribution.

He was from every standpoint an innovator. Immediately after his return from Europe he began private practice, and as his reputation had preceded him, there was no lack of patients. While heretofore there had been no separation between medicine and surgery, and every physician was his own apothecary, Morgan announced that he would have nothing to do with surgery nor would he dispense drugs. He had even imported one David Leighton, who had been trained in England and was equally versed in surgery and pharmaceutics. To him he sent his prescriptions to be filled.

This, too, was an innovation, and moreover an innovation which met with great opposition on the part of physicians, since it was a question of hard cash. It was from their medicines that physicians frequently derived the greatest part of their income. However, this was exactly what seemed to Morgan unbefitting a physician. It led, so ran his argument, to a lack of appreciation for the physician's service. The patient, who is charged a definite fee for his treatment, is not aware what portion of the sum is the cost of the drugs and how much is in payment of medical advice. He is only too much inclined to assume that the expense lies primarily in the cost of the medicine. And besides, Morgan goes on, is it not better to have the prescriptions filled by a skilled apothecary than by young students? For as a rule it was not the physician but his pupils who prepared the prescriptions.

Morgan was also busy organizing in other directions. In the same year that the faculty was established, in 1765, he initiated a medical society, which a few years later merged into the American Philosophical Society, in the organization of which he took a leading part; as in that of the College of Physicians in 1787, a medical academy in the manner of the London and Edinburgh colleges.

Now came the Revolution and the war with England. In 1775 Morgan was appointed by Congress General Director of Military Hospitals and Physician-in-Chief of the Army. A wide new field was opened to his gift for organization, a field full of thorns, however. The army was very much disorganized; the sanitary division especially so. Morgan went forward without fear or favor, fighting abuses wherever he found them. But he ran his head against a stone wall.

It is not easy to put over reforms in education; it is still more

5. JOHN MORGAN
1735–1789

6. BENJAMIN RUSH

1745–1813

difficult to convert the medical profession to an innovation. But the most impossible thing of all is to attempt to meddle with army institutions; especially for an outsider. Intrigues arose against Morgan, which caused his downfall within a year. He was dismissed by Congress, which appointed as his successor his colleague and rival, Shippen. Morgan retired full of resentment, took up his pen and wrote a violent pamphlet in his own defense.

Back in Philadelphia, Morgan resumed his interrupted practice. Since 1773 he had been attached as physician to the hospital where he had once worked as Redman's pupil and had mixed drugs in the pharmacy. But here too, evidently, he became involved in dissensions. He resigned in 1783. He withdrew more and more into retirement and died in October, 1789. (Fig. 5)

Benjamin Rush (*1745–1813*)

His successor in the chair of Practical and Theoretical Medicine was Benjamin Rush. (Fig. 6)

The faculty had become deeply involved in the revolutionary struggle. Students and instructors were at the front. More unfortunately still, party strife threatened the University itself. It was considered too conservative; and one day in the year 1779 it was incontinently suppressed, a new university, the University of the State of Pennsylvania, being set up in its place. A senseless proceeding this; the closing of the University of Paris during the French Revolution was a different matter, putting an end to what was already rigid under the accumulated tradition of centuries. Here, on the contrary, was a young institution, in its first stages of tentative growth, to which violence would not bring freedom, but destruction.

The new university made every effort to induce the staff of the former college to join its ranks. It met with no great success and those professors who gradually accepted the call, did so only with the purpose of keeping alive the idea of a medical school.

The college, however, had determined friends, with Benjamin Franklin at their head. In 1783, thanks to their exertions, its suppression was annulled. The professors returned in a body. Philadelphia now found itself in an impossible situation as the seat of two competing universities, each with its own medical faculty.

Eventually common sense got the upper hand. In 1791, after the excitement of war had subsided, the two universities were merged into the University of Pennsylvania, still one of the leading universities of the country. Both corps of professors were taken over; and in this way a most notable faculty was brought together. Shippen was again made Professor of Anatomy and Obstetrics, with Caspar Wistar, a prominent anatomist, as associate; Adam Kuhn assumed the teaching of theory and practice; and Rush became Professor of Institutions and of Clinical Medicine. Chemistry was represented by James Hutchinson; materia medica and pharmaceutics by Samuel P. Griffitts; botany and natural history by Benjamin Smith Barton.

For Benjamin Rush this marked the beginning of a new chapter; one in which all his activities were centered around medicine and which led to his becoming the founder of the American clinic. His previous life had been full of variety. Born of a Quaker family of English descent, he had, like Morgan, spent six years studying with Redman after taking his bachelor's degree at Princeton; then, again like Morgan, had gone to Edinburgh where he graduated in 1768; and after a study-tour in France he had, four years later than Morgan, returned to Philadelphia, where he was immediately, at the age of 24, given the chair of Chemistry at the College.

He had pursued his studies with fervor. Even as a very young student he had translated the aphorisms of Hippocrates into English. He was one of the first to attend Shippen's lectures on anatomy, and in 1762, during a fever epidemic, he kept a detailed diary which later provided him with valuable material. His objective differed from that of Morgan. He was interested not so much in shaping an outward form for the science of medicine as in enlarging its scope. He lived the early part of his life in the greatest retirement and would never have been seen walking with a silk umbrella. As he said once, medicine was his wife, science his mistress, books his companions; his study was his grave where he lay buried, forgetting the world and by it forgotten. Which did not prevent his later taking to himself a corporeal wife and begetting thirteen children. He remained in this retirement only while the fighter in him was still dormant.

For his was a fiery heart. The ideals of the Enlightenment burned in him as they did in Franklin. Liberty, the Rights of Man were to him no empty phrases. With Franklin he helped found a Society for the Protection of the Free Negroes, and was made president after Franklin's death. He suffered from the anomaly that there should be slaves in a country of free citizens. He was the champion of free schools and of religious toleration; he fought the abuse of alcohol and tobacco, as well as the too free use of profanity. Many of his writings are still very much to the point and deserve to be reprinted and read; as, for instance, the paper in which he criticizes the senselessness of the penal system, especially in the case of capital punishment. "I have no more doubt of every crime," he says, "having its cure in moral and physical influence than I have of the efficacy of the Peruvian bark in curing intermittent fever." Besides his public work he carried on a large practice. When the Revolution came, it found him ready. As a member of the Continental Congress of 1777 he was one of the signers of the Declaration of Independence. He later became Surgeon-General of the Revolutionary Army. But he soon resigned, having, like Morgan, become entangled in a net of intrigue. He returned to practical medicine, in which as teacher and physician he took an ever-increasing part.

The philosophers of the Enlightenment were of necessity dogmatists. They championed their doctrines with the conviction and zeal of soldiers waging the wars of religion. When these philosophers chanced to be at the same time physicians, their dogmatism might easily reveal itself in their medical beliefs.

This was the case with Rush. It is true that for Sydenham, whose works he had translated into English, he had the greatest admiration. But he himself was the product of Cullen's school, which was the cradle of neuropathology. Cullen's philosophical attitude, his tendency towards systematization, could not help making a powerful appeal to a nature such as Rush's. Another product of Cullen's school had been John Brown, whose *Elementa Medicinae* appeared in 1780 and was to bring about a revolution in therapy. The concepts of irritability, of sthenia and asthenia, would naturally capture the enthusiasm of a medical world which was just then beginning to think in physiological terms.

In 1793 a fearful epidemic of yellow fever raged in Philadelphia. Rush, who had seen the first cases in August of that year, drew attention to the impending danger, and was laughed at for his concern. The contagion spread at a terrific rate, and for weeks panic possessed the town. A graphic account written by the publisher and bookseller Matthew Carey describes scenes which bring to our minds Boccaccio's pictures of the plague in Florence. Those who could do so fled. Parents forsook their children and children their parents, but there was no town that would shelter the fugitives. Mad rumors were afloat as to means of protecting oneself. Women and children went about with huge cigars in their mouths; people chewed garlic all day long or merely kept some in their pockets or their shoes. In many houses gun-powder, tobacco or alum were constantly kept burning, or vinegar was sprinkled at intervals. People did not dare to walk along the walls of houses but would run down the middle of the street to avoid poisonous exhalations. Regardless of class the dead were buried without even the simplest funeral service. Thousands fell victims to the fever.

It is the same old drama of pestilence, which has been replayed so often all over the world.

As is always the case, there were shown in this extremity examples of great heroism. The physicians did whatever was humanly possible, Benjamin Rush above all others. He saw close relatives succumb to the infection; was himself taken sick; but he would not give up. While the epidemic was at its height he visited from a hundred to a hundred and twenty-five patients a day. A method of treatment was sought. Rush, too, had the problem in his mind and found his answer in following the principles laid down by Brown. The disease seemed to him to be a sthenic condition. He endeavored to remove the causes of excessive stimulation by means of blood-letting, cold air, cold drinks, restricted diet, and cold-water applications. The results convinced him of the correctness of his premises. The sick crowded to his door.

The epidemic died down. Rush, however, remained a convinced adherent of the Brunonian theories; he became their propagator. With the same passion with which he had championed social reforms, he now threw himself into the fight for medical ideals. For the battle was a serious one. He was violently attacked on account of his drastic remedies. Profuse bleedings and large doses of calomel were his main reliance. He subjected himself to further attacks by ascribing the ultimate responsibility for the epidemic to the filth of the city. In contrast to Morgan, he wielded a facile pen; and fierce polemics were the result.

The fight around the Brunonian theories was ended early in the nineteenth century, when the Paris clinical school showed the way out. Rush is the child of the eighteenth century Enlightenment; he is essentially a philosopher. His services to medicine are not to be sought in his theories, which were conditioned by his period and died with it. But he was not alone a philosopher and a theorist; he was a great physician and in the hands of a great physician all theories achieve results, since he will never be unbendingly dogmatic in his practice but, faithful to his professional intuition, will put aside his theories when the case demands it. Rush himself has often discarded old beliefs for new and has never hesitated to admit it. His observations on cholera infantum, on the relations between rheumatism and diseases of the teeth were anything but dogmatic and very far in advance of their time.

He was also a great teacher. Thousands of young medical men passed through his school and learned from him how to observe, and to reason from a clinical standpoint.

However, his greatest services lie probably in the field of social medicine. From 1783 on, he was physician at the Pennsylvania Hospital. During the thirty years in which he held this position, the mentally ill were his greatest concern. He saw to it that there was improvement in their living conditions and in the care of the sick; that adequate bathing facilities were provided to keep them decently clean; and that troublesome visitors were kept away. But above all he sought to cure mental illnesses. "We assume," he says in a letter, "that insanity has its seat in the mind. And nevertheless we attempt with remarkable inconsistency to cure it by physical methods. The disease affects the body and mind alike and can be cured only by methods which reach both." Work and diversion seemed to him remedies for mental illnesses. In this regard he was a pioneer in occupational therapy. It goes without saying that when the first dispensary was founded in America in 1786, Rush was among its supporters.

And finally, he is a part of the great hygienic movement which belongs to the medical history of the Enlightenment. He had seen at first hand the fearful effects of yellow fever and had reached the conclusion that such epidemics could be warded off as men had learned to ward off lightning. He said once, prophetically, "The time will come when courts of justice will punish cities and villages if they allow the sources of bilious and malignant fever to persist in their midst."

Rush has been called the American Sydenham. The designation is unfortunate. Rush and Sydenham belong to quite different categories. Rush, too, was of course a clinician, but he was beyond that a man of the Enlightenment, embodying its highest ideals.

John Morgan and Benjamin Rush are merely two men singled out of a group of prominent physicians; but to these two Philadelphia first of all owes the fact that, in the field of medicine, it became a model to the other cities of the Union.

Ephraim McDowell (1771–1830)

The next scene is laid in Kentucky on a farm. After the peace of Paris, settlers from Virginia had begun to push westward over the mountains and to clear the forests. At first there were very few; after the Revolution they came in greater numbers. Three counties were founded which, united into one state, Kentucky, were taken into the Union in 1792.

On this Kentucky farm, later known as Motley's Glen, Thomas Crawford led the life of a pioneer. His wife, Jane Todd Crawford, thought herself pregnant. She knew the symptoms. She had already borne five children. Her body swelled. Her time drew near. But she felt no life stirring within her. Her body grew bigger and bigger. Something was wrong. A neighboring doctor was called in; then a second. Neither had any advice to give, and they suggested sending sixty miles away for Ephraim McDowell, so that he might deliver her. He was known as a good surgeon. (Fig. 7)

He came on horseback, the instruments and medicines in his saddle-bags, as was the habit of pioneer-doctors. He arrived

December 13, 1809. He made an examination, and soon found that this was no pregnancy, but a tumor. What was to be done? There were no hospitals in that region, no professors whose counsel could be sought. Here everyone was thrown on his own resources. But the resolution with which the pioneers had faced Indians and wilderness was alive in their physicians as well; theirs was the same initiative, the same practical good sense. McDowell came to the conclusion that nothing short of an operation, the removal of the tumor with a knife, would be of any use. It was an unheard-of risk to take. No such operation had ever been carried out. The dressing of wounds, the care of broken bones and sprains, amputations, stones, ruptures, tracheotomies: these were at that time the whole scope of surgery. A serious abdominal surgery did not exist.

He talked quite frankly to the patient, did not hide from her the danger she was running; explained to her that this was an experiment and asked whether she were willing to submit herself to it. She was willing. The wives of pioneers were brave women. They shrank from no exertion. They did not even dread Indians. How could a pioneer's wife get along with such a growth in her body? She would be no good to anyone. Yes, she would let herself be operated upon.

McDowell asked her to go with him to his house in Danville. She climbed up on the horse. It was the middle of winter. The tumor rested on the pommel. The journey had to be slow and lasted several days.

Then came the great moment. The patient lay on the table. A nephew of McDowell's who had studied in Philadelphia and a young pupil assisted at the operation. The abdominal cavity was laid wide open. The patient gritted her teeth. There appeared a large pedunculated cystic tumor of one ovary. The tube was ligated and the cyst opened, evacuated, and finally removed. In the meantime the patient recited psalms. It lasted twenty-five minutes; then it was over.

Coming into the room five days later, McDowell found the patient making her own bed. On the twenty-fifth day she drove home. She lived thirty-one years longer.

That is the whole story. But here we have the first ovariotomy. The pioneer spirit had won a new field for surgery.

McDowell was thirteen years old when he came to Kentucky from Virginia. His father, of Scotch descent, was active in the local administration. His son was sent to study with a Dr. Humphrey in Staunton, Virginia. After this, in 1793, he went to Edinburgh, where he spent one year. He did not graduate. His chief interest was in surgery, and he attended the lectures which were given outside of the University by John Bell.

In 1795 he returned to Danville, a town of less than a thousand inhabitants, but at that time the capital of Kentucky. He soon acquired a large surgical practice.

During 1813 he operated upon a second case of ovarian cyst; in 1816 upon a third case. These operations were again successful. It occurred to him to make his findings public. He described them in a few pages, not in learned jargon, but in simple straightforward words. He was no literary man. The article appeared in a medical magazine published in Philadelphia, the *Eclectic Repertory and Analytical Review,* Vol. VII, in the year 1817. He was laughed at. Here was a man from the backwoods, telling tall stories. They tried to show him that he had overshot his mark. But he did not let himself be turned aside. In 1819 he brought forward two additional cases. This time he was heeded. He found followers, first in America, then in Europe, till gradually his operation became the common heritage of surgery and gynecology.

The University of Maryland, in 1827, conferred on him the honorary degree of doctor of medicine—his first academic degree. In Danville, where his work was done, there stands a monument, a slender pyramid bearing his portrait. His home, a simple frame house, has been preserved, and one can see the room where the first operation was performed. That is all. A homely story, very moving in its simplicity.

Daniel Drake (*1785–1852*)

The scene is again laid in Kentucky. A block-house, put together with rough logs. The Drake family had moved from New Jersey in 1788, bringing nothing but their two horses and the load of one wagon. They were simple, uneducated people. Their idea was to cut down trees and to plow the land. But their children should see better things.

Daniel was then three years old. He grew up in the woods, in the open air; and came into an intimate relationship with all natural things. He helped chop down trees and cultivate the soil. There were no schools, but now and then a wandering schoolmaster or preacher passed through the country, was given lodging by the settlers, and remained a while, teaching the children to read and write. Their calloused fingers learned to guide a pen.

An uncle of Daniel's was the storekeeper of the settlement. He had chosen the better part, earned a pretty income, and was able to send his son to study medicine in Philadelphia. When the cousin came home for the holidays, Daniel would pore over his text-books.

He, too, wanted to become a doctor. To be sure, the family had no means of sending him to Philadelphia, but his father had a scheme. On the trip down the Ohio he had become acquainted with a Dr. Goforth, who was also making his way west. He had settled first in their neighborhood, but later moved to Cincinnati, the city in Ohio which promised to have the greatest future. At that time, it held less than a thousand inhabitants. This Dr. Goforth, was willing, for $400 compensation, to take young Drake into his home and train him as a physician.

By December, 1800, when Drake was fifteen years old, the family affairs had gone so well that he was able to ride to town

7. EPHRAIM MC DOWELL
1771–1830

Iau Drake, M.D.

8. DANIEL DRAKE
1785–1852

and knock on his preceptor's door. The time for learning had arrived. He read all his teacher's little library: Cheselden's *Anatomy*, Haller's *Physiology*, the works of Boerhaave and van Swieten. Rush was forbidden, since Goforth had no use for his therapy. But in secret Drake devoured everything by Rush that he could lay his hands on and had no greater wish than to see and hear the author in person. As for the rest, he compounded salves, mixed drugs, and accompanied his teacher on his professional rounds. At the same time he went to school, to learn Latin. He was ambitious, and determined to better himself, and neglected no educational opportunities.

After only four years of study, Goforth took Drake into partnership. But Drake wanted more learning. Using his first earnings, and armed with a diploma certifying that he had successfully completed his period of preparation, he made his way to Philadelphia and for five months attended the courses at the University. He heard Rush and was enraptured by his lectures. Then he went back to Cincinnati, later practising for a while in the village where his parents lived. But the field was too limited for him. He returned to Cincinnati again and lived there until 1815 as a distinguished physician and an active member of a young and progressive community.

A western practice was no simple matter. The patients as a rule lived great distances apart. There was nothing unusual in a ride of fifteen to twenty miles through darkness and fog; one needed a good constitution. The fee depended upon the length of the ride; twenty-five cents a mile, half in cash, half in commodities. Or often nothing at all. Medical supplies were a problem in themselves. Drugs ordered from the East might take five months to arrive. The man who was no good at reckoning and at keeping an eye on his medicine closet soon found himself on the road to ruin.

Having grown up in the West, Drake was quick to realize that it was here, rather than on the eastern coast, that the nation's future would work itself out. This land, where men of many races and creeds, coming from the most diverse communities, had to face hard labor side by side, must one day be the melting-pot of the nation.

What were the conclusions to be drawn from this situation that concerned medicine? What responsibilities should be assumed by the physician?

With the eye of genius, Drake was the first to see what would be needed. This is his contribution. He foresaw that medicine had two great tasks to perform if the settling of the country was not to be left to develop in an accidental and chaotic fashion. And the first task was the investigation, from the standpoint of health and sanitation, of this spacious breeding-ground for men.

And what an enormous breeding-ground was provided by this largest valley ever fashioned by Nature, spreading from the Alleghanies to the Rocky Mountains, from the Great Lakes to the Gulf of Mexico, and watered by the Mississippi and its tributaries, great rivers themselves, the Ohio in the East, the Missouri in the West. "Ol' Man River," it was affectionately called; but it was a capricious master, whose sluggish calm was not to be trusted, who could storm wildly, break down the confining shores and flood the country, bearing all before it and leaving swamps and fever in its wake.

The second great task was to insure an adequate supply of competent physicians for the new country, not only for the present, but for the future. The whole idea was that the physician should become an integral part of the coming development, a pioneer by the side of the other pioneers, taking his share in the opening of the country as adviser in questions of hygiene.

In 1810 Drake wrote a little volume: *Notices of Cincinnati, its Topography, Climate and Diseases*. Five years later he published a larger book on the same subject: *Natural and Statistical View or Picture of Cincinnati*. It was a first experiment. Drake was working out his system in his own immediate neighborhood. He tried to cover the whole environment: the earth and what it bore, and the climate; and, on the other hand, its inhabitants, according to their history, the structure of their society, their economic life, and the nature of their diseases.

Drake returned to Philadelphia in 1815, and spent the winter attending courses at the University, using this occasion to obtain the degree of doctor of medicine. In 1817, his career took a sudden turn when he accepted a call to the chair of materia medica at Transylvania University, Lexington, Kentucky.

This was the first medical school to be established west of the Alleghanies. As early as 1783, while Kentucky was still a part of Virginia, a college had been founded at Lexington, which in 1798 became Transylvania Seminary. In 1799 a medical division was installed. Two physicians, Samuel Brown and Frederick Ridgeley, were appointed as professors.

This school is no longer in existence. It was first merged with the Kentucky School of Medicine and eventually became part of the University of Louisville. But it played an important rôle in the medical life of the West, and its library is still of great interest to the historian, not so much because of its rare volumes as because of the special character of its collection. Twice, in 1820 and 1839, large sums of around $25,000 were available for the purchase of books. At that time such a sum would go far. The money was chiefly spent in Paris—which had taken the place of Edinburgh—and in this way a library was formed which presents an excellent cross-section of medical literature in the first quarter of the nineteenth century.

Drake began teaching in 1817 and was a teacher for the rest of his life. His lectures were as effective as his writings, and were attended with enthusiasm. He now had an opportunity to train physicians for the new West.

He was not destined, however, for the ordinary routine of a professor's life. His was too restless and high-spirited a temperament. He was by nature a pioneer, an innovator, at home among the beginnings of a world. He could never bear to stay long in the same place. Thirteen times he was called to new positions; he filled nine professorships in five separate medical schools. There was hardly a department of medicine in which he had not given instruction. And what was more, he was himself the founder of medical schools: the Medical College of Ohio in Cincinnati in 1819, and the Medical Division of Cincinnati College in 1835. He travelled back and forth between Lexington, Louisville, and Cincinnati, besides spending the year 1830 in Philadelphia, at Jefferson College, founded in 1826 and a rival organization to the University of Pennsylvania.

The growing nation needed physicians, and medical schools sprang up like mushrooms. No less than fifty-three schools were founded between 1832 and 1852. Anywhere, all over the country, a couple of doctors would get together, found a school, admit paying pupils, and proceed to deal out diplomas. It was a profitable business.

This was not what Drake had had in mind. To be sure, the country needed physicians, but only thoroughly grounded physicians. What went on in many places was the most bungling charlatanism. In a series of articles, published in a small volume in 1832, Drake denounced the existing conditions. Without mercy he put his finger on the sore spots: the inadequate preparation of students, and, for that matter, often of teachers; the equally inadequate equipment; the absurdity of supporting a number of competing institutions in one place (a matter in which he himself had sinned); and the all-too-short period of training. Many schools required only two sessions of four months each. He demanded four years' training, practical demonstrations by the sick-bed, and asked for state control. The teaching profession ought not to be a business, but a public office, carried out for the public benefit.

His voice, as we will see later, was not heeded. Events had too headlong a course.

He went on teaching, and did his level best to raise the standards of medicine. He had not forgotten the second task required of medicine. What he had done as a young man for his own neighborhood in Cincinnati, he must now undertake for the entire West. He traversed the region from mountain-range to mountain-range, from the lakes to the ocean, back and forth, visiting every physician, talking things over, and sending out questionnaires. He came to be sixty-five years old. Finally, in 1850, there appeared as the fruit of thirty years' labor the first volume of his magnum opus, bearing the title: *A Systematic Treatise, Historical, Etiological and Practical, on the Principal Diseases of the Interior Valley of North America, as they appear in the Caucasian, African, Indian and Esquimaux Varieties of its Population.* This is a magnificent fresco, one of the greatest masterpieces of medico-geographic research. The first volume takes up in order: topography and hydrography; climate as an etiological factor; and physiological and social etiology, including a detailed account of the population, its mode of life, its clothing, its habitations, its means of livelihood, etc. The second volume, which did not appear until after Drake's death in 1854, is dedicated to the study of diseases: malaria, yellow fever, typhoid, eruptive disorders, tuberculosis, etc.

It was a great achievement. I know only one European book which could be placed beside this work of Drake's; that is Peter Frank's *System einer vollständigen medizinischen Polizei.* These are two very different pieces of work, developed, as may readily be imagined, from entirely different premises. But they resemble each other in largeness of aim and also in their more immediate purpose. Drake, too, was concerned with sanitation and hygiene. In this direction lay that part of his activity which held the greatest significance for the future.

In 1850 the meeting of the American Medical Association was held in Cincinnati. As Drake entered, he was greeted by a burst of applause, which it seemed could never end. He tried to speak, but tears choked him. His thoughts went back to his childhood in the forest, to his parents and sister. His life had not been in vain.

Morgan and Rush were pioneers in their own field, but their most decisive impressions had been received in Europe. Even McDowell had been to Edinburgh. Daniel Drake (Fig. 8), on the other hand, was a pure product of the American West, rooted in its soil, a man of the people, like Abraham Lincoln.

William Beaumont (1785–1853)

William Beaumont belonged to Drake's generation, having been born in the same year and dying one year after him.

His family had come from England as far back as 1635 and settled in Connecticut. William studied medicine with two practitioners, won for himself a license from the state of Vermont, and finally, in 1812, enlisted as a surgeon in the army. The war with England had broken out. Beaumont took part in several encounters and showed courage and unusual skill. He resigned when peace was concluded and started a private practice in Plattsburg, N. Y.

The outdoor life in the army had been very congenial to him, and we may imagine that his memory liked to dwell upon it. In 1819 the army was reorganized and Joseph Lovell, a competent young physician, was put at the head of the Medical Corps. Remembering Beaumont as a comrade of earlier days, he offered him a position in the service, which Beaumont accepted. The government kept a chain of forts along the whole western border. It had first been used against the French, later the English, and now served to hold the Indians in check. Most of the western cities had grown up in the shelter of some such fort. By this time, in 1820, the situation was quiet; and a friendly commodity-trade began to ply in these military settlements. Indians came bringing their own products, such as fur, in exchange for every sort of merchandise.

It was to one of these forts that Beaumont was ordered: Fort Mackinac on Michilimackinac Island, between Lake Huron and Lake Michigan, in the extreme northwest of the Union. The surgeon attached to such a fort usually had to serve as physician for the whole community.

It was here that the apparently unimportant accident occurred, which was the occasion of Beaumont's becoming a pioneer in American physiology. One day—it was the sixth of June, 1822 —a sudden shot was heard in the settlement store. A gun had gone off and an unfortunate young man had had the bad luck to be standing directly in front of it. Alexis St. Martin, a French-Canadian employee of the American Fur Company, received the whole load of buck-shot at close range in his left side. Beaumont was called at once, and was instantly on the spot, but found the man horribly mangled. The chest was torn open, the left lower lung, the diaphragm and the stomach lacerated. The stomach contents came out mixed with blood, shreds of clothing and bone-splinters. It was a sad sight. Beaumont did everything possible but the case seemed hopeless.

Strangely enough, the man recovered. His progress was naturally slow. At first he had to be nourished artificially, as otherwise the food would come out again through his stomach. Ten months later the wound was still open and a gastric fistula persisted. The man was wretched, feeble, and entirely without means of support. The authorities felt that he had been cared for long enough and decided to ship him back to his birthplace in Canada.

Many physicians would have considered the case closed. But not so Beaumont. He took pity on the young man. He saw that in his condition the journey would be fatal. Since all remonstrances with the authorities proved useless, Beaumont, with a sudden resolve, took the patient under his own roof and kept him there for two years, feeding, nursing, and giving him medical care, bandaging him sometimes twice a day. St. Martin gained a little strength and was able to walk about, though he was not yet in a condition to earn his living. The gastric fistula persisted.

Beaumont decided that he could make use of this fistula for experiments. Here was an ideal opportunity to find out what went on in the stomach.

While in the seventeenth century the process of digestion had been explained sometimes mechanically as friction and again chemically as fermentation or putrefaction, the eighteenth century had advanced a step farther by means of the studies of Réaumur, Stevens, and Carminati. It was known that the stomach secreted a special fluid which had anti-fermentative qualities and the property of dissolving food. During the following period there was disagreement in regard to the acidity of the fluid, to which Helmont had attributed great importance. Experiments were performed on animals, which were made to swallow perforated capsules containing special foods. After a certain amount of time the capsules were removed from the animals and the changes in the food could be determined. One method of obtaining the gastric juice was to have the animal swallow a sponge fastened to a cord and when the sponge was thoroughly soaked to pull it out again. Beaumont had the advantage of experimenting on a human being, but the disadvantage of working in the wilderness, far from laboratories and books. Another drawback was that his human subject was a most cranky patient. As soon as St. Martin felt better and took in the fact that he was being made use of, he became extremely arrogant, began to lead the most irregular life, and ran away over and over again. The relationship between the two men provides a spectacle at once tragic and absurd.

In May, 1825, Beaumont began to look forward to making his

findings public. In the summer he took two months' leave, and went east with the main purpose of showing his patient to a few scientists. But it all came to nothing, as St. Martin made his escape and was not to be found.

Two years later he turned up in Canada, married and penniless. Beaumont moved heaven and earth to get hold of him again. He was successful two years later. In 1829 St. Martin arrived with his wife and two children at Fort Crawford on the upper Mississippi, where Beaumont was at that time stationed. The fistula was unchanged. The experiments were begun again at once and continued without interruption until 1831. Again St. Martin made off; his wife was homesick. This time Beaumont had given his consent.

Beaumont had made great progress in his observations; but now he felt the need of consulting with chemical experts, and to this end wished to spend a year in Europe with his patient. Leave was granted, but almost immediately revoked, as an Indian rebellion had broken out in Michigan and Illinois. Before the fighting was over, there occurred the first cases of Asiatic cholera, which later grew to a serious epidemic. Every physician was needed. After the cholera campaign was at an end, Beaumont was given six months' leave and went home to Plattsburg. Here, to his joy, St. Martin made his appearance. It was too late for a trip to Europe. They went together to Washington and the work was continued. To keep St. Martin under surveillance, Beaumont had him made a sergeant in the army.

After making two hundred and thirty-eight experiments in all, Beaumont collected his observations into a book, printed in 1833 at his own expense and bearing the title: *Experiments and Observations on the Gastric Juice and the Physiology of Digestion.* It is a classic—simple, objective, and careful.

What were the conclusions? The stomach secretes mucus and gastric juice. The last is described in detail. It has the property of liquefying proteins; has an antiseptic effect; contains free acid salts; is to a great degree influenced by psychic occurrences. The processes of digestion both in and outside the stomach are described in great detail. It is noted that water leaves the stomach very quickly through the pylorus. The movements of the stomach are observed. Finally Beaumont takes up with full particulars the digestion of individual foods as well as the effect of such stimulants as tea, coffee, and alcohol upon digestion and in this way helps to lay the foundation for dietetics.

It is a beautiful book which can still be read to advantage, and which at that time aroused the greatest attention. Only a year after its publication, it was translated into German.

In 1844 Beaumont and his patient parted forever. St. Martin went back to Canada, never to return, no matter how deep the interest shown in him by the scientific world. Beaumont was stationed at various army posts, the last being St. Louis, until his resignation in 1839, after which he carried on a large practice in St. Louis until his death in 1853.

Would Beaumont have become a great man without Alexis St. Martin? It is hard to say. Chance cannot make a scientist. That Beaumont was of the right stuff is shown by the notes which he made as a beginner in Plattsburg and which evidence his gift for accurate observation and his conscientious wish to give an account of every detail which came before his eyes. A lucky accident gave a potential scientist his laboratory material. The fact that he recognized the opportunity and used it to the full in spite of difficult circumstances gives him his place among the leaders of medicine. (Fig. 9)

Samuel David Gross (1805–1884) and James Marion Sims (1813–1883)

We are now well into the nineteenth century and meet with two great figures in surgical history. They are not the first important surgeons America had produced, or rather, not the first physicians to have done good work in surgery. For in spite

9. WILLIAM BEAUMONT
1785–1853

of all Morgan's endeavors, there was no division between medicine and surgery until almost the end of the nineteenth century: the surgeon continued to carry on a general practice. Before the time of Gross and Sims America could point to prominent surgeons: Philip Syng Physick (1769–1837) in Philadelphia, a pupil of John Hunter's, who, though he published nothing, left a great tradition behind him, an eminent teacher and a surgeon who never shed an unnecessary drop of blood; John C. Warren (1778–1850) at Harvard, the first surgeon to use an anæsthetic; Valentine Mott (1785–1865) in New York, known for his ligating of great arteries; B. W. Dudley (1785–1870) trained in England and France, the pioneer of surgery in the West and teacher for over thirty years at Transylvania University, who was famous especially for his bladder operations.

What gives Gross and Sims their place in history is that they belong to the same generation as William Fergusson (born in 1808) and James Paget in England (1814), as Stromeyer and Langenbeck (both 1810) in Germany, Nélaton (1807) in France, and Rizzoli (1809) in Italy. That is to say, a generation which assisted at the rise of pathological anatomy, during its youth witnessed the introduction of anæsthesia and remained active far into the era of antiseptics. It was its task to clear the field, though the full harvest was reaped by the next generation.

Samuel David Gross (Fig. 10) was a Pennsylvania Dutchman descended from one of those Germans who had come over from the Rhine country in the eighteenth century. His childhood was spent on a farm. He was only a small boy when he first expressed the wish to become a doctor. But first he must study languages— English and German—for what was spoken at home was neither one nor the other, but a mixture of the two.

At the age of sixteen he went to train with a physician. This was still customary. He was not satisfied and changed his teacher several times, till he realized that the fault lay with himself. He was not sufficiently prepared. Though it was a bitter pill to swallow, he left off medicine to go back to school and study Latin and Greek. At last he was far enough along to take up medicine again. He matriculated at Jefferson College in Philadelphia, and graduated there in 1828. Now he had accomplished the first step.

A young doctor in Europe, after having passed his examinations, could spend a few carefree years in a clinic and as the pupil of some great teacher could train himself in his own specialty until he was equipped for an academic career. Here it was much more difficult. Hospital appointments were mostly in the hands of the older men. One could become the private pupil of a professor, as Gross had done while studying at college, but those whose means would not permit this, had no alternative after passing their examinations but to go into practice.

This was the case with Gross. But he was a born scientist, with an especial bent for anatomy and surgery. He determined to settle down in Philadelphia, which then offered the greatest opportunity to keep in touch with scientific investigations.

Philadelphia, however, had come to be a large city. There was no lack of physicians; and things were not easy for beginners. Gross spent eighteen months waiting for patients. Very few appeared and his savings shrank to nothing. It was not an idle time. He worked indefatigably night and day. He translated French and German medical books and wrote one of his own on anatomy and the physiology and pathology of bones and joints. Billroth in Berlin was to pass through a similar experience, but he made the time go by with music. Billroth was finally given an appointment at the Langenbeck clinic; for Gross there was no way out except to leave the city and return to the country.

He moved to Easton, near his father's farm, and there his practice went much better. Here, too, he was impelled to pursue his researches. A summer-house was turned into a dissecting-room. Every possible animal was used for experiment. Now and then, by going to Philadelphia, he could procure for his anatomical studies a human cadaver, which he had to call for himself and drive home in his wagon. Full of plans as always, he began to work on a book, a descriptive anatomy, which however was never published.

In Easton Gross felt isolated from the scientific world. He longed for work with a university. The West stood open and the new schools needed teachers. So in 1833 Gross went to Cincinnati to become demonstrator of anatomy at the Medical College of Ohio, one of the schools founded by Drake. Only two years later he was appointed to the Chair of Pathological Anatomy in the medical department of Cincinnati College, also founded by Drake. He was active there for four years, giving the first systematic course of lectures in America on pathological anatomy; and the outcome of this series was a work in two volumes, of over a thousand pages, and copiously illustrated: the *Elements of Pathological Anatomy*, which went through several editions, the first comprehensive work in this field in America, indeed in the English language. In 1829 a shorter treatise on the subject by William E. Horner had been published in Philadelphia.

Gross was now a famous man. He turned down several appointments in northern universities, but accepted a post in Louisville, Kentucky. It was the Chair of Surgery, his own immediate subject. He remained there sixteen years, except for one winter in New York, till he was called to Philadelphia in 1856 as Professor of Surgery in Jefferson Medical College. This was his own college. This call he must heed. He moved there with his whole family, returning to his point of departure, and stayed there until his death.

Gross has written an enormous amount. Whenever his hand was not busy with the surgeon's knife, whether for operations or experiments, it would take up the author's pen. He wrote innumerable short articles, covering the whole field of medicine, but especially pathology and surgery. In addition he wrote several larger monographs and hand-books.

Three great works were completed in Louisville: on intestinal lesions (1843), the result of experiments on animals; diseases, injuries and malformations of the bladder, prostate and urethra (1851), a comprehensive work, with many illustrations, which remained authoritative for a long time; and a treatise on foreign bodies in the organs of respiration (1854), the first attempt to sum up the knowledge on this subject.

In Philadelphia, in 1859, was published his surgical handbook: *A System of Surgery; Pathological, Diagnostic, Therapeutique, and Operative,* which went through six editions.

Gross's memory does not live by one achievement alone, as is the case with McDowell and Beaumont. During a time of great progress, his influence was predominant in many branches of medicine. The middle of the century witnessed a complete transformation of pathological anatomy and surgery. Gross was active in this reconstruction, he carried many bricks to the great building, laid out many cross-sections in his monographs, and in his text-books gave a synthetic picture of the whole plan.

And the literary side of his work was the most important. The thousands of physicians, who, often with inadequate training, were scattered over the face of the land, wanted books both for study and reference. Gross provided them. And the fact that they did not come from Europe but were written by an American from the American point of view, made them all the more valuable and easy to grasp.

Finally, Gross had great influence through the force of his personality. As a physician of high ideals and tireless industry, he was an example to all, showing what a farmer's boy could make of himself. Like all great physicians who have been aware of the meaning of their own period, he had a deep understand-

IO. SAMUEL DAVID GROSS

1805–1884

II. JAMES MARION SIMS

1813–1883

ing of history. He wrote and edited a number of biographical
studies of American physicians, and in 1876 he published an account of the development of American surgery during the
century which had just elapsed. Whenever there was a chance,
he would use an historical example to bring home to his contemporaries the nature of the developments in which they themselves were taking part.

At his death he left behind him the manuscript of his last
work, an autobiography, published by his sons in a two-volume
edition. It is a splendid piece of history. The European reader
will for instance be interested in the impressions of a trip to
Europe, which brought him in touch with the coryphants of
medicine; or in the pious pilgrimage to the home of Haller,
whom he held in such reverence that he named a son after him.

There is a statue of him in Washington, not far from the
Capitol. The tall figure with its noble scholar's head is cast in
dark bronze and stands out sharply against a green background
of surrounding trees. American surgeons raised this monument
to the services which Gross has rendered to surgery in America
and to medicine as a whole.

James Marion Sims (1813–1883) (Fig. 11) was, like Gross,
a great surgeon. Like him he had completed his medical training
in Philadelphia at Jefferson Medical College, graduating in
1835, seven years later than Gross. But while Gross from childhood had wanted to be a physician and had steered steadily for
that goal, Sims had drifted into medicine without enthusiasm,
driven by circumstances.

His family lived near Lancaster, South Carolina. His father,
the incumbent of several small public offices, dreamed of seeing
his son a lawyer, and made great sacrifices to send him to college. Sims would have preferred to go into business, but since
his father had spent so much money on him, he could not disap-
point him and was forced to study willy-nilly. He had not the

slightest inclination towards the legal profession, nor did he want to become a preacher. So there was nothing for it but to study medicine. He began his studies under a physician, then went to the medical school in Charleston, and finally to Philadelphia.

His examination completed, he bought a set of surgical instruments and a chestful of medicines, went home, and hung a large sign on his door. After some weeks he got his first case. An infant was suffering from acute diarrhœa. The father was a prominent man, a tailor, and the former Mayor of the town. Sims made the examination, and feeling quite at a loss, went home to his library, which consisted of seven text-books, and concocted a prescription. It did no good, nor did any of his subsequent prescriptions. The child died. One may imagine with what emotions he followed the funeral procession. A few weeks later a similar case presented itself. Again the child died.

Sims would now have liked to give up medicine for good. But he was without means. He had to earn his living by what he had learned. He left the place which had brought him so little luck, and went west to Alabama where he settled in the little town of Mt. Meigs. Here things went better. His practice thrived. He soon earned enough to be able to afford a marriage with a friend of his boyhood. A reputable physician took him into partnership under very advantageous conditions. He now lived in a log-cabin and practised his profession, still without any interest in its larger aspects. When a friend suggested going into partnership in the cloth trade and moving to Mississippi, he agreed, gave up medicine, and sold his house. But just as he was about to leave, the whole business went to pieces before it had even begun and there was nothing for him to do but to resume his practice. Everything went well enough until one day he and his whole family caught malaria. The place was swampy and miasmal. He decided to leave.

In December, 1840, he settled in Montgomery, the capital of

Alabama. Sick and without means as he was, he had to begin all over again. But he succeeded. At first only the free negroes came to consult him; then the Jewish population and later, gradually, the gentility. He was able to open a small private clinic. Five years later he had acquired the reputation of a good physician and above all of a skillful surgeon. He was the first Southerner to operate successfully on a club-foot, the first to perform a strabotomy. He had already met with success in operating on an abscess of the liver, had undertaken the resection of a jaw, and operated on a hare-lip. These things were being done in Europe, too, but under much more favorable conditions. He had to invent his own instruments and, as so often happens, it was a small group of special cases which led to his future career. Vesico-vaginal fistulas had always proved a trial to the surgeon. Much had been written on the subject, but only a few successful cases were on record. The malady was considered on the whole incurable. It was not uncommon among the female slaves of the South, and chance would have it that Sims came almost simultaneously in touch with three patients who suffered from it. He operated, but without success. The use of lateral posture and a speculum he had himself invented allowed him a better field of vision than had ever been given previously. A new catheter made it possible to keep the bladder emptied. But all in vain. The fistula would not stay closed. He had the idea of using silver wire instead of silk thread for his stitches. And now, with this sterile material, as we would say nowadays, he met with success. The cases, which had been under clinical care for several years, were all cured within a few weeks. This was in 1849. In 1852 he made public his cases in the *American Journal of Medical Sciences*, and the article met with the attention it deserved. Two years later, in 1854, Gustav Simon in Germany wrote a monograph on the subject.

But now that success had come, his practice thriving, and Sims had nothing left to wish for except that this state of affairs would continue, he was again the victim of misfortune. A son died. He himself was taken with a severe intestinal malady and was not far from death. A change of climate was urgently advised. He was forced to give up everything and go north. Sickness had eaten up his savings.

In May, 1853, he was in New York, ill and poor. He was now forty years old and the fight had to be fought all over again. His last cent went to purchase a house in a good situation. He was no longer a beginner. He knew how to operate and had made an important discovery. He tried to build up a practice, but his receipts did not suffice even for necessities. His colleagues were interested in his operation and came to see it demonstrated. But instead of sending him patients, they carried out the operation themselves and made the life of this Southerner, who was attached to no clinic and quite friendless, as difficult as possible.

At last there came a change for the better, and the way it came is so illuminating that it must be recounted. Sims had been pushed by his discovery quite inevitably into the field of operative gynecology. He had in mind the establishment of a clinic for indigent women. But how could this be accomplished in the midst of an indifferent and hostile community? One of his few friends had a scheme. He brought with him a newspaper man, who took the matter in hand. He rented a hall and sent seven hundred invitations to prominent physicians and laymen for a lecture by Dr. Sims upon the necessity of founding a Women's Clinic in New York. The newspapers were won over. It worked. Now that the plan was made public, no one could put forward any objection. A board of trustees was set up. Women raised the funds and on May 1st, 1855, the Women's Hospital of the State of New York, with thirty beds—all free—was opened, with Sims as head physician.

Now he could work and operate, and gained more and more

repute as a surgeon and gynecologist. His hospital and private practice increased daily. A journey to Europe in 1861 turned into a triumphal procession. In Paris he had to demonstrate his fistula operation over and over again, and the results were dumbfounding. Wherever he went, he was invited to operate, and he was soon as well known in Europe as in America. Crowds of women came to him for consultation. He was received by Napoleon III, and while the Empress Eugenie was ill with diphtheria, he was invited to spend fourteen days with her at St. Cloud.

After this, his life was led on two continents, now in New York, now in Paris. He was one of the most sought-after gynecologists. He took a distinguished part in the Franco-Prussian War as head surgeon of an English-American ambulance. In 1886 appeared his most important book, *Clinical Notes on Uterine Surgery*, which was immediately translated into German. During 1881 and 1882 there was published in the *British Medical Journal* a comprehensive work on hemostasis in the abdominal cavity, on abdominal ligatures and other problems of abdominal surgery. In earlier short publications he had described his method of amputating the cervix uteri and his gall-bladder operation, as well as giving a very clear picture of the symptom complex of vaginitis.

Gross and Sims differed much as men. Both were great surgeons. Both came from the people and had to struggle against poverty and other external difficulties. Both went through a pioneer period in the West. But while the life of Gross progressed in a straight line towards his position as a great teacher and productive writer, the life of Sims went up and down like the waves of the sea until he found his eventual success as practitioner and initiator in the field of operative gynecology.

Oliver Wendell Holmes (1809–1894) and Silas Weir Mitchell (1829–1914)

The scene of our previous sketches has been laid in Pennsylvania, Kentucky, Ohio, Michigan, South Carolina, and Alabama. It is time to look to the North again, to New England.

There, too, the evolution was rapid. Before the Revolution there were only two medical schools of academic standing in the colonies; Philadelphia, founded in 1765, and New York, in 1767, where the medical school was affiliated with King's College. The first university to establish a medical school after the Revolution was Harvard. This was done in 1783 at the instigation of the surgeon John Warren.

Further development is primarily identified with the personality of one man, who was a real pioneer in the field, Nathan Smith (1762–1829). Born in Massachusetts, he spent his childhood on a farm in Vermont, and went through the usual medical apprenticeship. He graduated from Harvard and spent some time in Edinburgh. He was equally outstanding as a physician and as a surgeon. In 1824 he wrote a classical monograph on typhoid, and later a similarly important one on necrosis. He, too, recognized the necessity of providing educational facilities for the doctors in connection with institutions of higher learning. His idea, a very sound one, was that each state should have one and only one medical school. He founded such a school in 1797 in the state of New Hampshire, at Dartmouth College in Hanover, the fourth medical school of the Union. There, for many years, he was Professor of Anatomy, Chemistry, Medicine and Surgery, all at the same time. He was the faculty.

In 1812 a medical faculty was added to Yale University, and Smith was appointed as Professor of Clinical Medicine. Maine and Vermont followed in 1821. Medical schools were founded in Bowdoin and Burlington, in both cases with the coöperation of Smith. He lectured in both schools.

Oliver Wendell Holmes (Fig. 12) was another Harvard man. He graduated from Harvard in 1829; it was at Harvard that he taught anatomy from 1847 until 1882, and physiology from 1847 until 1871. His whole life was centered in Boston.

He is known primarily as a poet, one of the author-physicians we come across so frequently. But he has a place in the history of medicine, since he took an active part in its development.

His medical concepts were formed in Paris, during 1833 and 1834. Like Edinburgh in the eighteenth century, Paris in the first half of the nineteenth was the Mecca of American students of medicine. The man around whom they chiefly gathered was the great clinician, Louis. From him they learned clinical observation, clinical methods of examination, pathological anatomy, and statistical methods. He was the object of their "reverence, almost idolatry."

Broussais, too, was still on hand but, to use the words of Holmes, he was like "an old volcano, which has pretty nearly used up its fire and brimstone, but is still boiling and bubbling in its interior and now and then sends up a spurt of lava and a volley of pebbles." His lectures were followed by those of Andral, and if towards the end of the hour the students became impatient, Broussais "looked almost carnivorous at these interruptions."

Surgery was represented by Lisfranc, "a great drawer of blood and hewer of members." When he had an attack of blood-letting, rivers of blood would flow. He "regretted the splendid guardsmen of the old Empire—for what?—because they had such magnificent thighs to amputate!"

Old Baron Larrey, the surgeon of the Napoleonic armies, was also still at his post. "To go round the Hôtel des Invalides with Larrey was to live over campaigns of Napoleon."

But Dupuytren was the greatest surgeon of all. "A square

solid-looking man with a fine head . . . he marched through the wards like a lesser kind of divinity."

Then there was Ricord, the syphilis man, whom Holmes called "the Voltaire of pelvic literature, a skeptic as to the morality of the race in general, who would have submitted Diana to treatment and ordered a course of blue pills for the Vestal Virgins."

Paris offered far more to these young foreigners than Edinburgh had ever been able to: theatres, music, strolls along the banks of the Seine, not to mention the superb wines, which are so light (compared with Boston rum and Philadelphia Madeira) that "nobody gets drunk, except as an experiment in physiology."

Holmes returned from Paris in December, 1835, and in the following year published his first book, a volume of thoughtful, witty and graceful poems. But he stuck to medicine, set himself up as a practitioner and, having plenty of leisure, wrote several prize-winning essays: on intermittent fever; on neuralgia; on the use and significance of direct examination. For several years he was attached to the Massachusetts General Hospital. In 1838 he became Professor of Anatomy at Dartmouth College, holding this position until 1840; it was no great burden, since he was obliged to give lectures only three months out of the year. At the same time his practice continued, just large enough not to be troublesome.

Then, in 1843, at a meeting of the Boston Society for Medical Improvement, he presented a lecture which placed him all at once in the full light of history. This lecture was printed with the title: *The Contagiousness of Puerperal Fever*.

A violently discussed case had occurred. A physician, after dissecting a woman who had died of puerperal fever, had taken sick and died, exhibiting similar symptoms. Holmes became thoughtful. "I therefore felt that it would be doing a good service to look into the best records I could find, and inquire of the most trustworthy practitioners I knew, and arrived at the results contained in the following pages."

The results, in a nutshell, were as follows: "A physician holding himself in readiness to attend cases of midwifery should never take any active part in the post-mortem examination of cases of puerperal fever. . . . If a physician is present at such autopsies, he should use thorough ablution, change every article of dress, and allow twenty-four hours or more to elapse before attending to any case of midwifery. . . . On the occurrence of a single case of puerperal fever in his practice, the physician is bound to consider the next female he attends in labor, unless several weeks at least have elapsed, as in danger of being infected by him, and it is his duty to take every precaution to diminish her risk of disease and death. If within a short period two cases of puerperal fever happen close to each other, in the practice of the same physician, . . . he would do wisely to relinquish his obstetrical practice for at least one month. . . . The occurrence of three or more closely connected cases, in the practice of one individual . . . is *prima facie* evidence that he is the vehicle of contagion. The physician should make *proper inquiries* concerning nurses and other assistants and give them *timely warning of every suspected source of danger.*"

Holmes' essay closes with the words: "Whatever indulgence may be granted to those who have heretofore been the ignorant causes of such misery, the time has come when the existence of a private pestilence in the sphere of a single physician should be looked upon, not as a misfortune, but a crime; and in the knowledge of such occurrences the duties of the practitioner to his profession should give way to his paramount obligations to society."

This was written in 1843, in the plainest possible language. Holmes had the satisfaction, during the year that followed, of seeing many physicians allow themselves to be convinced and to exercise greater care. Naturally there was no lack of opposition, as is to be expected in the case of a theory which blames the physician for the disease. In 1852 two Philadelphia professors raised their voices in protest against the belief in the contagiousness of puerperal fever. One of them went so far as to say that he would prefer to attribute the illness to accident or to Providence, of which he could form some conception, rather than to a contagion of which he could form no clear idea, at least in this particular malady. Holmes answered in a new edition of his essay which was published in 1855. His material was as impressive as before.

In Europe it is Semmelweis who is hailed as the savior of motherhood, the discoverer of the true nature of puerperal fever and the means of its prevention. There is nothing more futile than these bickerings over priority in science which spring for the most part from a narrowminded nationalism. Holmes, too, was not the first to recognize the contagious character of the disease. In this essay he aims to present confirming testimony out of the past and reaches back through the eighteenth century for his material. Nevertheless, it remains his contribution to have marshalled with convincing power, into a brilliant, immortal essay, all the arguments for the right doctrine, and to have specified successful preventive measures.

Semmelweis, who had never heard of Holmes, reached the same conclusions four years later, in 1847, activated by a similar incident—the death of a colleague from septic poisoning. Semmelweis's observations were first announced in December, 1847; the conclusive statement was published in 1861. The two men employ very similar arguments and speak in much the same spirit. But what gave such tremendous force to the teaching of Semmelweis was not his discovery of chlorine as a more effective hand-disinfectant; it was the tragedy of his life.

In the career of Holmes puerperal fever was a mere episode. His personal experience with the disease was limited. He had a brilliant and correct idea, which he championed with all the material available, and he fully realized that here lay his greatest opportunity to be of service to society. But in the life of Semmelweis there was no compensation for the hell through which he had passed in the Vienna General Hospital, a hell such as did not exist in Boston. He had undergone torture. He had fought and suffered for his theory against opposition compared with which the American opposition to Holmes amounted to nothing. He had died in tragic circumstances, a broken man. All this lent him the aura of a martyr.

Holmes, on the other hand, was made Professor of Anatomy and Physiology at Harvard in 1847, became Dean of the Faculty and developed into a more and more popular author. But before he came so far, he was a witness of an important medical event which took place in Boston, the introduction of inhalation anaesthesia, one of America's most important contributions to world medicine. The story is so well known that I need use only a few words.

The first to use inhalation anaesthesia for operative purposes was Crawford Williamson Long (1815–1878), a Georgia physician, who graduated from the University of Pennsylvania in 1839, practised for one year in New York, and after 1841 in a Georgia village. The euphoristic effect of laughing gas was known, and the inhalation of this gas was a favorite indoor sport. Long now discovered that ether had a similar effect, and one evening at a gathering of friends at his house, he suggested, there being no laughing gas at hand, that they might try ether. He noticed that if at such parties anyone were injured during his ether-intoxication, he would feel no pain. Evidently ether took away the sense of feeling. With the practical sense shown by these country doctors, Long made use of his observations and in March, 1842, performed a small operation, after having first dulled the patient's senses with ether. The experiment was completely successful and was repeated several times during the years 1842 and 1843.

However, Long did not make public his discovery, and it was not heard of beyond his immediate neighborhood. Why this silence? Today, with fully developed means of transportation and countless organs of publicity, even the most unessential observation is advertised. In those days conditions were different. With things as they were, what chance to get a hearing would a country doctor in a remote village have? McDowell, for instance, had waited years before communicating his discovery.

In this instance, there was no time to wait. The need of a general anaesthesia was so great that the discovery of a reliable narcotic was inevitable. Long's method was re-discovered a few years later, this time in Boston.

As early as 1800 Sir Humphrey Davy had pointed out the narcotic effect of laughing gas. Decades passed before, in 1844, the first attempts to use it were made. It happened that a dentist in Hartford, Connecticut, Horace Wells (1815–1848) had the distinction of introducing laughing gas-anaesthesia into dentistry.

Wells died insane a few years later. But a friend and colleague, William Thomas Green Morton (1819–1868) developed the idea. It is not accidental that dentists have been leaders in this field, for if anyone ever knew how to inflict the most terrible pain, it was certainly the dentists. Morton, in his efforts to work without giving pain, continued the experiments from 1844 on, and learned from the chemist, Charles Thomas Jackson, that not only laughing gas but ether, as well, would inhibit feeling. On September 30th, 1846, he extracted a tooth, using ether with complete success.

It was a fortunate circumstance that Morton practised in Boston instead of in the wilderness. He turned directly to the hospital and induced a surgeon, John Collins Warren, to undertake an operation at which he, Morton, was to make the patient unconscious. It was carried out on October 16th, 1846, and repeated on the following day. There was no doubt that now a

Oliver Wendell Holmes

12. OLIVER WENDELL HOLMES
1809–1894

13. SILAS WEIR MITCHELL

1829–1914

means had been found by which even more serious operations could be performed under anaesthetics.

Morton behaved badly. He tried to keep his substance secret, to patent and capitalize it, and to reserve all profits for himself. He was not a great man.

The discovery, however, was great, and its use spread like wildfire. By the 18th of November it had already been made known to the world in an article by Henry J. Bigelow, and the very fact that recognized surgeons like Bigelow and Warren stood sponsor for it, cleared the way for its reception.

It was Oliver Wendell Holmes who coined the terms anaesthesia and anaesthetics.

Returning to him after this digression, we find him established as a professor. For thirty-five years, until his retirement in 1882, he taught anatomy to the Harvard students, conducted the dissection exercises, gave instructions on the manipulation of the microscope, and, above all, for five days a week at one o'clock delivered a very popular course of lectures.

An anatomical lecture can be fascinating or terribly boring; it can sound like a fairy-tale or like a dull catalogue. Like Hyrtl in Vienna, Holmes in Boston knew how to discourse on anatomy with wit and eloquence, to make what was dead live, and to cast a spell on his hearers.

He was no research worker, no man of the laboratory. He developed more and more into a writer; he wrote poems, light essays, and novels. It is as an author that he is best known to America, as a representative of the literary group to which Hawthorne, Emerson, and Longfellow belonged. He survived them all, for he lived to be eighty-five years old. But he also deserves to be remembered as a physician.

Silas Weir Mitchell (Fig. 13) was another author, but a man of quite a different stamp, much more active in temperament and above all a great neurologist. As a young man he sent Oliver Wendell Holmes a small collection of his poems, and the latter advised him to put poetry aside and devote himself entirely to medicine. Mitchell took his advice. Not until his fiftieth year did he come forward with his poems, novels and short stories. By that time he was already one of America's leading physicians and one of the great neurologists of his time.

He grew up in a highly cultured circle in Philadelphia. His father was a prominent physician. After going to the University of Pennsylvania, he studied medicine at Jefferson Medical College, graduating in 1850. The course at that time lasted only two years. He then spent a year in Paris (1851–1852), where he became immensely impressed by the work of Claude Bernard.

He returned, started practice and devoted every available moment to research. There were as yet no laboratories in America. For that matter, Claude Bernard and Pasteur had also been forced to begin their work under very primitive conditions, but the resources at their disposal were enormous compared to what a scientist could muster at that time in the United States. In spite of hindrances, Mitchell found ways to join in many kinds of scientific pursuits. In 1853 he was made a member of the Academy of Natural Sciences; in 1858 he helped organize a biological section of this society. The year before he had been one of the founders of the Pathological Society in Philadelphia. Here, as everywhere, the scientific societies had played a most stimulating part. Their organization was always a harbinger of new knowledge. They became gathering-places for scientific investigation, the more essential since there were no organized scientific departments. Nowadays, every department or institute is a little scientific center, within which a group can benefit by the constant interchange of ideas. At that time all scientists were isolated, and met each other only within the societies. Mitchell was later to initiate the founding of the American Physiological Society, which took place in 1887 and bore rich fruit.

Between 1851 and 1863 Mitchell published twenty-two works which presented important findings: on the formation of uric acid; on blood-crystals; on the chiasma of the nerves of the larynx of the turtle; on the immunity of the pigeon to opium. The outstanding work of that period, however, was a toxicological study on the poison of rattle-snakes. He remained interested in these toxicological problems during all his life, and finally with Reichert in 1883 achieved the analysis of toxalbumen.

The Civil War broke out and occasioned the opening of a new chapter in Mitchell's life. The year 1863 found him at the head of a military hospital for nervous diseases. There followed years of unremitting and feverish activity, which drove him farther and farther into the field of neurology. In 1864 appeared the first result of his studies, a book on gun-shot and other injuries to the nerves. He continued his observations for many years and finally published the result of his researches in 1872 in a work which is perhaps his most valuable contribution: *Injuries to the Nerves and their Treatment.*

The war was now over, but Mitchell had been won over permanently to neurology. He became director of a division of the Orthopaedic Hospital, the Infirmary for Nervous Diseases, an institution which he found a small and penurious dispensary and left a great hospital. He led the busy life of a general practitioner, a frequently consulted specialist, and a beloved family doctor.

He was a prolific and effective writer. His contributions to neurology are many and valuable. He was the first to describe post-paralytic chorea, and erythromelalgia, the first to call attention to the fact that headaches are often caused by eye-strain resulting from uncorrected or insufficiently corrected defects in vision. He was known far and wide as the originator of the rest and fattening cure in the treatment of nervous cases, described by him in a pamphlet, *Fat and Blood,* which was translated into most European languages.

He was the author of novels, short stories and poems. They were written during vacations as a diversion from more strenuous work, and were widely read in their day. The poet and the physician found a united expression in a series of shorter works, lectures and speeches, in which he approached questions of general interest: the physician and the patient; death and suffering; hints for the overworked; and other like matters.

He was one of the curators of the University of Pennsylvania, and took an active part in the reform of nurses' training.

It was a rich and fruitful life, which came to an end on January 4th, 1914.

John Shaw Billings (1838–1913)

Europe has any quantity of books. It has always had them. There were books even during ancient times, though these are no longer in existence. In the Middle Ages the monks did the writing, and every monastery had its library. With the invention of printing came the making of many thousands of books. Every city, no matter how small, supported a library. Universities and learned societies have for centuries made their own collections.

In Europe books are taken for granted. They are used quite as a matter of course. In America, three hundred years ago, there were no books at all. The colonists brought with them very little besides their Bibles. In the eighteenth century, libraries like that of John Winthrop, Jr., were very much the exception. Gradually a real hunger for books made itself felt, and they began to do a little printing in the colonies. The first printing-press was started in Cambridge in 1638. Benjamin Franklin was one of the Philadelphia printers. And of course books were imported from abroad. Those who went abroad to study brought their text-books home with them. Pupils learned from the books, few enough for the most part, found in their master's library. It was only through books that America could share in

14. JOHN SHAW BILLINGS
1838–1913

the knowledge of Europe. Every learned institution collected its library; and the library committee exercised one of the most important functions of the institution.

As the West was opened up and schools were built in increasing numbers, the hunger for books grew insatiable. We have observed the efforts put forth by the Transylvania University to form its library.

Every book is a repository of knowledge and power. In Europe, where books were an old story, this was often forgotten. But in America, where no book was come by without a sacrifice, the attitude towards books became something quite different. Even now that there is no scarcity of books and the libraries are the best stocked in the world, this respect for books is still in evidence. The architectural plan of a university frequently indicates that the library is its logical center. All other departments radiate from it.

The pioneer of the medical library was John Shaw Billings (Fig. 14). He was an army surgeon and, naturally enough, a Westerner, who had begun to feel the need of books. He had grown up on an Indian farm in the middle of the pioneer country. Even as a child, he had shown an uncontrollable desire for knowledge. He learned Latin and Greek from an old clergyman; in 1852 he went for five years to Miami University, afterwards studying medicine at the Medical College of Ohio, founded by Drake, and graduating there in 1860. His unusual gifts had attracted the attention of his teachers, and he was not allowed, like the other students, to go immediately into practice, but was retained as a demonstrator of anatomy.

Then came the Civil War. Billings enlisted as an army surgeon, saw the whole war through, now in hospitals, now at the front, and was present at Gettysburg and other bloody battles. In December, 1864, he was ordered to the department of the Surgeon-General in Washington, where he was to remain for thirty years.

He found there a library of 1365 books. This was not a great number. But gradually the idea took shape in his mind that this collection could be developed into a national library of medicine. A European might question the suitability of the office of a Surgeon-General as the starting-point for such an institution. In this case it assuredly was. America is a union of separate states, each exercising wide powers of sovereignty. Medicine and Public Health had been organized in each state separately, while the Medical Corps of the Army was a department which had federal authority.

The library grew larger, as Congress agreed to bigger expenditures; and Billings spent most of his time travelling in search of books. It was a good time to buy. In 1876 the library already owned forty thousand volumes. Another problem became acute, the making of a catalogue which should also serve as an exhaustive bibliography of medicine. After careful preliminary studies, the first volume of the index catalogue of the Surgeon-General's Library was published in 1880. Billings had valuable assistants, Robert Fletcher and Fielding H. Garrison, men who stood by him in his work and carried it on into the future. The first issue of the catalogue comprising sixteen volumes was completed in 1895. A second edition was immediately begun, and finished with twenty-two volumes in 1916. The library grew larger and larger. Today it holds more than half a million books. A third edition was brought to a conclusion in 1933. A fourth is under way. Forty-eight volumes have been published so far.

This catalogue is a monumental work, unequalled in medical history since the libraries of Haller, and is indispensable to every medical investigator. The importance of the library itself can be appreciated only by those who live in America and use it constantly.

A year before the first volume of the index catalogue was completed, there appeared the opening issue of a parallel publication, the *Index Medicus,* a bibliographical periodical which keeps the physician informed of important new material in all medical literature.

Billings with his co-workers created a mechanism which, through the extraordinary part which it played in the development of medicine in America, has made itself felt all over the world. It is probably the only case in history where a military authority in one country has contributed so much to international knowledge.

Billings resigned from the army in 1895 and after a short term as visiting Professor of Hygiene at the University of Pennsylvania, he became director of the New York Public Library, a library of two million books, whose present quarters on Fifth Avenue were built according to his plans.

It would be a great mistake to consider Billings merely as a librarian and a bibliographer. Close as this work was to his heart, and though it constituted probably his greatest contribution, he was nevertheless an active leader in a number of other fields. He had learned many things from the army: war-surgery, military sanitation, and, above all, how to organize a project no matter what its nature. The army has always been the best school for organizers. One of his first tasks in Washington was the reorganization of the Marine Hospital Service. This department had charge of the health of the sailors in the Merchant Marine while in harbors and inland waters, and carried out the quarantine measures which protected the nation from foreign contagions. Billings was successful in doing away with abuses, and put the department in shape to assume increasing responsibilities till finally, in 1912, it became the U. S. Public Health Service. This we shall return to later.

Billings was the authority of his time on the subject of hospitals. The building of the Johns Hopkins Hospital in Baltimore, at the time the most modern institution for the sick in the United States, was begun after his plans in 1876. He was called in for advice wherever a hospital or a laboratory was to be erected.

Finally he was a leader in the development of vital statistics. He recognized the enormous importance of statistics to hygiene, and it is due to him that since 1880 the census of population has included medical data. For many years he assisted in the analysis of the material so assembled.

Billings has written a great deal. His bibliography contains two hundred titles. He is the author of several excellent articles on medical history. Still, he was no literary man, but a man of action, a great organizer, such as was needed in a country deep in the process of construction.

Sir William Osler (1849–1919)

It is difficult to write of him, without the privilege of having known him. The readiest pen may well falter. Will it be possible to draw this picture? Can a way be found to give expression to the feelings of thousands? It is a temptation to skip to the next chapter after merely setting down: Here was a man who embodied the ideal physician and who was beloved by all. But his influence on American medicine goes so deep that this book would be an organism without a heart, if his portrait were lacking. So there is no escape. (Fig. 15)

The physicians of the European continent do not know much about him. The older ones have heard of him as a clinician. They have read some of his works and are perhaps familiar with his text-book which has been translated into French, German, Spanish and Chinese. To the younger men he is almost unknown.

The physician, however, who leaves the Continent to enter the circle of Anglo-Saxon culture, will find himself all at once in a milieu where Osler's spirit can still be felt. If he travels through America he will see his picture in every physician's office. Medical libraries are proud to possess an old book, one of the medical classics, given by Osler and inscribed by his hand. A recently published biography had a sale equalled usually only by popular novels. He is the subject of countless anecdotes. A myth is beginning to form about him. Here at the Hopkins we still feel his presence, though he left us in 1905. The students know him well; he is the model constantly before their eyes.

The stranger who encounters this miracle will ask, "Who was Osler? What is this all about? Pasteur—of course, he is known to every child in France and his memory is revered as that of a benefactor who by his great discoveries shielded humanity from disease. Was Osler a discoverer? Is it his literary work which has cast a spell on posterity? Or does the secret lie in another direction?"

The outward tenor of his life was as undramatic as possible and can be described in a few words. He was a Canadian of Celtic blood, son of a minister, and was himself intended for the ministry. He grew up in a country parish on the edge of the primeval forest, and attended Trinity College in Toronto. Becoming interested in the natural sciences, he gave up the idea of joining the ministry and turned to the study of medicine. After attending McGill University in Montreal, where he graduated in 1872, he went abroad for further training. It was no longer Paris which drew to itself the American students. Vienna, and above all the German universities, were now the main centers of attraction. Osler went first to London, where for fifteen months he worked in histology and physiology and learned to handle the microscope, then later to Berlin and Vienna. Foreign though the German character must have been to him, he recognized the significance of the German clinics and laboratories. He heard Virchow lecture, and was greatly influenced by the clinics of Frerichs and Traube at the Charité. In Vienna, Rokitansky and Skoda were still active, but they were old men; and it was above all the specialists, the dermatologists, the ophthalmologists, the throat and ear specialists, like Hebra, Arlt, Jaeger, Schnitzler, and Politzer, around whom the foreigners gathered. Even today, it is first of all on account of its specialists that American students go to Vienna.

Osler returned to Canada in 1874, started a practice, became instructor and later Professor of Medical Institutions at McGill, his own university. In 1884 he was called to the University of Pennsylvania as Professor of Clinical Medicine, in 1889 to join the nucleus of the faculty of the Johns Hopkins Hospital, which did not open its doors until 1893. He remained in Baltimore till in 1905 he went to Oxford as Regius Professor. In 1911 he was knighted by the King.

It was an academic career, the most brilliant career within the reach of a medical man in an Anglo-Saxon country. The Regius Professorships of medicine in Oxford and Cambridge, which are not filled by the universities but by the Prime Minister himself, are the highest distinction which England can confer upon a physician. However, other men have achieved these distinctions. Osler's importance cannot be entirely explained in this way.

Osler has done much scientific work in pathological anatomy, in all branches of clinical medicines and many allied fields. He was one of the first to investigate blood platelets, and his name will remain linked to many clinical pictures: erythema multiforme, telangiectasis, cerebral palsies in children, chorea, angina pectoris, cancer of the stomach. But there were many great clinicians at work during those fruitful years when the natural sciences were being perfected and the laboratory was enlisted in the service of medicine.

Osler's text-book, *Principles and Practice of Medicine,* is an outstanding work and met with a success which its author had not anticipated. Still, there have been books in other countries. Strümpell's text-book, which appeared in 1883, enjoyed a reception in the German-speaking world in every way resembling that given by the English-speaking countries to Osler's book, and was likewise translated into a number of foreign languages. The two works are closely related in character and belong to the literary deposition of a great age in medicine. Both will one day be recognized as sources of important historical material.

The secret of Osler's influence must be looked for elsewhere. It lies in his personality, in his inimitable qualities as a physician, a teacher, and a man. The resemblance to Hermann Boerhaave comes involuntarily to one's mind. Boerhaave also made no great scientific discoveries. His books, however valuable, cannot explain his reputation. Nevertheless, he was the *communis Europæ magister*, the teacher of Europe, the magnet which at the beginning of the eighteenth century drew the whole world to Leyden; it was he who taught young people to observe and think beside a sick-bed, inspired them to accept the tasks of medicine and filled their minds with the precepts of medical ethics.

What Boerhaave had been to the Europe of his day, Osler became for America. Wherever he went, to Montreal, to Philadelphia, he was met with enthusiasm by the young students of medicine. Most pregnant of all were the years in Baltimore.

The importance of the Johns Hopkins Medical School to American medicine will be demonstrated more fully in the next chapter. A few words must be said here concerning its beginnings in which Osler took so prominent a part.

In the year 1873 there died in Baltimore a merchant called Johns Hopkins, who left his fortune of seven million dollars to provide for a university and a hospital. The board of trustees acted with discrimination, appointing Daniel Coit Gilman President of the University, and found in him without doubt the most capable man in America at that time. The University, at first limited to a philosophical faculty, was opened in very modest quarters in 1876. But the University from the outset was based on very different principles from others in America. It was a university in the European sense; a center of research, where masters and pupils could unite in the investigation of scientific problems. Gilman found eminent assistants who made it possible to bring his idea of a university to realization.

The graduate school being well under way, attention now turned to the medical department, which was to be centered in a hospital. Here again, America was to be given something new, not a mere school which should provide students with two years of medical education; this, too, was to be a center of research, this time of medical research. And the center of gravity should be, not in the lecture room, but at the sick-bed, on the ward, and in the laboratory.

We have seen that in 1876 John Billings had been called into consultation and his plans accepted. The hospital was begun the following year. It took many years to build, as the funds were very economically managed. While the walls were slowly rising, the board kept their eyes open for men who would be competent to carry out the ideas of this department.

William H. Welch was appointed as pathologist. He had received his training in Germany, had worked with Ludwig in Leipzig and with Cohnheim in Breslau, and had been connected with the Bellevue Hospital in New York. He came to the Hopkins in 1884 and, together with the biologist Newell Martin and the chemist Ira Remsen, began giving courses. The first structure to be finished was a building intended to house the basic sciences. It came to be the first institute of pathology in an American university. And from 1886 on, even before the medical school was opened, an active scientific life was developed, with Welch as its center, and regular courses in pathology were given to medical men.

In the meantime the hospital had been completed and now the fate of the whole institution hung in a great measure on the choice of a clinician. Osler was called from Philadelphia. He accepted on May 7, 1889, and was present at the opening of the hospital, a system of red-brick pavilions on high ground, its

15. SIR WILLIAM OSLER
1849–1919

16. THE JOHNS HOPKINS HOSPITAL, 1889

silhouette, with the dome of the main building rising above it, visible from a great distance (Fig. 16). It was a great day; all eyes began to turn expectantly toward Baltimore.

Work was commenced at once; but four more years went by before, in the fall of 1893, a memorable year, the medical school was ready to open its doors. The first class comprised eighteen students, three of them women. The faculty was first-rate, with Mall, who had worked with His and Ludwig, as anatomist; with Abel, a pupil of Schmiedeberg's, as pharmacologist; Welch as pathologist; Osler as clinician; Halsted, who had studied two years in Vienna, Leipzig and Würzburg, as surgeon; and Kelly as gynecologist.

They were splendid times, those first years at the Johns Hopkins. Everything was new; there was no shackling tradition. Everyone was young, and filled with an enthusiasm for his enterprise which carried all before it.

Here Osler had an opportunity to develop his personality to the full. He worked, lived and had a good time with his pupils, and made them into physicians and scientists. It was for them that he wrote his text-book in 1892. His clinic was a center of teeming scientific life. Of course, in Europe there were at that time and even earlier many such clinics. But not in America. Here was a medical school which put science before everything, in which from the outset the student shared in research work, where he received his instruction in the laboratory, in the wards. This was something new. What lent persuasive force to Osler's personality was the fact that in contrast to many European clinicians he was no one-sided scientist. He loved books of all sorts. He collected and read them. He was a born humanist, but not one of those neo-humanists, who believe that the world may be improved by one program or another. In him the synthesis of learning was consummated as something natural and inevitable. So his students learned from him more than methods of clinical examination; he introduced them to Thomas Brown,

Shakespeare, Montaigne, Cervantes, and Plutarch. His many writings of medical history are exquisite works of art, which bring to life the great physicians of the past, and have contributed more to the understanding of the evolution of medicine than many works by learned specialists. Soon after coming to Baltimore, he founded a medical history club, which met once a month. His historical interests were shared by Welch and the other Hopkins men, including Billings who came over from Washington, bringing with him treasures from his library.

The Bulletin of the Johns Hopkins Hospital constantly published historical essays as well as laboratory and clinical studies. It is to be noted that the very men who assured laboratory methods a place in American medicine are the ones who have shown this humanistic approach, and it is to this liberal note that the Hopkins largely owes its unique position.

When Osler left for Oxford in 1905, his loss was deeply felt at the Hopkins. But though absent in the flesh, his spirit remained present and was renewed in his pupils and in their pupils after them. The twenty years he had spent in America were a leaven which will never cease to work.

Osler's hospitable home in Oxford became the Mecca of American physicians. It was a heavy blow when in 1917 his only son fell at Ypres. He followed him two years later, in his seventieth year.

His books were sent back to Montreal, to McGill University, which had been his starting-point. His ashes rest among the books which had meant so much to him.

☆ CHAPTER FIVE ☆

MEDICAL EDUCATION

MEDICAL education has already been repeatedly discussed. We have seen that the first phase of its development consisted of a period of apprenticeship, whereby a young man would choose for himself a master and study with him for a number of years. We saw how individual physicians went to Europe and supplemented their training by studies at a foreign university, such as Edinburgh.

We saw later, as a second phase, the establishment of medical schools, as medical departments of previously existing universities. Let us summarize briefly: in 1765 the first faculty in the country was organized at the College of Philadelphia, later becoming the Medical School of the University of Pennsylvania. New York followed, when in 1768 King's College added a medical department, which, though it went to pieces during the war with England, was revived later, merged with the College of Physicians and Surgeons in 1814 and was eventually absorbed by Columbia University. Harvard followed in 1783, Dartmouth in 1798, Yale in 1810, and, as the first of the western colleges, Transylvania University, which in 1799 opened a medical department, reorganized in 1817.

So far the development had been entirely sound. The schools were well distributed and had, throughout, the university character. The professors were the best physicians in the country. We have seen many of them as leaders in their several fields. The schools were not intended to do away with the old apprentice method but rather to supplement its inadequacies. The students who came to the universities had as a rule four years of training behind them and had acquired a fund of practical experience. Many had already won a bachelor's degree. The medical school in a one-year course offered them the opportunity of increasing and rounding out their scientific knowledge and usually in addition, through its connection with a hospital, the possibility of further clinical training. In order to be near a hospital, the Harvard Medical School moved from Cambridge to Boston in 1807.

If these developments had been allowed to continue without interruption, conditions similar to those in Europe would soon have prevailed.

However, the interruption did occur through the opening of the West and the sudden expansion in that direction. The country needed doctors, many more than the few eastern schools could furnish. And besides the East was too far away. We have watched Drake as the founder of schools. The movement was as irresistible as an avalanche. Medical schools shot up like mushrooms after a night of rain. There were hardly any governmental regulations. Wherever a few doctors were gathered together, they could found a school, get a charter, call themselves professors, give medical instruction in some rented building, deal out diplomas, and pocket the tuition fees. It was a good business, not only on account of the fees, but because former students would enlarge the professors' practice by calling them in for consultation. It was such a good business that physicians found a teacher's chair worth paying a good price for and, naturally, it was often on the open market.

Instruction was, as may be imagined, quite insufficient. There was a complete lack of medical supplies. The schools were without funds. The only income was derived from the tuition fees and these were for the most part divided among the professors. The libraries were meagre; the laboratories non-existent; and, as a rule, no corpses were provided for anatomical demonstration, but at the best, a skeleton instead of the usual chest filled with bones. The majority of schools had no connection with a university, which might have guaranteed a certain standard of education; or else their connection was merely nominal. Nor were most of them connected with hospitals, so that their instruction was limited to theory. The time required was now as a rule two years, but since there was no division into grades, the second year was nothing but a repetition of the first, and besides, in many places the academic year lasted only sixteen to twenty weeks. No previous training was required of the students.

Still worse, these very inferior schools were replacing the old methods of practical training. Formerly an individual physician had his own group of pupils who for a number of years lived and worked in close touch with him. Now this contact was broken. A class received its instruction from a number of physicians in turn, and graduated without having been given any practical training. It is true that Europe still lay open; and some students now went to Paris. But a journey abroad was expensive and only a few could afford it.

Between 1810 and 1840 twenty-six new schools were founded; from 1840 to 1876, forty-seven. With the wave of immigration arose a corresponding number of schools: no less than one hundred and fourteen were founded between 1873 and 1890. In some states and in individual localities schools were literally heaped one on top of the other. In Indiana there were twenty-seven, in Illinois thirty-nine, of which fourteen were in Chicago alone. Missouri broke all records with forty-two. Louisville had eleven schools, as compared with Cincinnati's twenty.

It is difficult to give exact figures, as many of these schools collapsed soon after their establishment, some of them never existing except on paper. It has been calculated that in the course of a century the United States produced over four hundred medical schools.

The result may readily be imagined. The country was completely flooded with poorly trained physicians. There were plenty of discerning men who saw the danger of this situation. Voices were raised demanding reform. We have heard Drake make his protests and offer his sound suggestions. But these were voices crying in the wilderness. The country was too large and too heterogeneous; it was being settled at too headlong a rate for any early organization to be possible. The nation must first reach a period of comparative rest and obtain a certain equilibrium.

The process of reform was set in motion very gradually and from several quarters at once: the medical profession, the state, and the universities.

In 1845, following a motion made by N. S. Davis, the Medical Society of the State of New York invited all medical societies and schools of medicine in the Union to send delegates to a general congress of physicians to be held in New York. This step was provoked primarily by the realization that medical conditions had become intolerable and that above all there should be reforms in the training of physicians. In spite of initial opposition the meeting was finally arranged, and opened on May 5, 1846. It passed four resolutions: that it would be to the advantage of the medical profession to form a national organization; that it would be desirable for all medical schools as a unit to demand higher requirements for a doctor's degree; that it would be desirable for all young people who were accepted as medical students, to have had suitable preparatory training; that it would be advantageous for the medical profession to submit to an enforcement of professional standards.

The first point was carried: the congress had another meeting in Philadelphia in the following year, and organized the American Medical Association. It passed new resolutions for the reform of teaching. But they remained mere resolutions; lost in the increasing chaos of rapid development.

Nevertheless, the founding of the American Medical Association was of great importance. It provided physicians with a superstate organization, a forum for the expression of opinion, and above all else, a common professional conscience. At the very beginning a committee on medical education was formed, and even if the Association had no authority to enforce its wishes, it did exercise a moral authority. It was to have an important share in the reorganization of medical training during the twentieth century.

The intervention of the states proved to have greater, indeed paramount importance. We have seen that in the beginning of the colonial period, the practice of medicine was in no way controlled, anyone having the right to treat patients, but that even before the Revolution some states established certain standards, prescribing a minimum period of training and making the right to practise dependent on the acquisition of a license. New Jersey led the way by introducing a state medical examination in 1772. These were promising beginnings.

There was always the question as to where the authority to confer the license should rest. A doctor's degree from a European university of itself entitled the bearer to practise in the colonies; quite correctly, since the degree was the guarantee of a sufficient preparation. Now that medical schools which conferred diplomas were being established at home, it was natural that these, too, should be recognized. So, automatically, the schools came to confer the doctor's degree and the license at one and the same time.

There were, however, still a great number of medical students who never attended a university, contenting themselves with supervised work under a practitioner. From whom were they to get their licenses? When Daniel Drake began to practise, his only diploma was the certificate of completed studies given him by his master. This state of affairs persisted for a long time in many places in the West.

In the East, on the other hand, medical societies, formed as early as the eighteenth century, were given the right by the states to establish minimum training requirements and to award licenses. This was in itself a sound development. The medical profession was allowed to bring order into its own house.

But now followed the tremendous changes of the nineteenth century, which in this field, too, led to chaotic conditions.

The medical schools conferred the license to practise at the same time as the doctor's degree. Now we have seen that the number of schools grew beyond calculation and that many were inferior from the start. The more numerous the schools, the lower sank the average level. A school which had insisted on difficult examinations would very quickly have lost its pupils. And on the pupils depended its very existence. Voices were raised repeatedly demanding that the examinations for doctor's degree and the state license should be held separately and under different jurisdictions. It was no use; the schools raised a lively protest, in words fairly dripping with virtue.

And even in those localities where the licenses were under the control of medical societies, conditions became gradually worse. We will see later that during the nineteenth century there flourished not only religious, but medical sects. Each of these sects founded its own societies which claimed the same right as the legitimate medical societies to confer licenses. What was more, they exercised that right. Quackery had official sanction and those who could not procure a license from a medical society could always get hold of a perfectly valid license from some organization of charlatans. The height of absurdity had been reached.

After 1835 there was a marked tendency among the states to establish state boards of medical examiners appointed by the Governor. The idea was good, but premature. There was the problem of filling the positions. Political influences made themselves felt. In some places physicians nominated by the medical societies were appointed. Elsewhere, however, the various sects were represented on the commission, and in still other places, they had their own examination boards.

So nothing much was accomplished in this way. Towards the middle of the century these commissions were dissolved. They died of their own impotence. And again medical practice became a free-for-all proposition.

The reaction came in the seventies. Conditions had become unendurable. Something had to be done to protect society from the pseudo-physician. And as there were good reasons for not putting the medical examinations in charge of the schools, there was nothing left but to have the state again assume the sole right of licenture. Statutes were passed to this effect. Again examination commissions (State Boards of Medical Examiners) were appointed, first in Texas in 1873, in 1874 in New York and Kentucky, in 1875 in New Hampshire, and in 1876 in California and Vermont. By 1895 practically every state had its examination board.

The nation was more mature; its growth had become less rapid, so that the mistakes of the earlier days could be avoided. Naturally much still depended on the individuals composing the board and on their way of handling examinations. As is still the case, only written examinations were given, making it possible for students from inferior schools, if cleverly drilled, to obtain brilliant marks. Even today the problem of state examinations has not yet been solved satisfactorily, as we shall see later on. Nevertheless, the establishment of these boards was a great step forward. They at least gave the state an indirect control over the schools; there was moreover the possibility, even if not put to immediate use, of direct interference, since the state could make the right to take examinations dependent upon certain conditions.

The decisive step in reform had been taken. But it was at first a negative step; the eradication of the rankest growths. The country was still swarming with inferior schools and, even in the better ones, the instruction was by no means up to the highest standards of the time.

Now we understand the importance of the Johns Hopkins Medical School. It was the first positive step towards the reorganization of medical education. A model was provided, and it found imitators. Physicians from Johns Hopkins soon proved their superiority. Today they are found in leading positions all over the country. It was soon generally recognized that the teaching of medicine can never be an exclusively academic matter, that laboratories, dissection rooms, and clinics are indispensable for practical instruction. It was further recognized that medicine is a university subject requiring contact with other branches of science.

The realization of these facts had the fortunate result of closing automatically a large number of former medical schools. A school founded on a commercial basis could pay its way only as long as its expenses were at a minimum. As soon as public opinion demanded laboratories, hospitals, and other expensive equipment there was not the slightest chance of keeping down to the income derived from tuition fees, much less of making a profit. Other schools followed the example of Hopkins. The large eastern institutions were reorganized one after another. In the West and Middle West state universities were established which from the start included a medical faculty and which knew how to make use of the new methods.

In spite of all this, progress was slow. The opening of the twentieth century found plenty of abuses still persisting. Then in 1908 a great reform was set on foot. The Carnegie Foundation commissioned Abraham Flexner to prepare a report on the prevailing conditions of medical education in the United States and Canada. For two years Flexner travelled all over the country, visiting the 155 existing schools (including those in Canada). In 1910 he published his report, which exposed without hesitation all surviving abuses. But the book was more than a merciless piece of criticism; it offered a great number of creative suggestions.

And now the great reorganization began to be carried out in a systematic manner. Again many schools which, according to Flexner's report, had no future before them, closed their doors. Others, however, were put on a firmer basis with the assistance of the General Education Board, one of the Rockefeller foundations, which had Flexner at its head. The regional needs were taken into consideration.

As the South was badly provided for, the medical school of Tulane University at New Orleans was enlarged and expanded. With the help of wealthy patrons, Duke University was established at Durham, North Carolina, and the medical school of Vanderbilt University at Nashville, Tennessee, became a center for that section. In Rochester, New York, a modern university was founded, to which Eastman, the kodak manufacturer, contributed a large endowment.

The new schools needed professors, and looked largely to Hopkins for the supply. Often the faculty of a school would be essentially a graft from the Hopkins stem.

In the Middle West, the University of Chicago, Washington University in St. Louis, and the University of Iowa were all developed with money given by Rockefeller.

So it went on without a break. Wherever a sincere interest in reform was shown, abundant means would be forthcoming. And everywhere Abraham Flexner was the leader and adviser.

Hand in hand with this reorganization came the introduction of a system much discussed in America, and little understood in Europe—the so-called *full-time system*. The plan is very simple. Originally, professors of medicine in America, as in Europe, were physicians who earned their living by their practice and gave university lectures on the side. This is still the rule in England, and in France most professors are active practitioners. In Germany during the nineteenth century the teachers of the basic sciences came to relinquish the practice of medicine, while the clinicians continued to take private patients, leaving only a portion of their time free for university work.

The German system was the first to be tried at Hopkins, but it was exchanged in 1914 for the full-time system; that is to say, by the payment of an adequate salary it was made possible for the clinicians to do without private fees, leaving their time entirely free for research and study.

The most frequent objection raised against this system in Europe is that the clinician needs the experience given by private practice. There is nothing to prevent a full-time professor from seeing cases outside of the hospital. As in Germany, he can be called in for consultation, and he will accept cases which interest him scientifically or which can be used for demonstration. But he enjoys the advantage of having no material interest in these cases, and of being independent of large fees. If the patient is well off he pays the institution, instead of the professor, a moderate sum, but this source of income is not relied upon in the general budget.

Naturally, the full-time professor will never earn as much as certain successful practitioners. Those, however, who have chosen science for their vocation, have already made their decision; they have renounced wealth and are aware of satisfactions which no money can buy. But the man who has chosen outside practice is not lost to the university. Only the heads of the departments have full-time positions. The practitioner can be attached to a medical school as part-time professor and fill a valuable function in teaching and research.

A system which takes its professors out of business, which delivers them from the worry incident to the support of a family, and leaves them free to dedicate every energy to their task, is an ideal system which will undoubtedly be maintained.

After the World War the reorganization of medical schools continued at a tremendous rate. The money which came so easily during the prosperity period was as easily spent, and was readily obtainable for the use of universities. Many schools were still housed in buildings which no longer met their requirements. Money for buildings was easy to collect, for a building is a visible monument to its founder, linked with his name in perpetuity. An epidemic of building swept through the country. The Yale University Medical School was rebuilt. The Rochester Medical School was founded. The Western Reserve University in Cleveland and the Northwestern University in Chicago were given wonderful new medical buildings, to mention only a few. The new outward form sometimes prompted an inner reorganization and an effort to improve the teaching staff. Hundreds of millions were advanced in this way. The criticism is often heard that too much money was given for bricks and building and too little for men. This cannot be denied, but, thanks to the great building wave, now that money for such construction is no longer available, the whole country is newly fitted out with the most modern hospitals and laboratories. The costly equipment is there, and the people to use it are there, too, though the depression is for the moment imposing certain limits to their work.

The Johns Hopkins is arranged in a series of pavilions (Figs. 17 and 18). Baltimore has room to spread horizontally. The latest addition, the William H. Welch Medical Library and the Institute of the History of Medicine, is a simple beautiful building with a ground-floor and two stories. Baltimore can indulge in such a structure (Fig. 19). In New York, on the other hand, where ground had become so scarce and so absurdly expensive, another solution had to be found and buildings were necessarily extended towards the sky.

New York's two most important medical schools, Columbia University College of Physicians and Surgeons, connected with the Presbyterian Hospital and a group of other hospitals, and the Cornell University Medical College connected with the New York Hospital, are both gigantic skyscrapers.

The Presbyterian Hospital, up in the northern end of the city, is an agglomeration of tremendous and, in their simple functional outlines, most impressive buildings, a true medical center (Fig. 21). The Cornell center, New York Hospital, is something quite different. The last link in the chain of hospital evolution, not opened till the fall of 1932, it is a unified independent building of really overwhelming beauty (Fig. 20). At the first glance, and seeing the great pointed arches which are frankly reminiscent of the Palace of the Popes at Avignon, one may feel taken aback and inclined to wonder what the Gothic has to do with New York: why these sacerdotal associations? Has not New York a rhythm and a style of its own? But at a more prolonged view the building casts a spell; we find ourselves coming back to look again. Gradually we become aware of the meaning of the building, its profound symbolism, the great humanistic idea which it embodies in stone. At the center of medicine is the sick human being, the sole reason for its existence. The center of the building contains the hospital, with the two departments of medicine and surgery, which rise towards Heaven like a prayer for healing. From medicine and surgery the specialties developed; and from the central building the specialist clinics branch out as separate wings. Medicine is based on anatomy, physiology, pathology, and pharmacology. These departments are located on the ground floor of the building and enclose in their midst the library, that room where the wisdom of centuries has been stored for the benefit of future generations. Mental diseases have a place apart in the system of medicine and here, too, the psychiatric clinic has a separate building. And the pointed arches? Is not medicine immortal, a dispensation given to men in all times? Did not the Middle Ages bequeath to us our most complete expression of the unity of medicine and the divinity of the physician's mission? Greek

17. THE JOHNS HOPKINS UNIVERSITY SCHOOL OF MEDICINE
THE JOHNS HOPKINS HOSPITAL
SCHOOL OF HYGIENE AND PUBLIC HEALTH

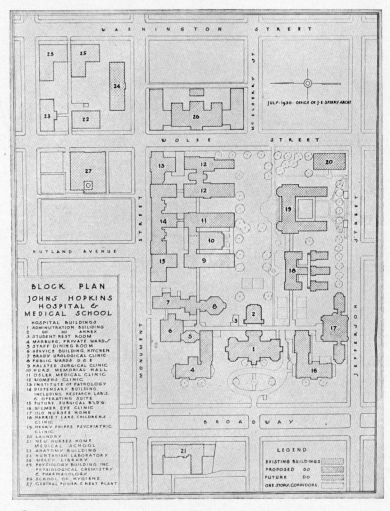

18. GROUND PLAN OF THE JOHNS HOPKINS UNIVERSITY SCHOOL OF MEDICINE

The projected buildings have in the meanwhile been completed

19. WELCH MEDICAL LIBRARY AND INSTITUTE OF THE HISTORY OF MEDICINE, THE JOHNS HOPKINS UNIVERSITY

20. NEW YORK HOSPITAL AND CORNELL UNIVERSITY MEDICAL
COLLEGE

21. COLUMBIA-PRESBYTERIA

The buildings from left to right are: Bard Hall, Medical Students Dormitory (at extr
Hall, School of Nursing; College of Physicians and Surgeons, School of Dental and O
Hospital; Sloane Hospital for Women; Vanderbilt Clinic; Squier Urological C

MEDICAL CENTER, NEW YORK

t); New York State Psychiatric Institute and Hospital; Neurological Institute; Maxwell
gery; School of Oral Hygiene, and Delamar Institute of Public Health; Presbyterian
and Harkness Private Patient Pavilion; Pediatrics; Ophthalmological Institute

science and Christian charity are the ground in which our Western medicine is rooted. In this building the snake of Æsculapius twines, not around a staff, but a cross. It is a fine thing and gives us confidence in the future to find such a monument today, in the twentieth century, in a city like New York. What Cornell will accomplish in the coming years it is as yet too early to tell. But by this building alone, the Dean, G. Canby Robinson, a Hopkins graduate who has previously reorganized the medical schools of Washington University in St. Louis and Vanderbilt University in Nashville, the Board of Trustees and the architects will win a permanent place in medical history.

The better the schools became, the smaller grew their numbers:

1910	*1914*	*1917*	*1920*	*1925*	*1932*
148	107	98	88	80	76

According to European conceptions, seventy-six is still a large number, but it is not as large as it seems. Ten of the schools mentioned are institutions giving only pre-clinical instruction, two are homeopathic, one is a college for women, and two are for negroes exclusively (Howard University in Washington and Meharry Medical School in Nashville). Above all it must be taken into account that compared to Europe, most of the schools accept only a limited number of pupils. Only seven institutions have more than five hundred students. The University of Illinois in Chicago has the greatest number, with five hundred and eighty-nine (in 1931–32).

Below will be found a list of the schools existing at this present writing (according to the Final Report of the Commission on Medical Education).

Alabama	University of Alabama School of Medicine	Tuscaloosa
Arkansas	University of Arkansas School of Medicine	Little Rock
California	University of California Medical School, Berkeley	San Francisco
	College of Medical Evangelists, Loma Linda	Los Angeles

	University of Southern California School of Medicine	Los Angeles
	Stanford University School of Medicine	San Francisco
Colorado	University of Colorado School of Medicine	Denver
Connecticut	Yale University School of Medicine	New Haven
District of Columbia	Georgetown University School of Medicine	Washington
	George Washington University School of Medicine	Washington
	Howard University College of Medicine	Washington
Georgia	Emory University School of Medicine	Atlanta
	University of Georgia Medical Department	Augusta
Illinois	Loyola University School of Medicine	Chicago
	Northwestern University Medical School	Chicago
	University of Chicago, Rush Medical College	Chicago
	University of Chicago, School of Medicine of the Division of the Biological Sciences	Chicago
	University of Illinois College of Medicine	Chicago
Indiana	Indiana University School of Medicine, Bloomington	Indianapolis
Iowa	State University of Iowa College of Medicine	Iowa City
Kansas	University of Kansas School of Medicine, Lawrence	Kansas City
Kentucky	University of Louisville School of Medicine	Louisville
Louisiana	Tulane University of Louisiana School of Medicine	New Orleans
Maryland	Johns Hopkins University School of Medicine	Baltimore
	University of Maryland School of Medicine and College of Physicians and Surgeons	Baltimore
Massachusetts	Boston University School of Medicine	Boston
	Harvard University Medical School	Boston
	Tufts College Medical School	Boston
Michigan	University of Michigan Medical School	Ann Arbor
	Detroit College of Medicine and Surgery	Detroit
Minnesota	University of Minnesota Medical School	Minneapolis
Mississippi	University of Mississippi School of Medicine	Oxford
Missouri	University of Missouri School of Medicine	Columbia
	St. Louis University School of Medicine	St. Louis
	Washington University School of Medicine	St. Louis
Nebraska	Creighton University School of Medicine	Omaha
	University of Nebraska College of Medicine	Omaha
New Hampshire	Dartmouth Medical School	Hanover
New York	Albany Medical College	Albany

	Long Island College of Medicine	Brooklyn
	University of Buffalo School of Medicine	Buffalo
	Columbia University College of Physicians and Surgeons	New York
	Cornell University Medical College, Ithaca	New York
	New York Homeopathic Medical College and Flower Hospital	New York
	University and Bellevue Hospital Medical College	New York
	University of Rochester School of Medicine	Rochester
	Syracuse University College of Medicine	Syracuse
North Carolina	University of North Carolina School of Medicine	Chapel Hill
	Duke University School of Medicine	Durham
	Wake Forest College School of Medicine	Wake Forest
North Dakota	University of North Dakota School of Medicine	Grand Forks
Ohio	University of Cincinnati College of Medicine	Cincinnati
	Western Reserve University School of Medicine	Cleveland
	Ohio State University College of Medicine	Columbus
Oklahoma	University of Oklahoma School of Medicine	Oklahoma City
Oregon	University of Oregon Medical School	Portland
Pennsylvania	Hahnemann Medical College and Hospital of Philadelphia	Philadelphia
	Jefferson Medical College of Philadelphia	Philadelphia
	Temple University School of Medicine	Philadelphia
	University of Pennsylvania School of Medicine	Philadelphia
	Women's Medical College of Pennsylvania	Philadelphia
	University of Pittsburgh School of Medicine	Pittsburgh
South Carolina	Medical College of the State of South Carolina	Charleston
South Dakota	University of South Dakota School of Medicine	Vermillion
Tennessee	University of Tennessee College of Medicine	Memphis
	Meharry Medical College	Nashville
	Vanderbilt University School of Medicine	Nashville
Texas	Baylor University College of Medicine	Dallas
	University of Texas School of Medicine	Galveston
Utah	University of Utah School of Medicine	Salt Lake City
Vermont	University of Vermont College of Medicine	Burlington
Virginia	University of Virginia Department of Medicine	Charlottesville

	Medical College of Virginia	Richmond
West Virginia	West Virginia University School of Medicine	Morgantown
Wisconsin	University of Wisconsin Medical School	Madison
	Marquette University School of Medicine	Milwaukee

And now we will take up the teaching of medicine in the United States at the present moment. I cannot go into detail; but must confine myself to the most fundamental aspects, especially emphasizing those points where it differs from the European systems.

I shall give the greatest space to describing the set-up at Johns Hopkins University, not only because I am most familiar with it, but because I have the impression that here has been found the most successful solution. The other universities have organizations which are similar, but never quite identical. All universities are autonomous. There are no state regulations in regard to the details of instruction. The State Board examinations set a certain standard, but methods of reaching this standard are the affair of each separate institution which, constantly on the lookout for better methods of teaching, can experiment at will and has authority at any time to make a change in the curriculum, without having to ask the approval of any government official.

First, a few words in regard to preparatory education. The American child, like the European, usually begins school in his sixth year, spends six years at elementary schools, and six more years at the high school. The divisions and the designations vary, but in general the high school is finished by the age of eighteen.

The future physician next enters college. The American college of arts and sciences was established after the English model during the colonial period, serving primarily as a preparation for the ministry, and is an institution unknown in continental Europe. The majority of the colleges were founded by private endowments and remain private institutions. Students may live inside or outside the college. In some country colleges, all students live in the college. But even in the cities most, if not all, colleges have their student dormitories. In the East the greater number are for either male or female students separately; while in the West, co-education is the rule. The curriculum extends over four years, which the student spends as freshman, sophomore, junior, and senior. The objective is the acquisition of a bachelor's degree, in either the arts (B.A.) or the sciences (B.Sc.).

The college is a sort of cross between the German *gymnasium* or the French *lycée* and a university. The age of students corresponds to the last two years of the *gymnasium* or *lycée* and the first two years of a European university. The college is not intended to prepare for any special profession, but to give a broad cultural background. Research is not part of its plan; though great scientists are found among the instructors. Its whole purpose is cultural. Many students go into business immediately after graduation.

The supervision of studies is much closer to elementary schools than is the case with European universities. It is true that the student has a certain freedom in the choice and arrangement of his courses; but he is given advice and kept under observation. He has to learn something. He does not enjoy the academic freedom of doing nothing whatever.

The idea of the college is excellent in itself. It is certainly an advantage to put off the narrowing effects of specialization. But here, as elsewhere, it all depends on how the idea is carried out. The number of colleges is legion. The 6457 medical students who began their professional studies in the Fall of 1929 came from over eight hundred different colleges. And these institutions vary a great deal. While some are on a very high level and, conducted in a liberal spirit, do most valuable work in education, we find countless others which are utterly inferior, whose inadequately trained staff can offer only the most out-of-date instruction, whose pupils—they can hardly be called students—are plagued with interminable examinations so meticulously marked that their whole progress becomes a matter of arithmetical calculation.

The result is that the young people who take up medicine are very unequally prepared. The American Medical Association has published a list of the colleges which meet the requirements which must be demanded of medical students. It is constantly checked and is published in the *Journal of the American Medical Association.* But there is still a certain, though decreasing, percentage of students graduating from unrecognized schools.

The college is the germ of the American university. It is true that most colleges are independent institutions, which have no connection with a university. But such universities as there are, usually grew up around a college.

Here we touch on a fundamental difference between European and American universities. The European university is a product of the Middle Ages, a time when a *universitas litterarum* really existed. The traditional interrelation of the four faculties of theology, jurisprudence, medicine, and philosophy has been more or less preserved, and even if these have today developed into separate schools, preparing for this or that profession, there is still the endeavor to keep the idea of the *universitas* alive, and, illusion though it may be, to foster the tradition that science is not pursued merely for the sake of professional advancement but as an end in itself. How long this idea can be maintained is problematic. The rise of the natural sciences has already split the faculty of philosophy into two divisions; no harm has been done. We see another aspect of the problem in Leipzig, where a veterinary school has been accepted as a "faculty" in the old sense. At the same time, the European university has understood how to preserve its unity and its scientific character and to admit no interests foreign to its nature.

The nationalization of the universities had, with many disadvantages, the one great advantage of assuring a certain minimum standard.

It is quite different with the American university. It developed as additional departments were established; a medical school, a law school, eventually a divinity school. The majority of institutions were privately endowed and were enlarged gradually according to needs and means, with no regard to the European pattern of four faculties of learning. Johns Hopkins began with a faculty of philosophy, followed later by the medical school. Even now, there is no school of law or theology. Divinity schools are usually quite separate as there is no state church in the country—but innumerable creeds. Instead, Hopkins has a school of engineering, a school of business economics, and a college for teachers and, besides the medical school, an independent School of Hygiene and Public Health, to which we will return later.

Other universities have still broader educational facilities: conservatories of music, art schools, and schools of dramatic art. And most of them hold university extension courses for adult education, like the *Volkshochschule* in Germany.

In this way enormous aggregates have come about, conglomerations of schools, like Columbia University and the University of Chicago. Naturally, not every division of such a group can be on an equally high level.

The college still functions as the integrating part of the university. As it stands half way between high school and a postgraduate school, it has a tendency to gravitate toward one or the other. It has become the fashion to criticize the college as an unnecessary burden on the university. That is justified when the college standard tends to be lowered towards that of the high school. It would seem to me to be desirable to give college-teaching an increasingly academic character. Eighteen-year-old human beings are after all no longer children; it falls to the colleges to teach these young people independent thinking, and to cultivate their individuality.

Those who intend to study medicine must go to college to prepare themselves in physics, chemistry, and biology, subjects which are taught in France in the "*p.c.n.*" (*physique, chimie, histoire naturelle*) and in Germany in the first year of the medical course. Since the American student has several years' time, he can prepare himself very thoroughly, adding bacteriology, mathematics and psychology to the required subjects. Above all, he has a better opportunity than the European student for practical laboratory work. At Hopkins, the future medical students, while still in college, are given introductory courses and lectures on medical history by members of the medical school faculty and begin their acquaintance with problems of medicine and of the medical profession.

Then comes the critical moment when the student has to compete for admission into the medical school.

The Johns Hopkins School of Medicine, like most schools in this country, has strict regulations as to number. Each year, seventy-five students are admitted, and since the course lasts four years, the total number of students never exceeds three hundred.

Naturally, an effort is made to admit the best students among those applying. The choice is determined in the following way. To begin with, there are high requirements for admission. Though many schools demand only two or three years of college education, Hopkins requires a full course and a bachelor's degree from a recognized college. The candidate must further demonstrate that during his college studies he has acquired a certain minimum amount of knowledge in the following subjects: biology, chemistry, physics, French, German, and Latin. Mathematics is desirable, though not obligatory. The Medical School next gets in touch with the candidate's college instructors, asking for at least two references—still more in doubtful cases —in regard to the work, personal character, and ability of the candidate.

As a rule, many applicants are turned down at this point. But after the first sifting process there still remain several hundred candidates who meet the requirements. The sifting process continues. Only those with the best references, who come from first-class colleges and have done unusually good work, are kept under consideration and are now invited to a personal interview. The school should have the whole country to draw from, and yet no candidate can be expected to take a four-day journey for a possibly unsuccessful errand. Hopkins graduates in leading positions in the larger cities have been given the responsibility of holding these interviews. At last the seventy-five most promising candidates are accepted, among whom about ten percent are women—a large number considering the fact that women comprise only 4.3 percent of the total number of medical students in the country.

The new students are very carefully examined by the Dean, his assistant, and a committee of the teaching staff. Every student is an expense to the school, since the tuition fees obviously do not cover the outlay. Therefore, the greatest possible assurance is desired that the expense is not for nothing; that the money really serves to provide the community with first-rate doctors.

There is naturally no absolutely certain method of choosing the best material. Still, the results at Johns Hopkins have been very good, and mistakes extremely rare. It must be kept in mind that the candidates, after four years in college, are usually in their twenty-second year and it is not so difficult to estimate their capacities, while in Europe the students usually enter the medical school at the age of nineteen.

The rejected candidates will attempt to enter some other school. Usually they have sent applications to several places at once, to have more than one string to their bow. In 1929–30, 13,569 candidates sent 31,481 applications. Only 6457, or about half of them, were eventually admitted. More than 7000 were turned down everywhere. What will be their next move? Some, who have behind them only two or three years of college, go back for further study and a year later make another application, perhaps under better auspices. Others give up the idea of studying medicine. A third group goes abroad.

This explains the great stream of American students who go to European universities. In the year 1931–32 no less than 1481 Americans studied medicine abroad. Naturally, Canada (308) and Great Britain (339) attract the greatest number, on account of their language. Switzerland comes next with 214, Austria with 188, Germany with 183, Italy 155, and France with 58. The rest are divided among the other countries.

These students get their doctors' degrees abroad and then come home and take their State Board examinations. The poor results are compromising to European universities. This seems to me so serious a question that I am repeating in full the statistics for the years 1927–31 published by the Council on Medical Education and Hospitals of the American Medical Association (*Journal of the American Medical Association*, vol. 99, 1932, page 743).

The identity of language may account partly for the good results shown in Great Britain, but these must to a still greater degree be attributed to the higher entrance requirements and the fact that English universities have lately begun to reject all American candidates who cannot furnish a certificate from a recognized American medical school showing that he is in every way acceptable to the school and rejected only for lack of space.

The other European universities should use more caution in admitting American students and should enforce a stricter standard.

Country	University	Number Examined	Percentage Failed
Austria	Universität Graz	7	57.1
	Universität Wien	65	33.8
Cuba	Universidad de la Habana	18	33.3
Czechoslovakia	Deutsche Universität, Prag	16	31.3
	Karlova Universita, Praha	12	41.7
England	Licentiate of the Royal College of Physicians and the Royal College of Surgeons	10	0.0
France	Université de Paris	21	33.3
Germany	Albert-Ludwigs-Universität, Freiburg	5	20.0
	Albertus-Universität, Königsberg	12	66.7
	Christian-Albrechts-Universität, Kiel	7	57.1
	Friedrich-Wilhelms-Universität, Berlin	38	39.5
	Universität Würzburg	13	61.5
	Rheinische-Friedrich-Wilhelms-Universität, Bonn	6	33.3
	Schlesische Friedrich-Wilhelms-Universität, Breslau	7	85.7
	Thüringische Landesuniversität, Jena	5	60.0
	Universität Leipzig	10	50.0
	Ludwig-Maximilians-Universität, München	18	38.9
Greece	National University of Athens	55	78.2
Hungary	Magyar Királyi Erzsébet Tudományegyetem Pecs	5	20.0
	Magyar Királyi Petrus Pázmány Tudományegyetem, Budapest	31	35.5
Ireland	University College, Dublin	20	10.0
Italy	Regia Università di Bologna	12	41.7
	Regia Università di Modena	8	75.0
	Regia Università di Napoli	176	76.7
	Regia Università di Padova	12	75.0
	Regia Università di Palermo	34	73.5
	Regia Università di Pavia	7	85.7
	Regia Università di Roma	42	57.1
Japan	Nippon Medical College, Tokyo	6	50.0
	Tokyo Charity Hospital Medical College	7	100.0
	Tohoku Imperial University, Sendai	6	100.0
	Tokyo Imperial University	8	37.5
Mexico	Escuela de Medicina de Guadalajara	16	43.8
	Escuela Libre de Homeopatia, Mexico	6	16.7
	Universidad Nacional, Mexico	30	6.7

Country	University	Number Examined	Percentage Failed
Portugal	Faculdade de Medicina do Porto	12	75.0
Rumania	King Ferdinand I Universitatea, Cluj	5	40.0
Scotland	University of Edinburgh	20	0.0
	University of Glasgow	6	33.3
Spain	Universidad Central de España Madrid	15	46.7
Switzerland	Universität Bern	10	50.0
	Universität Zürich	5	60.0
	Université de Genève	10	30.0
	Université de Lausanne	6	50.0
Syria	American University of Beirut	9	33.3
Turkey	Université Istanbul	5	80.0
U.S.S.R.	Charkovsky Medical Institute	24	54.2
	Dragomanov Medical Institute, Kiev	29	58.6
	First Medical Institute, Leningrad	9	44.4
	First Moscow Medical Institute	14	71.4
	North Caucasian Medical Institute, Rostov-on-the-Don	9	55.6
	Odessa Medical Institute	11	63.6
	Saratov Medical Institute	8	62.5
	Second Medical Institute, Leningrad	8	50.0
	Tomsk Medical Institute	12	50.0
	Voronezh Medical Institute	6	33.3
	Totals	984	52.9

Number of schools with no failures	2
Number of schools with 1–25 per cent failures	5
Number of schools with 25–50 per cent failures	25
Number of schools with 51–100 per cent failures	24
Total number of schools	56

Now to the studies themselves. When the Johns Hopkins was organized, it had the choice of three systems of instruction: the English, which as a whole still throws emphasis on training in a hospital and subordinates scientific studies to clinical work; the German which, before commencing clinical work, lays a thorough foundation in the basic sciences; and the French, which is something half-way between the two. The German system was decided upon; but the greatness of the men who built up Johns Hopkins consists in the fact that they did not simply imitate.

They took over the spirit, but not the outward forms of German teaching.

While in German universities the mediaeval *Lectio,* or formal lecture, is still very much to the fore, clinical teaching not much else but a lecture with demonstrations, and the practical courses treated as supplementary, at Hopkins the situation is reversed. The lecture is little used now. The existence of text-books has been discovered and the fact that there is not much use in holding forth on what can be found everywhere in print. The students are recommended books, and it is taken for granted that they have read them. Much time is saved; and emphasis can now be placed on instruction in the laboratory and in the hospital wards, with the possibility of work in small groups. This naturally demands a large staff. Johns Hopkins has at present (1932–33) for 289 students, 374 instructors, including the assistants and instructors who perform all the functions of teachers. In Germany the teaching staff could be noticeably strengthened by making more use of the *Privatdozenten* and medical assistants.

The curriculum is planned to allow the students long uninterrupted periods without being chased from building to building. When they are working in anatomy, they stay from nine to five at the anatomical institute; for pathology, they stay from ten to five at the pathological institute. They participate in every activity of the department. A medical school is a group of physicians who are occupied with scientific research and the treatment of patients. The students receive all their instruction by spending four years as an active part of such a group.

The professor and director of a department directs the teaching of his own specialty, keeps an eye on all the classes, holds interviews with co-workers and students, gives a few courses himself, and occasionally delivers lectures or clinical demonstrations on difficult subjects. The students are not to be mere passive recipients of facts; but are to find them out for themselves, with the knife and the microscope, in the laboratory and on the ward. Since their number is small, they are never without an instructor of whom they may ask questions, who makes suggestions, gives assistance, or demonstrates. The number of students is a constant upon which one can depend. It never rises to more than 75 in a single class. The dissection rooms and laboratories are planned for this number. Each student works with his own microscope. He must begin by getting used to his instrument, which in Europe is not the case.

For the instruction of these students there are available, for example, ten instructors in anatomy, twelve in pathology, thirty-eight in psychiatry, thirty-four in ophthalmology, five in medical history. As the wards are much smaller than those in German university clinics, the members of the staff are not overworked but have plenty of time for the individual patient and the individual student, time also for research.

The course lasts only four years and to use this limited time to the best advantage a certain amount of systematization is necessary. The school's program, which takes only the required courses into account, provides a scaffolding of the absolutely essential subjects. It is arranged so that only half of the available time is taken up by the required courses. The responsibility for the other half is put upon the student himself. All the departments offer a large number of elective courses which enable the student to fill the gaps in his knowledge or to pursue special interests more intensively. He may do research work as part of his curriculum. The courses are very wisely limited to the hours between nine and five, while in Europe they sometimes start at six o'clock in the morning and last till late into the night. There is no value in the piling up of information. The student must have time to assimilate what he has heard and seen; he must have leisure for reading.

The academic year runs from the beginning of October to the beginning of June and is divided into four terms of two months each, a plan which allows great elasticity in the arrangement of studies.

The first year is given to anatomy, physiology, psychology, and bacteriology. The second year is dedicated to the study of pathology. Pharmacology is included, and with it begins the approach to clinical work. What is called Elementary Medicine is taught. The students are given introductory courses in medical treatment, and learn methods of examination and how to use the ophthalmoscope. After studying physiology in the first year, they learn in the second how to apply physiological methods to medicine. The third and fourth years are devoted entirely to work in the clinics.

Tempting as it is to describe the curriculum in detail, I must confine myself to singling out a few particulars which seem to be specially characteristic or to offer extremely practical solutions—particulars that impressed me when I came from Europe.

It goes without saying that in anatomy each student dissects the complete half of a cadaver and its cavities and that in the histological course he examines not only preserved and colored specimens, but fresh tissue as well. In Europe many universities have great difficulty in obtaining a sufficient number of cadavers. In Holland cadavers had to be imported from the colonies. Another advantage is that instead of one large dissection room, as is usual in European universities, there are a series of small rooms for two or three cadavers. The students disturb each other much less. The fortunate diversity of the teaching staff makes it possible to add to the usual program courses in comparative anatomy, anthropology, X-ray anatomy and anatomy of the nervous system. As the last is known to present special difficulties to the students, it is illustrated physiologically by experiments on animals. The correlation between anatomy and physiology is much closer than in Europe.

In pharmacology, besides the lectures which have to be supplemented by reading, there is held during one term a biweekly afternoon laboratory course, in which the students make observations on the effect of the most important drugs and poisons through animal experiments performed by themselves.

Bacteriology is taught in the department of pathology. Instruction in pathology centers on the autopsies which are carried out by a small group. When the reports have been written, and the microscopic and bacteriological examinations have been made, the individual case is discussed with the whole class. General pathology and pathological anatomy are taught as follows: a series of lectures and demonstrations on general pathology are held at the beginning of the school year. Then the class divides into small groups, each morning into a separate class-room. Each room is devoted to one disease or one group of diseases. So a student may find a room which contains everything needed for the study of tuberculosis, beginning with individual case histories, which he can follow up through photographs and macroscopic and microscopic specimens. The literature on tuberculosis is displayed. Whenever experiments can be made, they are introduced into the course. The group remains in such a room for two weeks, in the charge of a teacher who gives instruction on the disease in question; then it progresses to the next class-room and another group of diseases. Once a week the whole class comes together. The week's work is discussed. Difficulties which have arisen are elucidated. Reports are made by individual students. There are also weekly clinical-pathological discussions with the senior students.

Instruction in internal medicine is divided into three stages. The second-year courses in elementary medicine and in methods of examination have already been mentioned above. In the third year the actual clinical work begins. The class breaks up into groups of 25 students each, so that while one group is occupied with internal medicine, another may be in the surgical and a third in the obstetrical or one of the other special clinics. The morning is spent in the dispensary, the afternoon on the ward or in the laboratory, where each student during his term at the clinic has a fixed place to work. Clinical lectures are held once a week. As the third stage, in his fourth year, the student acts as clinical clerk. He goes on rounds and a number of patients are put in his charge. At this stage, too, there are weekly clinical lectures and besides this the student takes part in the clinical pathological discussions. This is the minimum required. There are still a large number of elective courses at the disposal of the student, whether to bring him up to standard or for more exhaustive study.

Following the same idea, surgical instruction is likewise arranged in three sections. Very ingenious is the course in operative surgery, which is studied not only on human corpses as is the case in Europe, but with living animals. It is assumed that a case is surgical. One student plays the part of the family physician, another of a surgeon. The physician refers the case and discusses it with the surgeon. They decide to operate and consider the operation from every angle before carrying it out on the animal. A third student acts as anaesthetist, a fourth as nurse, a fifth as first assistant. They disinfect themselves, put on aprons and masks, and the operation is performed according to the rules, exactly as if a human patient were involved.

Instruction in the specialist branches is similarly arranged, except that they are given less time. For example, the instruction in psychiatry, which runs through all four years, has an excellent plan. In the first year the student is taught the elements of psychobiology in order to round out the anatomical and physiological picture of the human being. In the second year he becomes acquainted with methods of psychiatric examination and learns to recognize the chief reaction mechanisms. In the third year he sees clinical cases demonstrated and works in the dispensary. Finally in the fourth year he must make complete examinations of six ward cases and give a report on them.

In 1929 an independent Institute for the study of the history of medicine was erected at Johns Hopkins University, very practically located in the same building as the Medical School Library. It offers a four-year training. An introductory course acquaints the beginner with the main phases and leading ideas of medical history.

Seminar courses are held for each class which relate to the subject of the current year (anatomy and physiology, pathology, clinical medicine), in which the students are led to undertake original work and an effort is made to give a background to the material with which they are engaged. Courses on the social aspects of medicine are given to the fourth-year students. Once a week there is a research seminar, which gives the students an insight into the research work of the Institute, and acquaintance with the methods of medical history. Certain lectures, held partly at the Medical School and partly at the University, seek to bridge the division between the two departments. In this way an attempt is made to give the students a broad cultural background leading them gradually from the historical into the sociological field.

Another institute must not remain unmentioned as it, too, represents an interesting experiment which has already borne good fruit; that is the Institute of Art as applied to Medicine, under the directorship of Max Broedel, who came to Baltimore in the nineties from the Leipzig Art Academy and Ludwig's laboratory. Here the students can learn to draw. But it serves above all to train medical illustrators, who are taught every branch of medical illustration. A great school of medical art has had its inception in this institute and Max Broedel's pupils can be found all over America.

The division into small groups has the further advantage that the instructor gets to know the students very well. Examinations play a much smaller rôle than in Germany or France. Two examinations are given, one at the end of the second year, in the basic sciences, another at the end of the fourth in clinical medicine. The results of the examination only partially determine the grading of a candidate. Equal weight is given to the judgment of the instructors in the obligatory as well as in the elective courses. Any independent achievement of the student, such as special scientific work, is also taken into account. A student may for that matter be put out of the class at the end of a year without an examination, if his teachers have found him incapable. The examinations are not primarily intended as a means of appraising the students. Their purpose is rather to lead the students to review a subject and grasp it as a whole. After a successfully completed course of study the candidate is given his medical degree.

The course lasts four years, but naturally anyone is at liberty to prolong his studies. This does not happen often, as the student is usually already in his twenty-sixth year and has at his disposal other possibilities for further training.

A characteristic difference from Germany has been frequently mentioned. The students do not go from place to place, but complete their medical studies at one and the same university. This is as it should be. The difference in the plan of studies and above all the limitation in the number of students admitted make a change of university difficult. It is, however, not impossible. If, for instance, a vacancy occurs in the third year at Hopkins, a student from another medical school may be admitted for the rest of the course, providing he can meet the requirements of the class. A Hopkins student may also without further question spend the second half of his fourth year studying abroad. He may also at any time, with the consent of the Dean, spend a term at another institution such as a hospital. Only he must see to it that he conforms in some degree to the program of study.

Such changes are therefore quite possible, but they are not frequent. There is a great advantage in spending the whole four years at one and the same school. It must also not be overlooked that preparation for medicine is divided into three sections, college, medical school, and, as we shall soon see, an internship. These three periods can be spent in separate places; in fact, this is usually the case. Very few Hopkins medical students have taken an A.B. at Hopkins. A student for instance goes to Harvard or Yale, studies medicine at Johns Hopkins Medical School, and finally becomes an interne at a hospital in New York, California, or elsewhere. The American system gives ample opportunity for change of environment.

After finishing medical school, the student receives his doctor's degree. He has not yet the right to practise. First he must pass the State Board examination. Seventeen states and territories require, besides the completed course of study at the medical school, one year of internship before the examination can be attempted. Twelve medical schools confer the doctor's degree only at the end of a year of internship. Even where such a year is not demanded, 95 percent of all medical students spend at least one year in a hospital.

The student enters a hospital to serve his time as interne. He is given board and lodging, but no salary. Naturally not every hospital is suitable for the training of medical men. The American Medical Association, as the result of an investigation, has made a list of suitable hospitals which is added to from year to year. In 1932 it comprised 696 hospitals with 211,174 beds and 6261 internships; a sufficient number considering that in the same year the number of graduates was 4936. Several states have detailed regulations for the program of the interne which require that he have practice in every field of medicine and in addition be given laboratory work. But even where there are no such regulations, the internship is regarded as a period of learning. The student is supervised and, by being given increasing responsibility, is gradually prepared for the independent practice of his profession.

The state examinations, in contrast to Europe, are given not by university professors but by a State Board of Medical Examiners, which consists for the most part of practising physicians. The examination covers as a rule all the main fields of medicine, including the basic sciences, and consists entirely of written work. In 1931, 5576 candidates took the examination. Six and three-tenths percent failed.

The constitution of the United States does not admit of a form of license which would be valid for the whole country. The passing of an examination, therefore, gives the right to practise only in the state in question. When a physician moves to another state, he has to submit to another examination. Gradually, however, it has become the custom for those states which have equally high requirements to recognize the result of each other's examinations, so that a practitioner with a license from one of these states is granted a license to practise in another without taking a new examination.

Furthermore, in 1915 the National Board of Medical Examiners was established, which sets maximum requirements; and its license is now recognized by 41 states and 3 territories.

At the beginning of this chapter it was shown why the right to confer licenses was taken away from the medical schools. The State Boards have played an important part in the reform of medical education. Today, however, the situation is changed. The state examinations, in their present form, have outlived their usefulness. To judge a man's fitness for medical practice, one must first of all know him, the longer the better, and in medicine, if anywhere, a written test is less appropriate than a practical one, at the bed-side of a patient. The medical schools have now made so much progress that they can again be trusted with the privilege of issuing licenses. The state would not need to renounce its right of control. It could limit the right of licenture to the schools which met its requirements and could be represented at the examinations by a commissioner, as is done in Europe.

America is no longer in the first stages of youth. It already has traditions which now and then restrict its free development. But fortunately the elasticity is still great enough to break through these restrictions before they can do much harm.

I have described the Johns Hopkins plan in detail as a paradigm. The other schools are run on the same principle; that is, on the theory that instruction in the basic sciences should antedate work in the clinic. Of course one finds extraordinary differences in the quality of students, professors, and equipment. We have seen that some schools have much lower standards in their entrance requirements and that many have not yet taken over the full-time system. In some places the laboratories may be excellent, while the clinical opportunities are still inadequate. Very few schools have as liberal a spirit as Hopkins. In many the teaching is much more formal, the students are under stricter control and are plagued with examinations. While Hopkins, where interest is focussed chiefly on science and research, has become the school which furnishes the country with the greatest number of academic teachers, many other schools, especially in the Middle West, are used in the main to prepare students for the practice of medicine, so that the emphasis is put rather on the dispensary than on the ward work, a point of view which is in itself altogether sound. On account of the dispensary patients especially, the medical school or a section of it is often separated from the rest of the university. There has been the tendency to build universities away from big cities, in the country or in small towns. But clinical teaching requires the proximity of a larger town. So the basic science courses and the clinical institutes are sometimes found in separate cities, which naturally has disadvantages.

It has already been mentioned that there are great differences in the plan of the curriculum and in the classification of the material. Every school makes experiments in teaching and one meets with many interesting ideas. To describe them in detail would fill a whole volume.

One word in regard to the cost of tuition. There are no fees for individual courses; but one fee for the whole academic year which entitles the student to visit all courses given by the school. Tuition costs $600 at Johns Hopkins; in ten universities it costs over $500. These are mainly the great endowed universities of the East. The western universities, especially the state universities, are cheaper. In 22 universities the charge is between $200 and $300; in six schools it is under $100. However, the state universities ask a surcharge of from twenty to three hundred dollars for students from another state. At Columbia University in New York it has been calculated that the living expenses of a student, including a tuition fee of $520, would amount to a minimum of $1277 in an academic year, $1538 on the average. Many students, especially in the West, work their way through school, and a great number use the summer months to earn their expenses.

In one department of medicine America has led the way from the beginning. The subject of *American dentistry* must be briefly touched upon. It is not long since American dentists were preferred abroad. An American, Thomas W. Evans, was dentist at the court of Napoleon III. The course of development was at first chaotic in this field also, similar to that of medicine generally. Until quite far into the nineteenth century there was no sort of regulation. Anyone could practise dentistry. The doctor, the surgeon, any craftsman who felt himself qualified, any sort of quack was able to pull teeth. False teeth were primarily the affair of artisans, goldsmiths, and workers in ivory, who could make the sets themselves. It was France which produced Pierre Fauchard, whose book *Le Chirurgien Dentiste* (1728) marks the beginning of modern dentistry. Therefore at first it was towards France that one turned for news of technical improvements.

But during the nineteenth century the situation was completely changed. The technical skill of Americans maintained itself in this department also. They imported less and less and learned to manufacture at home. And their product was superior. A dental profession with a definite professional consciousness began to develop. Many physicians made a specialty of dentistry, or dental surgery, as it was called. Two such physicians in Baltimore, Chapin A. Harris and Horace H. Hayden, tried to establish a school of dentistry as a department of the University of Maryland in 1839. But the idea met with no understanding on the part of the University. So in the next year, 1840, an independent College of Dental Surgery was founded in Baltimore. Four physicians made up the staff. In the same year was founded the American Society of Dental Surgeons, the first organization to represent the profession as a whole, since before there had only been separate local societies. In the following year, 1841, Alabama became the first state to make the right to practise dentistry dependent on the acquisition of a state license. The publication of the first magazine of the profession, *The American Journal of Dental Science*, began in 1839.

In this way the year 1840 marks a turning point in the history of American dentistry. It was, to be sure, only a tentative beginning. The Baltimore college had few pupils and the majority of dentists continued to be artisans. The Alabama licenture remained on paper. The society died out in 1856. The journal went by the board in 1860 after the death of its founder.

But a beginning had been made. The way of future development had been shown.

As early as 1855 a new organization had been founded—the American Dental Convention. The American Dental Association followed in 1859. In 1868 three states—Kentucky, New York, and Ohio—introduced the licenture and, what was more, insisted upon its being carried out. One by one, though very slowly, new schools were established. In 1865 there were four which gave dental degrees. Of great importance was the fact that in 1867 Harvard opened a dental department. Dentistry was hereby raised to academic rank. This recognition had special significance, coming as it did from Harvard, the oldest university in the country. It was Oliver Wendell Holmes who gave the address at the first graduation exercises.

As in the case of medicine, it was not the object of these first schools to offer a complete dental education, but rather to round out and supplement the period of practical training. Harvard, for instance, began by giving two courses of four months each, but required three years of previous training.

From now on progress was much faster. In 1868 there were ten schools, by 1884 there were twenty-two, many of them connected with universities. Their number increased rapidly, and as in medicine a whole series of schools sprang up purely as business enterprises, providing inferior teaching, but able to sell the coveted doctor's degree. And since American dentists were highly esteemed in Europe, these degrees actually became articles of export, finding grateful purchasers abroad.

Till here, too, an iron broom swept the floor clean. The factors working for reform were similar to those in medicine: the state licenture, efforts on the part of professional groups, and the establishment of model institutions. As early as the first years of the twentieth century the majority of swindling enterprises were discontinued. Finally, just as in medicine, an investigation was made possible by the Carnegie Foundation. In 1926 appeared the report of William J. Gies, a book of almost seven hundred pages which gives a cross-section of contemporary dentistry and points out the right lines of future development.

Today there are thirty-one first class dental schools, with few exceptions departments of universities. Besides these there are seven additional schools which are not yet up to the highest standard.

If one reviews the history of medical education in the United States, it is evident that extraordinary difficulties have been surmounted within a very short period. Fifty years ago American schools counted for nothing in world medicine. Twenty-five years ago there were only a few schools which could measure themselves against European institutions. But today the standard of instruction equals that of most European countries and in many places and on some points is definitely superior. And its development has by no means come to a standstill. Every school has its committee on medical education which keeps constantly on the watch and never flags in its effort to perfect the system of instruction. Every school is in a state of healthy competition with all the rest. And since reforms do not need to be confirmed by the state, there is no delay in carrying them out.

Today, however, progress is already at such a point that each year five thousand physicians leave the universities to practise medicine, fully equal to the demands which will be made upon them.

☆   **CHAPTER SIX**   ☆

THE PHYSICIAN AND THE PATIENT

THE foregoing chapters have dealt with the evolution of the American medical profession. We have seen the physician in Boston and Philadelphia during colonial times. We have seen the pioneer doctor riding across country with his saddle-bags. We have learned how much the nation needed physicians and how schools were founded, from which they poured in thousands over the face of the land. And finally we saw how the erstwhile artisan developed into the modern physician equipped with every weapon of science.

Like everything in the new country, the medical profession was allowed to develop without system, by fits and starts, and in bursts of violent energy. The number of practitioners increased at a prodigious rate during the nineteenth century; and today, in spite of the closing of many schools, is greater than in any European country. It must be remembered that America is a thinly settled continent. While England alone has 742.2 inhabitants to the square mile, Germany 360.7, and France 106.9, the United States has only 41.3 inhabitants within the same area.

For a total population of somewhat over 123,000,000 there are now 156,440 licensed physicians. In other words, there is a doctor for every 780 inhabitants. For comparison the parallel figures of several European states are given below. The proportion of population to every physician in European countries is as follows:

Sweden	2,890
France	1,690
Germany	1,560

England & Wales	1,490
Switzerland	1,250
Austria	880

In the meantime the number of American physicians is steadily on the increase, and at a higher rate of progression than is the case with the population as a whole. Two thousand nine hundred and fifty-two physicians died in 1931. In the same year 4735 physicians were graduated from recognized medical schools. To this must be added 233 physicians graduated in foreign schools. It is calculated that, if the situation remains unchanged, in fifty years the population will have risen to 147,000,000 and the number of physicians to about 22,000,000. That would give one physician to every 670 inhabitants. There is no doubt that America is more than amply provided with physicians, even when it is taken into consideration that on account of the great distances between points, more physicians are needed than would be the case in a densely populated country—a point that must not be overstressed, since with modern means of communication one man can take care of a much larger area than was possible even thirty years ago.

This enormous number of physicians is a dominating factor in the present situation. What happens when a country has too many doctors? According to theory, it should make medical assistance readily available. It might further be expected that, the supply being greater than the demand, the wares, in this case medical service, would become cheap. For society this should mean reasonable and adequate medical care; and for the physicians intense competition which should lead, by natural selection, to a survival of the fittest.

This is correct in theory, but turns out to be quite different in practice. And for a number of different reasons.

First, there must be considered the distribution of physicians, both from the geographical standpoint, and from that of specialization.

The physicians are naturally not distributed evenly over the country. Though in the beginning and the middle of the nineteenth century the frontier, the western border, was the decisive psychological and economic factor in American life, during the second half of the century the development of the great cities determined the trends of progress. (This was occurring in Europe as well, the only difference being the much faster rate of development.) While in 1880 the proportion of urban to rural population was 28.6 to 71.4, this was changed by 1930 to 56.2 urban, 43.8 rural. The medical profession followed this movement towards the big cities; they concentrated in one spot. With modern means of transportation a city is able to provide medical care for a very large rural territory. In Europe, where the cities are close together, this possibility is of no importance. But here, where wide areas are thinly settled and far from any city, it necessarily developed that in spite of the great number of physicians, certain parts of the country are not taken care of. In California there is a physician for every 483 inhabitants; in Montana and South Carolina, on the other hand, the proportion is one physician to every 1430 inhabitants.

There are many reasons behind the movement of physicians into the cities. In certain sections and under the competitive system, a physician simply cannot support himself by a country practice. It is true that competition in the city is intense, but there is also a better prospect of earning at least a living. The distances are smaller. The population has more ready money. To this must be added important psychological factors. The city alone offers unlimited opportunities for a career. The most competent man can work his way to the top and attain an increasingly large and remunerative practice. And though only a few may reach this goal, the bare possibility is in itself enticing. In the country a physician may be ever so competent; there are strict limits to his rise in the economic scale.

At the university the students live for four years in close

touch with science. They work at the hospital, where every technical resource is at their disposal, and where they can turn for advice at any moment to an expert in each special field. In outside practice the young doctor is suddenly thrown on his own resources, and finds himself forced into many compromises. Much that was possible inside a hospital and described to the students as absolutely essential cannot always be carried out in other places. Only first-rate physicians with an unusual all-round training and marked initiative can manage to keep up their scientific standards even in a country practice. For many, there is great danger that their practice will gradually deteriorate to mere routine. The theories impressed by the universities fade out: the diagnoses become approximations, the treatment is limited to a number of prescriptions, diets and other directions which are determined rather by instinct than by logic. One discovers after a while what an incredible natural power of recovery resides in the human organism.

To be sure, to a pioneer spirit, the country offers possibilities and satisfactions not to be found in a city. The country doctor may become the savior of his district. He knows his families from the oldest to the youngest. He has brought the child into the world, has accompanied him through the perils of infancy, has followed his progress through school, has been an adviser at the time of his betrothal and a present help in every trouble. He is at the bedside during the final sickness, and closes the eyes of the dead. And he is more than a physician. He is the exponent of the great ideas of hygiene; it is his task to bring the people of his district to healthier and happier ways of living. If he still has his interest in science, he will have plenty of opportunity to cultivate it and put it to use. Periodicals and postgraduate courses will keep him informed, and his own practice provides an observation material so different from that given by a hospital that it is well worth studying. McDowells and Beaumonts are still possible.

However, a city practice is much simpler, with hospitals and laboratories close at hand, to which the physician can always turn for an adviser to share in the responsibility of doubtful cases. And how much easier it is to keep in touch with scientific developments!

And above all the city physician does not need to master the whole field of medicine; he can specialize in a single subject and as specialist enjoy the added perquisite of larger fees.

Medical specialization developed relatively late in America. A physician who limited himself to one field was not taken seriously in the old days. We have seen how for a long time surgeons combined a general practice with their surgery. For a long time there was no opportunity for training in special lines. To become a specialist, one had to go to Europe. Today things have changed. There are now over 39,000 specialists; that is almost exactly one quarter of the medical profession. At the same time the specialization is much less rigid than in many European countries. Less than half restrict themselves to their particular specialty. The greater number combine it with a general practice. The sharp professional distinctions found in Germany, which make the designation of specialist dependent on a specified training and moreover do not allow the specialist to step outside his own narrow field, have a great advantage in that they protect society from the pseudo-specialists, but at the same time they have the disadvantage of making of the specialist a nothing-but-specialist, and of closing to him many wide fields of medicine that should have been opened to him by his medical license. The onesidedness of specialization is hereby intensified. It is obvious that back of these restrictions there is a materialistic rather than an idealistic motivation.

In America there is as yet no legal restriction to the assumption of any specialist title. Any physician can go to Vienna, register at a special clinic, and whether he spends his time in the clinic or vacationing on the Semmering, at the end he will get

a handsome diploma from a society calling itself the American
Medical Association of Vienna, which will hang in his room
and give him the prestige of a specialist. These abuses are of
course exceptional.

Efforts to work a reform in specialist practice have lately
been under way. The great organizations of surgeons and physicians, suggested by English models, the American College of
Surgeons, and the American College of Physicians are typical.
Both exercise great care in the admission of members and accept
only such physicians as have received real scientific training.
Membership in such a college therefore constitutes a guarantee.
Other societies of specialists have taken similar action. The
ophthalmologists in 1917, the otolaryngologists in 1924 and the
gynecologists and obstetricians in 1930 have severally formed
committees who examine candidates in these specialties and confer diplomas. Some universal regulation will have to come from
the American Medical Association, it is to be hoped in a liberal
spirit. The Association has already prepared a list of 353 hospitals with 2092 interne-positions which presumably offer satisfactory training for specialization.

Though there was for a time a great increase in specialization, the latest statistics show that this has already passed its
peak. Of the physicians who graduated in 1915, only 22.5 percent are general practitioners; 35.6 have a specialty besides their
general practice; 40.9 are pure specialists; 1 percent does not
practise at all. Of those practising in New York who graduated
from Columbia University between 1900 and 1919, 43 percent
are pure specialists; of those who graduated between 1920 and
1928, only 10 percent. Similar, but somewhat lower figures are
obtained by examining the total number of New York physicians. Naturally a proportion of the most recent graduates will
still take up some specialty or other; but a tendency towards a
decrease in specialization is very marked.

It might be expected that the over-supply of physicians would lead to a reduction in the cost of medical care. It has not turned out that way. The number of physicians increased and yet the prices kept rising; for the reason that at just this time medicine became, certainly more successful, but also more complicated. The training period became longer, and the invested capital was consequently larger. Whereas a physician formerly needed two rooms, a stethoscope and a few simple instruments to carry on his profession, today he cannot practise with an easy conscience without a laboratory, an X-ray outfit, and a whole arsenal of expensive apparatus. The outlay has increased tremendously. Higher production costs can only be met by increased sales. But in medicine there are natural restrictions to output. A single physician can handle only a limited number of patients; and the fees of these patients must cover his office expenses and provide his livelihood. In other words, the commodity remains expensive and can only be bought by those who command the means. And since the commodity is expensive, and the number of sales is relatively low, it goes badly with both producer and consumer.

An effort to decrease overhead costs had to be made. Just as small independent businesses cannot survive unless they consolidate with other firms, so physicians have combined with each other. At first the getting together was a purely external affair; they moved into the same building. It is a foolish expense for each physician to maintain his own laboratory, his own X-ray, and his own office staff. It is much more economical to have an apparatus that serves a number of physicians in turn, rather than one that lies idle. But this requires that the apparatus and the physicians are in close proximity, for it would not only be a nuisance, but most uneconomical, to have to chase the patient all over the city for his various examinations.

This was the origin of the *Medical Arts Buildings* (Fig. 22) now found in many cities, some of them skyscrapers, housing a doctor behind every door, in which, particularly in the smaller cities, a large percentage of the medical profession carries on its practice. Since these buildings are planned expressly for that purpose, they are most practically arranged. The patient can find there general practitioners, his family doctor if he has one, but also every sort of specialist, including dentists. Every examination can be made without loss of time. The examining physician can get the laboratory findings within a few minutes. A pharmacy and a medical supply store are in the building. There is usually a garage in the basement. In the top-story there are lunch-rooms for the doctors and the personnel. In many cities the local medical society has its office in the Medical Arts Building, with its library and meeting-rooms. In these most modern buildings one sometimes even finds collections on medical history.

These medical buildings originated in the Middle West and were soon copied by the Far West and more gradually by the rest of the country. There can be no doubt that this is a wise and practical arrangement which will one day be adopted also in Europe.

The consolidation of physicians was carried still further and led to what is called *Private Group Clinics*. Partnerships between physicians practising the same specialty occur in Europe, particularly if they have a private clinic together. But this is a quite different situation. The word *clinic* must not be allowed to create confusion. It does not mean a clinic in the European sense of a hospital, but refers to the fact that physicians representing different specialties have formed a group which has a practice in common, space in common, and a common interest in the expenses and profits of the undertaking. The group as a whole liquidates even when a patient is seen by only one of its members.

This group-medicine development has sprung up mainly since the war, and began in the Middle West. Today there are about

22. MEDICAL ARTS BUILDING, ST. PAUL

200 such groups, comprising from 2000 to 2500 physicians and dentists. Many consist of a physician, a surgeon, a gynecologist, an ophthalmologist, an ear, nose, and throat specialist, a dentist, and a pathologist who has charge of the X-ray and laboratory examinations. There are smaller groups and also large ones of fifteen or more doctors. The groups as a rule have no hospital of their own, but for the most part are affiliated with one to which they can refer their patients.

The manner of dividing the profits varies to an extraordinary degree, as it naturally depends upon whoever has provided the capital for office, apparatus, and instruments. It is a simple matter when the clinic is the property of one physician, who pays the others a fixed salary. As a rule there is some method by which the physicians share in the receipts. In many cases the clinic is organized as a joint-stock company, with the physicians as shareholders. Each draws a salary and the surplus income is apportioned as dividends.

Though still new, this group medicine has already proved its medical as well as its economic value. The patient visiting such a clinic is assured of all that is humanly possible in diagnosis and treatment. The outstanding advantages of a hospital, the coordination of specialties and the more complete equipment for examinations are carried over into everyday practice. The personal relation between physician and patient is not lost, for it is obvious that in each case one physician will have the ultimate responsibility, with the others acting as expert advisers.

It is also quite clear that such a group can work more economically than an isolated physician. The majority have a business manager, who can handle their affairs much better than the average physician who is by nature a bad business man. For that matter, the lowering of the overhead is as much for the good of the patient as of the physicians. Complete examinations can be carried out at a much lower cost than is usual in private practice. The physicians get on the average a higher income. To be sure it must be taken into consideration that with these medical groups we are dealing with a certain élite. Obviously, such a group will be particular in admitting a new physician, since it must act collectively as sponsor for him. Work in close association with physicians of varying professional interests is of course stimulating to all concerned.

Lately several of these clinics have entered into agreements with groups of employed persons according to which the clinic, in return for a lump sum, undertakes the medical care of the group.

It is all a recent development, a phenomenon of the post-war period. However, long before the war there already existed one such group, the *Mayo Clinic* in Rochester, Minnesota, which became the inspiration for the whole movement.

The Mayo Clinic is the creation of a gifted family of physicians. The elder William W. Mayo (1819–1911) came from England in 1845, having studied physics and chemistry in Manchester. In his new home he took up medicine, studied for a time with a practitioner and graduated from the University of Missouri in St. Louis. He practised in different places of the Middle West, finally settling in Rochester in 1863, where he soon became the leading physician and surgeon of the district. His two sons, William J. Mayo and Charles H. Mayo, studied medicine, and both became prominent surgeons.

A cyclone, which visited the district in 1883 at the cost of many lives, led to the building of a hospital. St. Mary's Hospital was opened in 1889, with the three Mayos as physicians-in-charge, five Catholic sisters and room for forty-five patients. Such was the beginning of a development, the importance of which no one could then have had the slightest notion. The new hospital became a center of surgical activity. Four years later it was already in need of enlargement. Five years later a new wing was added. After 1900 it developed more and more rapidly and the

23. THE OLD MAYO CLINIC

24. THE NEW MAYO CLINIC

At the left the old clinic, behind it the Kahler Hotel, at right the new hotel and hospital building

whole character of the institution was changed. Till now it had been a partnership—formed in 1887—among three physicians, specializing in surgery, and merely giving medical treatment on the side. After 1900 co-workers in other fields were associated with the project. The range of activities steadily increased. New specialists were constantly added, and a medical group came into existence, a clinic in the sense in which we have been using the word, but on a gigantic scale. In 1929 it comprised no less than 386 physicians. The emphasis was placed on diagnosis, for which a separate building was erected in 1914 (Fig. 23), which, however, soon proved to be too small, and a new building of fifteen stories with 288 examination-rooms and 21 laboratories was substituted (Fig. 24). The realization that an exact diagnosis is the prerequisite for successful treatment had led to this development. The correctness of the theory was demonstrated by the result. Patients streamed towards Rochester. In 1929, the clinic was visited by 79,000.

When the Mayo Clinic is discussed in Europe—usually by people who have never been there—it is as a rule used as an example of over-mechanized medical treatment, a medication run on a factory-belt. It is true that the patient goes through a number of clinics—as many as his case demands, but the reports are all finally gathered into one hand. One man is responsible for the synthesis of the findings, the diagnosis, and the treatment. What happens is identical, with the procedure of every serious European hospital, except that the technical means are more nearly perfected.

And above all, diagnosis is made a means, not an end in itself. It serves four large hospitals, which are economically independent of the clinic, but which are in charge of physicians who belong to its staff.

That an institution serving such a tremendous number of patients would offer ideal opportunities for scientific research and also for training of physicians, was at once recognized by the

Mayos. From the outset great emphasis was put on research. Numerous papers are published each year. In 1924 an Institute for Experimental Medicine was built near the city on a model farm belonging to the Mayos. In 1915 the Mayo Foundation for Medical Education was established, bringing the Mayo Minnesota Clinic into close relation with the University of Minnesota at Minneapolis. Every year a number of carefully picked young doctors are admitted as fellows of the Foundation and it is made possible for them to perfect themselves in some specialty.

The clinic is attended not only by well-to-do patients; it is open to everyone. The fee demanded depends on the medical care involved and the financial status of the patient. About 30 percent make no payment whatever, 25 percent pay just enough to cover the costs. The physicians have a fixed salary. The surplus income is used for maintenance and expansion of the equipment, and any residue goes into the endowment fund.

So, in the middle of the Minnesota hill country, arose an institution, unique of its kind, a twentieth century Salerno.

This getting together of physicians has undoubtedly resulted in a lowering of overhead costs and more reasonable fees. But the whole movement is still in its beginnings, and by no means universal; and even group medicine is still too expensive.

The American nation in the year 1929 spent no less than three billion, six hundred thousand dollars for medical purposes. In the same year thousands of people died of preventable or curable diseases, thousands were without physicians; in Massachusetts, one of the best governed states in the Union, more than a third of the chronically sick were left to their own devices, with no medical assistance. How much worse the present situation must be can be easily imagined.

So there has developed the paradoxical situation that, in an era when medicine can marshal more effective remedies than ever before, great sections of the community are still without medical care and, as another side of the picture, the very existence of many practitioners is threatened. Medicine is by way of being shattered because of the force of its own impetus.

When a commodity becomes too expensive it disappears from the market. But medical assistance is a commodity which society cannot very well do without. Society has an interest in the health of each one of its members.

It is time to consider very seriously whether, after all, adequate medical care is still possible under conditions of free competition. The judiciary and the schools have long since ceased to be business concerns. Will medicine come next?

Business principles have never been followed consistently in medicine. The physician can never measure his fees exactly according to the service rendered, but must take the financial status of his patients into consideration. He has always treated a certain proportion of his patients without remuneration.

Since the beginning of the Christian era welfare agencies have taken charge of the sick poor. And in America especially, the states and, to a still greater extent, the private organizations, have provided an extraordinary amount of medical care. Over 6½ million patients are treated free of charge every year in the out-patient departments of hospitals. Several million more are taken care of in state or private charity dispensaries not affiliated with any hospital. More than one-fourth of all hospital care is given free.

The realization that many diseases constitute a danger for society as well as for the individual has led the state to assume the responsibility for combating these diseases. We will study the organization of preventive measures in a later chapter. Tuberculosis and venereal centers were established with analytic laboratories and serum institutes. The object of these centers is primarily diagnostic; but they have more and more branched out into therapy, naturally without charge.

Today 15 percent of all physicians are on a fixed salary, partly in the service of the state, partly in private institutions. It has been found that the average income of salaried physicians is higher than that of those practising independently.

In the prosperous year of 1928, 14 percent of all families had a yearly income of less than $1000. In the event of sickness welfare agencies took care of these families. About 10 percent had incomes of $5000 or over. Such families could pay for the doctor of their choice and for whatever care might be needed. Between lie three-fourths of the population. To these families, especially today, sickness means an economic catastrophe which eats up the last savings and throws the household budget on the scrap-heap. Members of many of these families cannot afford hospital fees, and will either keep away from doctors or leave their bills unpaid.

The annual cost of medical care cannot be estimated beforehand, for sickness comes unannounced, like a thief in the night. Many, pushed to the wall by sickness, might have gotten together the price of adequate treatment if, for many years, they had saved a small part of their monthly income for this purpose. But practically no one does this. No one believes in misfortune until it comes.

Ways have been sought out of this dilemma, the object of which has been to spread the cost over a period of time. Many hospitals and physicians have instituted a system of instalment-payments. Sometimes the patient may begin paying in advance, as when a woman is expecting a child. Or the patient signs a bill of exchange, which is discounted in the usual way.

To one remedy—namely, compulsory insurance—America has shown an unalterable prejudice.

The European nations have tried to solve the problem of medical care for the economically weaker section of the population through health-insurance. Though big mistakes were made, inevitable in such mass insurance of which there had been no previous experience, and though the administration of the insurance was accompanied by certain abuses, we must acknowledge the remarkable benefit resulting to public health.

Health-insurance is not only a rational solution of the problem, but for the state, that is, for the taxpayer, it is the cheapest solution. The cost of medical care is borne by the worker, who is made to put by a part of his wage—of course the employer's contribution has to be considered as part of the workman's wage —against a time of sickness, and, as he pays these premiums, he earns the right to assistance and ceases to be a recipient of charity. Through health-insurance the economically weaker fraction of the population is assured adequate medical care in any contingency, and at a price within its reach. The physician, for his part, need no longer give gratuitous treatment. He is paid for each case, though the individual's fees are necessarily small.

Health-insurance, as handled in most European countries, though without doubt an extraordinary advancement, is still a long way from providing the ideal situation. It includes only part of the population. And since the physicians, who cannot liberate themselves from their traditions, insist on being paid for each case and each service separately, an extremely complicated system of accounting and administration is necessary, requiring a large staff of officials. In normal times the sick benefit fund, which, though supervised by the state, is in itself a private corporation, works very well. During economic crises, however, when on account of unemployment there is no income from premiums, the fund fails, exactly at the moment when it is most wanted. The state has to intervene and assume the burden. European health-insurance is no more than a compromise.

The next step towards the solution of this problem, involving as it does the whole existence of society, seems to me to be clearly indicated. Insurance protects a fraction of the people against the economic dangers of disease. But in periods of crisis society is forced to protect itself as a whole. Would it not be more sensible to extend the benefits and costs of insurance to the entire population? Should not everyone according to his means contribute to the common welfare? The premiums, if fairly divided, without additional burden to any individual, would suffice to put into action every resource of modern medicine for diagnosis, therapy, and above all, prevention. And, moreover, the physician would be taken out of the economic struggle.

It is unworthy of his professional standing for the physician to be forced to express the value of each individual service in terms of money, as if he were a storekeeper. Medicine must be freed from economic fetters, like the teaching profession, the judiciary, and the clergy. It is an insult to their profession when it is repeatedly stated—strangely enough by physicians themselves—that free competition is essential. Are physicians really supposed to be inferior to professors, judges or clergymen? Those whose minds are on riches had better join the stock exchange.

Health-insurance, in fact every kind of social insurance, was taboo in America until a few years ago. The European observer finds this hard to understand, since America is the promised land of insurance companies. People insure themselves against every possible risk, and insurance agents swarm like mosquitoes in August. What has delayed insuring against sickness?

One apparently contributing cause is the fact that every European insurance experiment goes here by the incorrect label of "State Medicine," and "state" in America is, alas, largely considered synonymous with party control, election campaigns, nepotism, and corruption. One makes the sign of the cross at the idea of state intervention, though the state is humbly invoked whenever the individual is in trouble.

There have naturally been many abortive attempts to establish health-insurance. They began very early. Congress passed a measure in 1798, making health-insurance obligatory for mariners. However, the law remained in force for only a few years.

Then came a long pause. In 1911 the first workmen's compensation law was passed in New York and Wisconsin. The other states followed suit and, with the exception of four predominantly agricultural states, by now all of them have compensation laws. About the same time, in 1912, the discussion of the introduction of compulsory health-insurance began. The question was studied, but it was found that employers of labor, insurance companies, trade-unions, and the medical profession were at one in their opposition to such insurance. The discussion died out about 1920.

Private insurance exists in every form. Fifty-five million people carry life-insurance. Since the companies have a direct interest in the prolonged life of the insured, they have begun to pay attention to the health of their clients, and many provide them with periodic medical examinations.

Now and then individual life-insurance policies have an accident- and health-insurance clause. In the event of sickness the company pays a pre-arranged sum, which the insured spends for medical care.

Private sick-benefit funds exist here as in Europe, but they are not popular. Their services do not amount to much. They do not offer what the insured has most need of, that is, protection against the economic injury of a severe illness which brings heavy expenses and a prolonged loss of earning power. A number of religious and other societies provide medical care for their members, but their services are also usually inadequate.

Much better results are obtained by certain industrial insurance plans. Many businesses have collective insurances for their employees. Many industrial enterprises have extended accident insurance to cover cases of illness, whereby either the employer carries the cost or it is drawn from the employee's wage as a premium. Of 5,000,000 wage-earners in 3600 enterprises in 1912, about one-third received medical attention in some form. This tendency is on the increase. Later statistics have shown that at least 5664 enterprises with 4,200,000 employees provide medical examinations or more extended medical service. More than half of these enterprises, employing 3,100,000 people, require a medical examination before giving a position, and at regular intervals during employment. In over 2000 enterprises some provision is made for the care of sick employees.

The Endicott-Johnson Corporation in Binghamton, New York, may be taken as an example. It is one of the largest shoe- and leather-factories in the world, employing 15,000 people. Since 1918 the management has instituted a medical service as part of its welfare program, which gives free treatment to the employees and their families, altogether about 40,000 people. The medical personnel comprises about 100, among them 28 physicians, including a number of specialists, 4 dentists, 5 dental hygienists, 2 physical therapists, 67 trained nurses, 4 bacteriologists, 4 pharmacists, 17 technicians, and 16 on the clerical staff. The company maintains three hospitals of its own, a dispensary, and a first-aid station, as well as several day nurseries. In 1928, the expenses amounted to about $800,000. Besides this, about $40,000 was paid to specialists called in for consultation and $250,000 to hospitals and sanatoriums not belonging to the company, to which some of its employees were sent. Ninety percent of the workers and their families made some use of the service during the course of a year. In 1928, the service included 87,400 house calls and 118,740 office visits. The per capita expense for the number entitled to this service was $22.76. But it must be taken into consideration that dental care is restricted to the filling, extracting and cleaning of teeth.

The medical department of the Endicott-Johnson Corporation has aroused great interest, since it represents the organization of the medical care of a large group which of course could be similarly handled outside of a factory, as a community activity. Especially valuable were the figures obtained. Twenty-two dollars and seventy-six cents is not much, since it has been calculated that for the complete medical care of one person the average cost is $25.30 a year; if the $10.70 needed for dentistry is added, the sum comes to $36.00.

Other business enterprises have taken similar steps. It is a fine thing that such medical establishments exist. Naturally they do not solve the fundamental problem. They are welfare agencies, luxuries which a business can afford in prosperous times. It is doubtless preferable from the standpoint of public health to provide the worker with free medical care rather than to raise his wage proportionately and let him look out for himself. But these welfare agencies are dependent on economic conditions; there is no assurance of their survival. The worker has the privilege of medical assistance only during his employment by the firm. When he loses his job, he loses his privilege, just when he is most in need of it.

So today the situation, in spite of interesting and often successful experiments, is more chaotic than ever. The organization of medical service is built everywhere on presuppositions which belong to the past. The physician has not yet found his place in modern society.

This has been recognized for several years, and in 1928 a committee was formed to consider the problem: the Committee on the Costs of Medical Care. It consisted originally of 42 members: 14 physicians, 6 representatives of the Public Health Service, 8 representatives of different institutions and organizations, 5 economists, and 9 representatives of the public at large. The Committee was at work for five years at a cost of nearly a million dollars, which was provided by a number of foundations. First, the current situation was taken stock of, and an inquiry into all aspects of medicine was made. A mass of material was brought together, which was made available in twenty-eight separate publications. The list will be found at the back of this book. Such material is not available in any other country, and it is equally absorbing to medical men and to sociologists. It has provided most of the data of this chapter.

When the proposed five years were over, and the findings were assembled, the Committee summarized the facts and made recommendations for further proceeding. Here contradictory opinions asserted themselves. A unanimous vote could not be obtained. The majority of the committee recommended "that medical service, both preventive and therapeutic, should be furnished largely by organized groups of physicians, dentists, nurses, pharmacists, and other associated personnel. Such groups should be organized, preferably around a hospital, for rendering complete home, office, and hospital care. The form of organization should encourage the maintenance of high standards and the development of preservation of a personal relation between patient and physician." It recommended further "the extension of all basic public health services—whether provided by governmental or non-governmental agencies—so that they will be available to the entire population according to its needs." The costs of medical care should be placed on a group payment basis through the use of insurance, taxation, or both, without preventing those who prefer the former fee-system from continuing to use it. Cash benefits should be separate and distinct from medical services. The study, evaluation, and coördination of medical service should be considered important functions for every state and local community, and agencies be formed to exercise these functions. The coördination of rural with urban services should receive special attention. The report closes with suggestions on medical education, chiefly with the idea that the coming physician interest himself more in hygiene and less exclusively in disease; and with recommendations for the training of dentists, pharmacists, nurses, midwives, and hospital administrators. It is a compromise-report; but it is very good on the whole. It recognizes the medical as well as the social superiority of group medicine. It is aware that the costs can only be raised collectively. It emphasizes prophylaxis. It is elastic, which is necessary on account of disparities between the different states, and it opens the way to experiments.

Two minority groups of the Committee published separate reports. They express the traditional beliefs of conservative physicians. State competition with private practice is rejected, but the state to a still greater degree is to take charge of the needy sick and free physicians from this burden. The health centers are considered a dangerous imitation of industrial monopolies. Medical service should center around the general practitioner. Health-insurance may perhaps be unavoidable, but the solution of all these problems should be exclusively the affair of the medical societies. In other words, the patient should have nothing to say in the matter.

One member of the Committee, Walton H. Hamilton, an economist at Yale University, finally made a personal statement, which marks the culminating point of the whole volume. In a discriminating analysis he points out that medical care is not a technical problem, which can be considered separately, that it is much more a sociological problem. He describes the progress of medicine from a craft to a free profession. In the society of yesterday the family doctor was a fixed institution. His profession was to him a divine vocation, calling him to help where help was needed, without regard for compensation. In the then so much simpler structure of society he could make a modest but assured living, and his practice was untouched by commercial considerations. If there has been a change it is not the fault of the physicians, who on the contrary have retained their idealism in spite of an unfavorable environment. It is society which has changed. The physician one day found himself in the midst of an industrialized world, governed by stringent economic necessities. He had to live and support his family; he was forced to make compromises. Practice became a competitive struggle. A commercial spirit, foreign to its nature, was thrust upon medicine.

Here lies the kernel of the problem. The physician must be released from the economic sphere, in which he does not belong; he must be freed from economic restrictions, so that he may again follow his ideals and perform his work as a servant of society. Compulsory insurance, for everyone, is the solution. In society as it now is we are all mutually dependent on each other. Public health is everyone's health. We each have our proportionate responsibility for its preservation.

Everything else is secondary. Group medicine is there, whether we like it or not. It has shown its superiority and it is a question of guiding its development and going ahead with the systematic establishment of health centers.

So goes Hamilton's report. He has not only studied present conditions, but has interrogated history. He has looked at medicine, not as an independent phenomenon, but as an active part of a great complex of forces, and has understood relations of which others had been unaware.

What is to happen now? Everyone is agreed that something must happen. The business depression, which is steadily lowering conditions of health and at the same time leaving the physician to starve, will hasten the event. Since the Constitution does not allow any regulation covering the Union as a whole, the states will have to settle the problem individually. There will probably be experiments. Some of the states will probably manage as heretofore and thereby miss the right moment for reform. In others perhaps the official Health Service will expand and take over an increasing number of functions. In the Middle and Far West, where group medicine is already in an advanced stage of development, further gains will be made in this direction. A few preponderantly industrial states will probably have to resort to insurance. The ultimate result of these experiments cannot as yet be foreseen.

An interesting development began in the summer of 1933, when the Federal Emergency Relief Administration issued rules and regulations "governing medical care provided in the home to recipients of unemployment relief." The initial sentence states that "the conservation and maintenance of the public health is a primary function of our Government." The administration recognized that the health conditions prevailing in four million American families on the relief rolls are a matter of great importance to the people's health. Before, there was no organization whatever to secure adequate medical care to the unemployed. In case of sickness they went to the doctors without being able to remunerate them. The doctors behaved splendidly. From one end of the country to another they gave free medical care to the unemployed at a time when they were very hard hit themselves. Yet there can be no doubt that many unemployed did not get the care they needed. According to the new regulations the recipients of unemployment relief are entitled to free medical and dental care, to bedside nursing care in the homes, and they receive medicines and medical supplies free of charge. The doctors who treat such patients send their bills to the local relief official and are remunerated according to a tariff. It is obvious that such a scheme must have a very beneficial influence. The sick unemployed gets the medical care he needs and the doctors, on the other hand, are relieved of a great burden. These regulations, however, have not only a practical but a moral significance as well. The doctors become gradually accustomed to a system which today is an emergency measure but will undoubtedly become permanent in one way or another. And they are brought to realize that state interference in medical matters need not necessarily be bad, but may benefit the doctor as well as the patient.

American medicine is at a cross-roads. Scientifically, it has, by unremittingly purposeful effort, caught up with Europe, and is now leading in many lines of work. It is armed with the most superb equipment, with modern hospitals, laboratories and schools, manned by a large, competent, and well-trained corps of physicians. It has behind it a history, long enough to have borne fruit, short enough not to be oppressive, with the way into the future still open. Its task is a grateful one, for the majority of the population has faith in science and in the physician as its representative. The skeptical attitude towards the physician, so common in Europe, is seldom met with in America. And now American medicine is faced with the greatest task of all: it must put this artfully fashioned apparatus to work; now that the scientific problem is solved, it must find the social solution. It is an enormous problem, requiring a great deal of courage; for it is a question of treading on new ground, of going along new, untried paths. A new frontier has been opened, and calls for another generation of pioneers.

In the evolution now in progress, a great responsibility devolves upon the American Medical Association. We have witnessed its founding in Philadelphia in 1847. It was a small group which came together at that time, set up professional standards, and formulated suggestions for the improvement of medical education. Today it has grown to a huge organization. The counties have their County Medical Societies which are all connected by a state organization. These state organizations in turn are united in the American Medical Association, which a physician automatically joins by becoming a member of a local society. It is very democratically organized. The various societies are represented by delegates. The executive functions are carried out by a board of directors. The association has an annual meeting. The headquarters are in Chicago, in a large building with about five hundred employees. In its own press is printed every week the *Journal of the American Medical Association*, with its 100,000 copies, surely the most widely disseminated medical periodical in the world. A Spanish edition is primarily intended for Latin America. In addition, the Association prints and edits a whole series of scientific archives, publishes the *Quarterly Cumulative Index*, the continuation of the *Index Medicus*, and also the excellent popular magazine, *Hygeia*, which contributes a great deal to the hygienic education of the people.

Of special importance, however, is the work done by individual departments and committees. We have several times come across the activities of the Council on Medical Education and Hospitals. It assembles from official sources all data in regard to licenses and graduations, all students who matriculate at a medical school and all changes of address of physicians, forming a tremendous archive, which registers the biography of every medical man from the beginning of his studies till his death, whether he is a member of the Association or not. *The American Medical Directory* is an annual publication resembling the *Medical Register* in England, the German *Medizinalkalender*, and the French *Medicus*. The society also collects lecture-announcements and reports of foreign as well as of American schools, and literature on the subject of medical education and preparatory training. Since 1905 it has been assembling all available information in regard to hospitals in the United States and Canada. In this way the department is a great clearing house for all questions of this sort.

The Council of Pharmacy and Chemistry has an important function. It was organized in 1905 in order to protect physicians and the public from fraudulent medicines. It is formed by a group of clinicians, pharmacologists, bacteriologists, and chemists, has its own laboratories, and does excellent work in investigation. There is a special committee for the study of food-materials and food-preparations. The fact that every year industry puts numberless new apparatus for physical therapy on the market, has led to the establishment of a special department for the testing of such apparatus, to protect physicians and public in this direction as well.

A Bureau of Legal Medicine and Legislation compiles all laws and judicial decisions relating to medicine and gives legal information to physicians. A Bureau of Investigation gathers data and gives information in regard to every form of quackery. The Bureau of Health and Public Instruction fosters public instruction in hygiene. The Bureau of Medical Economics studies economic questions. A museum collects samples of food and drug preparations and other related objects. The library subscribes to over six hundred periodicals, whose contents are listed in the *Index,* and to some extent referred to in the *Journal.* They are left unbound, so that the individual numbers can easily be lent out. If a country physician, far from any library, asks for literature on any subject whatever, it will be sent him by the next mail.

In this way the headquarters of the American Medical Association is a great center for all questions relating to medicine. It collects data in order to be able to give information. Any one, physician or layman, can at any time turn to Chicago with any sort of question and will be sent an exhaustive answer. It is financed by the sale of periodicals and by advertisements, which, however, are accepted only after careful investigation.

Such a huge organization, representing a large number of physicians, obviously has great power. When the American Medical Association raises its voice, it speaks in the name of 100,000 physicians. It is equally evident that its size makes it inevitably conservative. Large bodies move slowly.

The attitude which the Association will take in regard to the reorganization of the medical care of the population will have enormous weight. It can accelerate changes or put on the brakes. It cannot stop them altogether, as they are determined, not by the decisions of the physician, but by the laws of social development. The responsibility is therefore very great. And it is to be hoped that the leading men will have the courage and the foresight to look squarely at these problems, not only from the narrower perspective of the physician's office, but from the wider viewpoint of the general welfare.

Another manifestation must be appended to this chapter, since it belongs to the picture of American medicine: that is, the various medical sects.

There are quacks in every country. There always have been and there always will be. A minority of the population will always be impervious to reason, and will seek help from the quack. Quackery is prohibited in most European countries. It occurs nevertheless, but illegally, and is kept within bounds by the law. In Germany a mistaken liberalism has led to an unrestricted license to perform cures, and the result is a thriving charlatanism.

In America certain individual sects have been able to win for themselves a legally valid position. But before going into their history, we must have a word on the subject of homeopathy, which does not belong strictly to their category, since the homeopaths, though doctrinaires, are nevertheless physicians. Homeopathy originated in this country in 1825, when a physician of Danish extraction, Hans Burch Gram (1786–1840), settled in New York, after having learned homeopathy in Copenhagen. He was a mystic, a Swedenborgian, a man of spotless character, deeply convinced of the truth of Hahnemann's doctrine. He translated his *Character of Homeopathy* into English, but in such inept language that the little book never came to be understood till it appeared in a new and improved edition.

With the chaotic conditions and the low therapeutic standards which at that time prevailed in medicine, the new doctrine necessarily fell on fertile ground. It spread in the course of a few decades over all the United States and found many adherents. As early as 1833 a Hahnemannian Society was founded in Philadelphia. Many more were to follow. In 1855 the first homeopathic school was founded in Allentown, Pennsylvania. The teaching was given in German. This school did not last long, but its place was taken by the Homeopathic Medical College of Pennsylvania in Philadelphia. Around 1835 the first homeopathic pharmacy was likewise opened in Philadelphia, and in 1848 the first homeopathic dispensary was founded in New York.

This was the beginning. Many schools were established. In 1900, when Flexner began his investigation, there were still fifteen existing. The number decreased, but the quality improved, and at the present time the homeopaths have several first-class schools, which were listed in the last chapter. The American Institute of Homeopathy, founded in 1844, came to be the central organization which gave impetus to the formation of countless societies in the various states and counties.

Naturally there was no lack of friction between the homeopaths and the rest of the medical profession. In many localities it would come, now and then, to bitter contentions. Peace has long been restored. The homeopaths are thoroughly trained physicians. They are much less dogmatic, now that they are no longer on the defensive, and there is no doubt that there are many competent practitioners among them.

Homeopathy is a European importation. The other sects belong to a different order; they are pure American products.

Andrew T. Still was born in Virginia in 1828, and grew up in Missouri, leading the life of a frontier farmer. Later he moved to Kansas, and had a great deal to do with the Indians, learning their language, and treating this and that ailment as occasion arose. He liked doctoring and took a medical course in Kansas City. Then came the Civil War, in which he served first as captain and eventually as major. After the war he went back to farming. He had mechanical ability and was interested in inventing machines. However, he liked doctoring more than anything. An unfailing source of wonder was the structure of the human body, especially the bones. He dissected every dead Indian that he could get hold of. And one day—it was in the year 1874—the whole truth was revealed to him; it was revealed that God had made the human body perfect and complete, and had filled it with a whole arsenal of natural remedies. A man's illness is caused by the fact that something in his organism has been shifted slightly out of place, especially in the bony system and most particularly in the spinal column. This affects the nerves and influences the circulation. The treatment consists in getting the misplaced bones back into position by means of manipulation. The rest is taken care of by the remedial properties of the organism.

This was a simple doctrine, within the comprehension of everyone not born an idiot. Still called it osteopathy.

He travelled over the country as a savior, pulling bones into place. The first students gathered around him. He taught them his art for $100 apiece. His five children became disciples. His following became larger and larger, and in 1892 the American School of Osteopathy was founded in Kirksville, Missouri. It is thriving; at the turn of the century it had several hundred students. But what is more, around 1900 there existed twelve osteopathic schools. And as a culmination, Vermont in 1896 passed a measure whereby the diploma of the American School of Osteopathy carried with it the right to practise medicine within the state. The other states followed. In 1897 the American Association for the Advancement of Osteopathy was founded, eventually organized on the pattern of the American Medical Association.

And what is the present situation? In 1930 there were 7644 osteopaths, coming from seven schools. They are doctors, not of medicine, but of osteopathy (D.O.) They have to take examinations before boards, which in some states consist only of osteopaths, in others of both osteopaths and physicians, and in still others of physicians alone.

But what is most remarkable is the change which has come over osteopathy during the last decades. It is a unique process. The requirements demanded of students of osteopathy became larger and larger. The curriculum now lasts four years, and the material is practically the same as that given in a medical school, except that osteopathic treatment is added. Though osteopathy began as a doctrine that explained the origin of all sickness according to a single principle, and prescribed treatment on this principle alone, today it has come to be a method of treatment like any other. The osteopaths, like the homeopaths, have become physicians. Their schools are medical schools, though it is true that they are rather poorly equipped. In localities where their state examinations are given by regular physicians, they take the same examinations as other medical candidates. But by giving up its original doctrine osteopathy has lost much of its persuasive power. Its appeal is no longer to faith alone. The movement has therefore come to a standstill and the number of osteopaths remains more or less constant.

It is quite otherwise with the thriving sect of the chiropractors, which at the present time numbers 16,000 adherents. It is an offshoot of osteopathy and likewise a product of the Middle West. Its founder was D. D. Palmer, a grocery-store keeper in Davenport, Iowa, who one day discovered in himself magnetic powers, and for ten years carried on magnetic cures, until in 1895 he discovered the true cause of disease. His son, B. J. Palmer, developed the doctrine and organized the sect. The theory is very simple. The cause of every sickness is a change of position of one or more vertebrae, which press on the nerves as they branch out from the spinal cord and so interfere with nerveforce. The diagnosis consists in determining which vertebra is affected, and the treatment is confined to rapping the bone back into place. That is all there is to it.

The chiropractors, too, have their national organization and a large number of schools. The sect was at its height between 1916 and 1923. In 1920 it had no less than 79 schools, whose number has declined to 21 at the present time. The Palmer School in Davenport is the most important. The training as a rule lasts eighteen months, after which the degree of D.C. (Doctor of Chiropractic) is conferred upon the candidate. Whoever studies twenty-four months can attain the degree of PH.C. (Philosopher of Chiropractic) in Chicago. And studies lasting as long as thirty-two months may be rewarded with a degree *cum laude*.

In 42 states a state license is insisted upon. In 32 the examination boards consist exclusively of chiropractors. In 6 states the practice of chiropractic is illegal; however, it flourishes just the same.

The relation of chiropractic to osteopathy is perfectly plain. But while the latter has made its truce with medicine and its adherents have gradually become physicians of the second rank, chiropractic has held fast to its original faith and so far has resisted every temptation to make concessions. This has added to its strength, and thanks to this alone it is today the most powerful medical sect in America.

In addition there is the great host of naturopaths and charlatans of every color, who base their theories, if they have any, sometimes on a diagnostic, and sometimes on a therapeutic principle. The same sort of people is found in Europe. It was in Europe that the principles of drugless treatment had their origin; but their most prolific growth took place in America. Naturally these people, too, have their schools and their diplomas, with the degree of N.D. (Doctor of Naturopathy). They have their own organizations, and in seven states there is a special license for naturopaths. But their chief function is to furnish the main contingent of the huge army of illegal quacks.

Based on altogether different principles is the lay treatment given by religious societies. The above-mentioned sects likewise work mainly by means of suggestion, that is, with mental means. But they do it unconsciously. In religious medicine, on the contrary, the method is conscious.

There has always been religious medicine. Its history can be traced back to primitive medicine, which was a mixture of empiricism, magic, and religion. With the progress of civilization medicine fell into its component parts. On the foundation of empiricism arose a science of healing which excluded the supernatural. Magic seeped down among the lower classes, where it survives as superstition. The belief in witches, magic, and demonic possession is deeply rooted in America, especially among the farmers of Pennsylvania. And that many magic rites are still practised by the negroes is natural enough. Religious medicine has always had its definite place in every civilization. In Greece we find the cult of Æsculapius. The Catholic Church has evolved a variety of forms of faith-healing. Countless invalids travel to Lourdes every year, and an American Lourdes is growing up in Montreal. It is quite evident that similar tendencies were bound to develop within Protestant circles. Christian Science, the most powerful of these movements, had its inception in America, but has, however, obtained a foothold in Europe and is beginning to assume serious proportions.

Christian Science was founded by a woman, and its adherents are largely women. The history of Mary Baker Eddy (1821–1910) is well known. Born in New Hampshire, she grew to be an hysterical woman, who led a life of suffering, until she found her savior in Phineas Parkhurst Quimby. Quimby is the spiritual founder of the whole movement. He was a watchmaker in Maine. He saw a Frenchman work some magnetic cures, became enthusiastic, undertook cures himself, and discovered that the procedures were quite unnecessary, faith was sufficient in itself. He cured Mary Baker, who became his disciple, and after his death in 1866, carried on his work and from it developed her own doctrine. In 1875 she published her book, *Science and Health with Key to the Scriptures.* She moved to Boston, where the Mother Church was founded. The sect grew. Today it has 1265 churches in the United States and about 700,000 adherents.

Christian Science is not a therapeutic system, but a religion, a religious sect; nevertheless its strongest appeal rests in its promise of healing, not only sickness, but every sort of evil. For evil does not exist at all. There is no matter. There is only spirit. Spirit is God. God is good. God is omnipresent. Sickness, sin, death, do not exist. They are human errors. When a person is sick, he is in error. When he is brought back to right thinking, he will necessarily feel well again.

There are 8848 Christian Science Healers in America, 90 percent of whom are women. The majority have their training in the Massachusetts Metaphysical College, the Boston headquarters of the sect. There is no doubt of their successes, and they have been very adroit in making concessions. Infectious diseases and surgical cases they leave to medicine. Even so they retain a large field of action. The laws of most of the states expressly enjoin that every form of religious medicine shall be tolerated.

For many more forms exist. The success of Christian Science has led other Protestant churches to lay stress upon the cure of physical and mental ills. These tendencies are summed up under the designation of New Thought; and it is calculated that, outside of Christian Science, about 1000 additional people are active as faith-healers.

So we have in America, along with medicine proper, very strongly entrenched healing cults. There are about 36,000 healers; that is, almost a fourth as many as the 156,440 physicians; and it is estimated that the population pays them about $125,000,000 every year for their treatments.

These sects enjoy a unique legal position in those states which give a license, not only to the physician, but to the osteopath, the chiropractor and the naturopath, and in this way show official toleration for the healing cults.

It is not so easy to get a clear picture of the factors behind this sectarian medicine. One cause is no doubt the weakness of Americans for every kind of sectarianism, which is equally manifest in their religious life, and which, in other fields too, has resulted in the formation of countless groups and societies with the most diverse aims.

A more universal factor is the lack of judgment in a great many people, who will always follow the prophet who has the most persuasive line of talk. The sects work with an effective advertising system planned to entrap the credulous and the suggestible.

It is understandable enough that the insufficiencies of medicine, which must frankly acknowledge its continued helplessness in the face of many diseases, often leads invalids to seek help elsewhere, hoping for miracles, and applying to those people who pretend to be able to heal everything.

These psychological causes are universal. But if, within a given period, lay practice develops to an unusual degree, the question must always come up, whether there is not something at fault in the medicine of the moment, which may be in part responsible.

Since 1900 medical science has made tremendous advances. Everyone turned with enthusiasm to the laboratory. It was natural that too little attention was given to the psychological side of medicine. Christian Science fell on grateful soil. In similar fashion, the way was cleared for the naturopaths and the osteopaths by the lack of medical appreciation of the value of physical therapy, massage and other methods. Quite generally the impersonal objectivity of medicine, together with its uncoordinated specialization, has driven many patients into the arms of the lay practitioner, who has perhaps more leisure for an individual approach.

There is no question of the evils of medical sectarianism. It is dangerous to the health of the public for people who know nothing about disease to be turned loose on the sick. Therapeutically, the sects have nothing to offer which medicine cannot give as well. The money spent on them is thrown away.

These evils cannot be overcome by law alone. It is essential that medicine should undermine the sources of sectarian popularity, by increasing its own efficiency, improving its organization, and paying closer heed to every necessity of sick human beings. To be sure, there will always be a residuum, for there is no cure for stupidity.

☆ **CHAPTER SEVEN** ☆

HOSPITALS AND NURSING

THE first hospital in Philadelphia was founded in the middle of the eighteenth century. It was the earliest hospital within the boundaries of the future United States, but not the first in America. For not only in Spanish, but also in French America there had been hospitals long before this. As early as 1639 an Hôtel-Dieu had been established in Quebec. A second Hôtel-Dieu was built in Montreal in 1644, through the efforts of Jeanne Mance, a heroic woman who played an important rôle in the life of the young colony. Three additional nursing institutions were established during the course of the seventeenth century, the Hôpital Général de Quebec (1692), the Hôtel-Dieu des Trois Rivières (1697), and the Hôpital Général de Montréal (1694). The nursing was done by nuns, for the most part belonging to the Augustinian and Ursulan orders. The physicians living in the colony provided the medical staff.

In the predominantly Protestant English colonies, the beginning was much slower. But the example of Philadelphia was quickly followed. New York, as has been mentioned, came next in line. A group of physicians, among whom Peter Middleton, John Johns, and Samuel Bard were particularly active, set themselves to founding a hospital. They were all three professors at King's College and were well aware that among the advantages of a hospital would be its value to medical education. *The Society of the Hospital in the City of New York in America* was founded in 1771. The funds were raised in New York and London. The government granted a yearly subsidy to continue for twenty years. By 1776 the hospital could be opened in a provisional structure. After the interruption of the Revolutionary

204

War the project was resumed in 1791 (Fig. 25). Today the New York Hospital is connected with the Cornell University Medical College. The superb new building in which the two institutions are brought together has been described in a previous chapter.

At first the hospital accepted every type of invalid, including the insane. The results of putting the mentally ill under the same roof with other patients proved unfortunate. A separate building for the insane was erected in 1808. This division of the New York Hospital has not only survived to the present day but, as the Bloomingdale Hospital in White Plains, located in a beautiful park in the suburbs, has grown to be one of the most up-to-date and attractive mental institutions in the world.

The Pennsylvania and New York hospitals were both intended from the outset as institutions for medical care. In addition, poorhouses existed in both cities, and as the destitute who were housed there frequently needed medical care, visits from the medical profession were brought about as a matter of course. In this way poorhouses gradually developed into regular hospitals.

This happened in Philadelphia, where the almshouse founded by the city in 1751 eventually became the Philadelphia General Hospital.

It was the same in New York. In 1735 a *Publick House and House of Correction of the City of New York* was founded, an institution which was at once almshouse and penitentiary. It had an infirmary and John Van Buren, who had studied with Boerhaave, was put in charge of the sick.

In the summer of 1794 New York was visited by the plague, and a pest-house was put up on a piece of ground which went by the name of Belle Vue. It was used by the city in further epidemics of plague, yellow fever, and cholera.

In 1811 the Workhouse and House of Correction were moved to the same piece of land. Remarkable complications ensued.

Conditions were scandalous. The nursing was in the hands of female prisoners. The mortality was at times enormous. Committees were appointed to investigate the situation. Towards the middle of the century reforms were set on foot, and the prisoners were moved to other institutions. From that time dates the beginning of Bellevue's development into what is now a gigantic city hospital for the indigent sick, the largest hospital in New York, with a capacity of over 2000 beds. The patients present a real pageant of races. One sees men from every nation, with every color of skin: negroes from the Sudan, Chinese, Polish Jews in their kaftans, gypsies in costume; nothing is missing.

Such an enormous material could of course be put at the service of medical education. Individual courses were given very early, and in 1861 Bellevue Hospital Medical College was founded; today, since its union with the New York University Medical College, it numbers about 500 students.

It was mentioned in an earlier chapter that the Harvard Medical School had moved from Cambridge to Boston, chiefly in order to be near material for clinical instruction. This was at first given in the poorhouse, there being as yet no hospital. The professors performed their professional services at the poorhouse and instructed their pupils at the same time. This was no more than a makeshift, and within the first year, James Jackson and John Collins Warren worked out a plan for a hospital. It met with a favorable reception. During the following year a charter was granted to the Massachusetts General Hospital; the cornerstone was laid in 1817 and the first patient admitted in the Autumn of 1821 (Fig. 26). It was under the dome of this building that the first ether-anaesthesia was administered in 1846.

The work of this hospital increased tremendously during the course of a century. New additions had constantly to be made, and today it presents an enormous complex of buildings which have a special interest for the historian. Each new wing

25. NEW YORK HOSPITAL, 1791

Compare with the present building in Figure 20

26. MASSACHUSETTS GENERAL HOSPITAL, 1821

was intended to embody the latest hospital improvements; and, as these structures derive from the most diverse periods, there is a splendid chance to follow the history of hospital building.

Parallel with the development of hospitals came the establishment of dispensaries for the free treatment of the indigent sick. The earliest was the Philadelphia Dispensary, founded in 1786. It was financed by annual membership dues. Six physicians were appointed to serve every other two months without compensation. In addition there were four consulting physicians, a surgeon, an apothecary, and a treasurer. A similar institution was founded in 1791 in New York. Later the hospitals came as a rule to have their own dispensaries.

These first American hospitals were frequently model institutions. The European hospitals were much older, sometimes survivals from the Middle Ages. In consequence many are still mediaeval in character. America, unhampered by any tradition in this field, was free to benefit by European experience, and could start out with the very best. The Pennsylvania Hospital and the Massachusetts General were justifiably admired by strangers.

During the nineteenth century there took place an extraordinary increase in the number of hospitals. The population was multiplied by the wave of immigration and the need for hospitals was very great. A hospital was built wherever funds could be raised for it, without restriction or regulation, and naturally hospitals springing up in this way were of very uneven quality. Some institutions were excellent in every way; others had no equipment whatever. Even in the beginning of the twentieth century conditions were by no means generally satisfactory.

One of a country's prime necessities is that all hospitals shall maintain consistently high standards. Whatever hospital a patient enters, he should be assured that, no matter what he is able to pay, he will receive the best that medicine has to offer in examination, treatment and nursing. Hospitals are the temples of medicine. What may not always be possible in private practice must be possible in a hospital. Accidents and delays which may be forgiven in private practice are inexcusable in a hospital. And since hospitals are temples of medicine, they serve not only therapy, but research. Even the smallest hospital is in duty bound to further the increase of medical knowledge.

The improvement in American hospitals during the last fifteen years must be ascribed first of all to the American College of Surgeons. The circumstances that led this organization to turn its attention to the hospital situation are extremely interesting. The College was founded in 1913 for the advancement of surgery. It laid down very strict membership requirements. Only actual surgeons with extensive surgical experience were to be admitted as members of the College. Applicants were to hand in one hundred detailed histories of patients on whom they themselves had operated. It then appeared that many candidates could not satisfy this requirement because, in the majority of hospitals, no detailed case-histories were kept. This small difficulty threw a bright light on the whole situation. It was suddenly realized that something was wrong. Further investigation proved that many institutions were poorly equipped, without laboratories or X-rays, and that there was no system for coordinating the work of the physicians.

The American College of Surgeons undertook to effect a change, on the principle that there exists a minimum standard of requirements, which a hospital must meet if it is to be equal to its task. As the result of several years' study, the precise nature of these requirements was determined and a *minimum standard* was established, whose main features are as follows:

Membership upon the staff of a hospital must be restricted to physicians and surgeons who are graduates of medicine in good standing and legally licensed to practise in their respective states, competent in their respective fields, and worthy in character.

The physicians of a hospital, regardless of whether the hospital is "open" or "closed" shall be organized in a definite group or staff, in the sense that they collaborate with each other, and together initiate rules, regulations, and policies governing the professional work of the hospital. Staff meetings should be held at least once a month.

Accurate and complete records of all patients shall be written. Directions are given as to what these histories shall contain.

Diagnostic and therapeutic facilities under competent supervision shall be available for study. These shall include at the least a clinical laboratory providing chemical, bacteriological, serological and pathological services, as well as an X-ray department.

This program being laid down, it was now a question of putting it into practice. During 1918, 692 hospitals of 100 or more beds were investigated, and it was shown that only 89, or 12.9 percent, met all requirements. The College did not allow itself to be discouraged by this report, but held fast to its standard and continued to send out its representatives year after year, extending its inquiry into wider and wider circles. From 1922 on, hospitals of 50 to 99 beds were included in the report; since 1924 those containing 25 to 49 beds, since 1925 the government hospitals as well. Those institutions which come up to the minimum requirements are reported as *fully approved;* those who have accepted the minimum standard, but because of external circumstances may, in one point or another, not have been able to carry it out, but who give assurance that this shortcoming is temporary, are *conditionally approved;* the rest are reported as *not approved.* The inquiry is repeated every year for every hospital within this range.

The existence of an institution which not only was able to

check all facts relating to hospitals, but was also in a position to give competent professional advice, had extraordinarily fruitful results. A few figures will explain this most clearly:

		Hospitals visited		Approved or conditionally approved	Percentages
1	100 or more beds	1918:	692	89	12.9
		1932:	1565	1469	93.9
2	50 to 99 beds	1922:	812	335	41.3
		1932:	1035	648	62.6
3	25 to 49 beds	1924:	307	49	15.9
		1932:	864	177	20.5
4	Government hospitals	1925:	100	90	90.0
		1932:	116	116	100.0

Naturally it is often difficult for small hospitals, with a restricted personnel, to come up to the standard set by the American College of Surgeons; yet here, too, within a few years a noticeable improvement has taken place. It is of vital importance that today almost all the larger hospitals are equal to their task. It must further be taken into consideration that a large number are far above the minimum standard, and that many are superlative as regards buildings and sanitary equipment.

This whole *hospital standardization* is a purely private and voluntary affair. But obviously it is to the interest of every hospital to assure itself of the collaboration of the College and to have its place on the list of approved institutions. Physicians and patients give the preference to such hospitals, and recently the Association of American Railroad Companies recommended the surgeons in their employ to send their patients only to institutions approved in this way.

Indeed, even hospitals in foreign countries—Australia, New Zealand, China, Cuba, Panama, Uruguay—have asked that their names be put on the list.

This whole line of procedure would seem strange to a European observer. In Europe they have the shorter way of State

Control. It would not work in America. It would need a constitutional amendment and would meet with all sorts of difficulties and oppositions. Only a private organization can reach unchecked across state boundaries, and, in any case, the results have been all that could be asked; a standard has been set, which to be sure is matched in many European countries, but by no means in all of them.

The activities of the American College of Surgeons have so far included only those hospitals with 25 beds or over. In 1928, 6852 hospitals were registered with the American Medical Association, divided according to their size as follows:

Size	Number of hospitals	Beds
25 and less	2453	38,918
26– 50	1585	16,222
51– 100	1247	93,813
101– 200	772	112,179
201– 300	306	76,350
301– 500	189	72,556
501–1000	115	82,587
1000 and over	185	355,309
Total 6852		892,934

The numbers are somewhat larger today. In round figures, there are now about 7000 hospitals containing 900,000 beds, while in 1909 there were about 4300 with 421,000 beds. The number of beds has therefore doubled in twenty years. It is calculated that a capital of three billion dollars has been invested in hospitals. They employ 340,000 people including 14,000 physicians, counting only those on full-time service.

There is now one hospital bed for every 137 inhabitants of the United States; but the distribution by states is very unequal. In Wisconsin a few years ago there was one bed for every 154 inhabitants, in South Carolina at the same time one bed for every 749.

The distribution of proprietorship is interesting. Only 26

percent are managed by the federal, state or local government. Thirty-eight percent are non-profit-making associations, and 36 percent are private hospitals. The picture changes when looked at from the number of beds. Sixty-three percent of all beds are government owned; 28 percent are controlled by non-profit making associations; and only 9 percent are in proprietary hospitals or hospitals run for profit. In other words, the larger institutions are, for all practical purposes, non-profit making.

The economic problem involved is serious, as the expenses are extremely high. The capital invested per bed varies according to the equipment of the hospital from $3000 to $12,000. The average is about $5000. In the latter case it would need, for interest and amortization of the capital, $400 a year for each bed; that is, if the beds are 50 percent occupied, $2.20 a day; if 75 percent are occupied, $1.46; at the least $1.32 and .88 respectively, at the most $5.26 and $3.50 respectively.

These hospitals cost six hundred and fifty-six million dollars a year to run. That amounts to $3.25 a day in public hospitals, and $5.00 a day in private hospitals. These prices naturally cannot be met by the general run of patients. Society as a whole has been forced to assume a part of the burden. Three hundred million dollars are raised every year by taxes. The state has taken special charge of those invalids whose condition makes a prolonged hospital stay imperative, that is, the tubercular and the insane, the latter's duration of illness averaging 1200 days. The costs in these chronic diseases are not so high. The cost in the case of mental disease in a public hospital averages $1 a day, in other hospitals $4; in the case of tuberculosis $2.50 and $4 respectively.

Fifty-four million dollars yearly are raised by voluntary contributions and interest on endowment. But there remain three hundred and two million dollars, which must be borne by the patients. And that is a very large amount. We meet again the same unfortunate situation that was brought to our attention in the last chapter. Indigent patients are given free hospital care. The small number of wealthy patients can afford whatever they like. For the middle class, that is, for the great majority of the population, hospital care presents a tremendous and often insupportable burden.

People have tried to find a way out. An interesting experiment was made by Henry Ford. In 1909, since the hospitals in Detroit could not keep pace with the growth of the city, it was decided to build a large new hospital. Money was collected. Ford signed a check and building was begun two years later. But in 1914 the money was used up, and the work had to be interrupted. New sources of supply were investigated, and a request to the city, asking it to take over the institution, was under consideration. Here Ford stepped in. He paid back everything to the original contributors, and himself took over the responsibility for the hospital. He wanted to work out a new plan. It ought to be possible to use the same economic ideas in the sphere of medicine that had been tested in the automobile industry. A hospital was to be founded, which would be self-supporting, where the patient should be no recipient of charity, but should pay for what he got, and where medical care, like Ford cars, should be cheap and good.

The hospital was completed, and, since America had entered the war, was immediately handed over to the Administration as an army hospital. It was given back after the war, and opened as the Henry Ford Hospital on January 1, 1920. The experiment had begun.

The hospital contains only single rooms, each connected with a bath. All rooms are of equal size, and have identical arrangements and furnishings. Every twenty-four rooms form a unit. There are altogether 600 beds available. The entire personnel, including all physicians, is on a full-time basis and a fixed salary.

Hospital care is often made particularly expensive by the fact that medical attendance and the often considerable extras are added to the price of the room. Here this was all done away with. The patients paid a uniform price of $4.50 a day, which included everything: room, nursing and treatment. Only operations were paid for separately, but according to a fixed price. A serious operation was to cost $125, lighter ones less in proportion. It was expected that the hospital would expand—there was room enough for more buildings—and that the prices could be correspondingly lowered as had been the case in the automobile industry.

However, these expectations were not fulfilled. There had been a miscalculation. The prices were raised instead of lowered. Some of the rooms were remodelled so that they could hold three or four beds. The Henry Ford Hospital is an excellent hospital with a staff of preëminent physicians and surgeons, but the economic experiment for which it was founded was a failure. It proves that a large hospital cannot pay its own way.

During the last few years a new tendency has made its appearance, which goes by the name of *middle-rate plan*. It was first tried in Boston in the Massachusetts General Hospital, where in the spring of 1930 a division of 330 beds, called the Baker Memorial Unit, was opened according to this new plan for patients of moderate means. It is something between a ward and a private division, and is designed to provide a hospital for the middle class.

Here, too, the charge covers room, doctor, and all extras. The hospital management determines the physician's fee, which shall under no circumstances exceed $150, no matter how much attention the case demands. In the case of room and nurse the actual cost to the hospital is taken into consideration. The patients only in exceptional cases are put in single rooms, and never in large wards. Rooms with several beds are the rule. Every luxury is avoided. It is in no way a matter of charity. The patient pays for exactly what he gets. The lowered price is made possible because the physician demands smaller fees, and the patient is satisfied with more modest quarters and less individual care.

Two thousand four hundred and seventy-six patients were admitted during the first year. The average duration of illness was 13.37 days and the average payment of patients $177.60 ($98.42 for the hospital, $59.62 for the physician, $19.62 for nursing). In the second year 3326 patients spent on the average 14 days in the hospital and paid an average amount of $189.75. The higher charges were caused by an unusually large proportion of surgical and obstetric cases.

The average income of patients admitted during the first year was $2057. However, each admission was handled individually and consideration was shown, not only to the patients' incomes, but to other sources of aid and to particular financial responsibilities.

The payments from patients covered 74 percent of the hospital expenses during the first year and 81 percent during the second year, and it is calculated that the hospital can be operated without loss as soon as 55 to 60 percent of the beds are occupied daily.

In the meanwhile several hospitals in other cities have introduced this plan. There is no doubt that by these means a lowering of prices is brought about. However, the patients' expenses are still too heavy, and it is significant that the report from which the above figures are taken closes with the wish that some form of insurance will be found which would spread the burden of payment over a longer period and make it easier to carry.

All hospitals have had to turn their attention to the question of lowered charges. Many were built at extravagant expense during the prosperity era and are now standing empty. Whole divisions have had to be closed. Palaces were erected for hospitals, as they had been for schools. They were intended to transcend utility; they were to serve as concrete symbols of the nation's wealth, and its interest in the health and the culture of its people. It is a beautiful thought, but a penalty for the disregard of elementary economic principles was inevitable sooner or later. To be sure the schools are full, but the teachers are badly paid. And in the hospitals the wards are crammed and the luxurious private rooms stand empty.

Only a few decades ago a hospital had two sharply divided classes: the general wards and the private rooms. Accommodation, food, nursing, privileges in the two were as different as can possibly be imagined. The patient in the general ward was a recipient of charity and had to pay a part of his debt by serving as teaching material for doctors and nurses.

The enormous increase in the middle class element has effaced these distinctions. The private room was turned into a semi-private room by the addition of a few beds. As the ocean liner has had to interpose the cabin and tourist classes between the first and steerage classes, and as the hotels have had to offer a sliding scale for their rooms, so the hospitals have had to establish graduated fees, proportionate to the financial resources of their patients.

Though it has been possible to arrange accommodation for stipulated lower prices, the unknown extra expenses continue to weigh on the patient. The patient can choose the room suited to his means before he is admitted to the hospital, but he cannot tell what extra care his case may demand, how many laboratory examinations and how much nursing will be necessary. The amount for these special services can be so large that the estimate based on the choice of a simple room may prove an illusion. To lessen this unknown quantity, a number of hospitals have begun to include certain definite special services in the price of a room. Others have gone still further and have established lump sums for certain typical cases. A hospital in Los Angeles charges $115 to $180 for a confinement case in a private room, $80 to $90 in a semi-private room. The price includes all hospital services during a ten-days' stay: nursing, use of the delivery-room, anaesthetic, bandages, medicines, laboratory, and the feeding, nursing and clothing of the infant. Other hospitals charge lump sums for all services connected with a tonsillectomy. Others, again, offer all necessary diagnostic laboratory examinations for a fixed price.

Many hospitals started a plan which is known as "Group Hospitalization." It was recommended by the American Hospital Association in 1933 and is becoming more and more popular. Under this plan a hospital makes a contract with organized bodies of people. Each member of such a body contributes a small annual sum and in case of sickness requiring hospitalization has his expenses paid. At the present time more than a hundred hospitals in over twenty-five communities are working under such a plan and in more than fifty other cities the plan is under way.

In spite of lowered fees it will often not be possible to get the patient to pay the full amount that he owes. Hospitals often have to accept deductions, and a few institutions like Johns Hopkins Hospital have special endowment funds to make up such losses. Many hospitals accept payment on the instalment plan but, as might be expected, without much success.

No matter how it is handled, there is no getting around the fact that hospital treatment is begun with a financial inquisition. And though this may be carried out with the greatest possible tact, the situation is painful for all concerned, and contrary to the spirit of medicine.

This, too, is a modern phenomenon. Formerly a hospital was a welfare agency. The needy sick were sent there because of their poverty, and physicians gave them their time without compensation. The well-to-do patient was cared for at home. For a long time even operations were performed in the patient's home. The development of surgery, especially antiseptic and aseptic treatment, brought even the well-to-do patient into the hospital. The private division resulted; but, since the patient had means and usually brought with him his own doctor, no long preliminaries were necessary.

Now that the entire population is going to hospitals, a situation has arisen which though logical from the medical point of view is extremely confused when looked at from an economic standpoint. The hospital has become a compromise between a welfare agency and a business enterprise, but an enterprise which cannot possibly pay. If during times of economic depression there is a drop in the number of hospital patients, this is a clear indication that the hospitals are not equal to their social responsibility; for hospital treatment ought not to be a luxury reserved for periods of prosperity. Some way out will have to be found, for hospitals as well as for the practitioners.

In travelling through the United States today, one can see the most diverse types of hospital, from the antiquated corridor-system to the pavilion and the skyscraper. We have seen that the number of hospitals has been doubled during the last twenty years. About 2700 hospitals were built after 1909; many, if not most, of the older hospitals were remodelled, enlarged, and modernized during the same period. This means that America has at her disposal the newest equipment. I should like to mention a few points which particularly struck my attention.

While the old hospital was a cold sombre building, still bearing the impress of its monastic origin, where one was reminded at every step that here was an abode of pain, today every effort is made to keep the atmosphere friendly and cheerful. The change is quite comprehensible, since hospitals are now a place to get well in, instead of, as formerly, primarily a place in which to die. The emphasis has been laid on healing. In the latest hospitals the entrance hall is like a hotel lobby. One finds comfortable chairs, flowers for sale, a newspaper-stand, a telegraph office, sometimes the branch of a bank, as in a hotel. In a Cleveland hospital, ladies from the city have formed a voluntary committee, and in attractive uniforms receive visitors and act as guides.

In the Mayo Hospital in Rochester, where the majority of patients are from out of town and usually come accompanied by relatives, hotel and hospital are very practically combined. The hotel is located in the lower floors, the upper floors belong to the hospital.

Large public wards are gradually disappearing. Interesting statistics show that in hospitals planned in 1908, 28 percent of the beds were in wards holding ten or more beds. In 1918 the proportion was 15 percent, and in 1928 only 7 percent. And where larger units have been retained, they usually consist of four groups of four beds each, which are separated from each other by walls reaching half-way to the ceiling, and can be entirely isolated by curtains, as is also the case with each individual bed. It goes without saying that each ward has single rooms for seriously ill or disturbing patients.

Antisepsis led the hospitals into a veritable orgy of white. Not only for practical reasons, because white shows the dirt, but mainly because white is the symbol of purity and innocence. That is all over. We have found that even a colored tile can be scrubbed. The hospital rooms have become cheerful and the operating rooms have lost their chilly aspect. Sometimes they go further still. In the surgical clinic of the Western Reserve University in Cleveland I noticed that not only have the operating rooms colored walls, but the aprons, the caps, the masks covering the mouths of physicians and nurses—the whole washable outfit is of a pale grey-blue shade. They operate entirely by artificial light for the reason that it has to be used in any case in forty-five percent of all operations, and that it is better to get the surgeons used to one constant source of illumination.

Similar arrangements are found at the University of Michigan, in Ann Arbor, and in many other places where new clinics have been built.

In many hospitals the kitchens are located, not in the cellar or on the ground-floor, but in a separate building or on the top-floor. The hospital is kept free of kitchen smells. A modern hospital ought to be absolutely odorless. Whoever has travelled in southern Europe will remember the atmosphere of certain hospitals, permeated with a mixture of cooking, water-closets and carbolic acid.

Naturally, in a country of such advanced technical development, the technical details of a hospital, such as ventilation, elevators, running water, baths, sound-proof floors and much besides have been brought to complete perfection. Every room has its radio connection and, in order that in a room with several beds the patients will not disturb each other, a special radio apparatus is supplied which can be placed inside the pillow. The physicians are summoned by light signals. The first time that one goes through a skyscraper hospital, one is afraid of getting lost, but the whole arrangement is so logical that it does not take long to find out how quickly any objective can be reached.

Special attention has been given the records, which are in charge of a numerous and well-trained personnel. Any history can be found at a moment's notice and be sent by mail-chute to the physician wherever he may be. Difficulties arise which are unknown in Europe. Here is a linguistically interesting example. In a Michigan hospital the patients are of course registered alphabetically, but only by consonants; the vowels are left out. The working class of Michigan is largely made up of immigrants from the most different countries, all of whom are likely to change the spelling of their name. It has been observed that it is usually the vowels which are changed, the consonants remain relatively stable. A man who immigrated with the name of *Huber* will perhaps in a few years sign his name *Hoober*; *Meyer* will become *Myer*. They could not be found in an ordinary register. Much labor is also saved by the adding-machines in the working out of case-history statistics.

It is hardly necessary to say that all the new hospitals are equipped with faultless laboratories. More noteworthy perhaps are the recreation grounds and gymnasiums designed for the recreation of doctors and nurses. They are provided even in New York, where space is scarce.

The administration of a large hospital is a big job which demands a wide background of experience and education. In America the superintendents are usually trained physicians. Hospital management has become a medical specialty, a career for a physician. It is work which naturally requires preparation in other fields as well—in economics and sociology—exactly as the physiological chemist or the pharmacologist must study chemistry, the roentgenologist physics, and the medical historian philology and history. The larger the part played by hospitals, the more inviting this career will become, and the higher the class of men to whom it will prove attractive, especially as in America the individual hospital is free to initiate its own experiments. The Committee on the Costs of Medical Care has recommended that special departments of universities be set up for the theoretic and practical training of hospital administrators.

Another development must be mentioned, which to me seems very important. It has come to be realized that the treatment of a patient is not concluded when he leaves the hospital. He comes from a definite environment, which is perhaps largely responsible for his illness, and has to go back into this environment and again become an active member of society. Not until this is accomplished can the treatment be considered finished. Many cases need after-care and control; some require a change of occupation or environment. These are tasks beyond the narrower bounds of medicine, but of decisive importance to the final success of the treatment.

With this fact in mind, a number of hospitals have organized special social service departments. This development is still in its beginnings, but there are already 554 institutions for the sick which have such departments, employing about 2000 social service workers. The institutions for mental disorders are not included, since with them social service has long been a matter of course.

The social workers (as a rule they are women) have two tasks to perform. First, they take down the social histories, which form a substantial part of the whole case-history. The physician consults them as specialists in all questions which concern the occupational and home environment of the patient. Secondly, when the patient leaves the hospital, they have the important function of forming the connecting link between the hospital and his home. They follow him into the factory, the farm, or the office, and learn whether he is now equal to the demands of his environment. Most important of all, it falls to them to persuade the patient to return to the hospital for follow-up examinations. The American College of Surgeons insists that all cases of broken bones should be kept under observation for six months after being discharged from the hospital in order to determine the final result of the treatment. It has given directions for the follow-up examinations after cancer operations. The patient should be seen every two months during the first half-year, every six months during the next three years, and finally once a year for the rest of his life. The College suggests that similar periodic examinations are desirable in other diseases as well, such as heart and kidney diseases, tuberculosis and arteriosclerosis. This requires that contact with the patient be constantly maintained, and herein consists the function of the social worker.

The profession of social work demands not only a great deal of tact and sympathy but a many-sided technical training. For this reason it is an academic profession. Ten of the twenty-eight schools of social work give special courses for training in medical social service. A college degree is required for admission.

The success of hospital treatment depends not only on the physician and the technical equipment but to a great extent on the nursing which is given the patient. Nursing is a factor in medicine which cannot be over-estimated. No country can measure up to its medical responsibility unless it has at its disposal an intelligent well-trained body of nurses.

European nursing is of religious origin. The church deacons, the members of religious orders took charge of the sick. It was a work of Christian brotherly love. Wherever the Catholic Church is active, devout sisters are found, who go about their nursing in a spirit of self-sacrifice.

On American soil, too, the first nursing was done under the auspices of the Catholic Church. In Mexico, at the Hospital of the Immaculate Conception, founded by Cortez shortly after his conquest, the nursing was in the hands of monks; and we have seen that in Canada sisters from various orders cared for the sick under the leadership of Jeanne Mance.

The Reformation caused a breakdown in hospital activity. Hospitals were closed; the monks and nuns were driven away; and it was a long while before a substitute could be developed.

In Protestant America, for this reason, there were no organizations for the care of the sick during colonial times. One did the best one could. Sick people were nursed by their relatives, their neighbors, or by hired persons without any special training. When the hospitals were opened in Philadelphia and New York, untrained men and women were engaged as attendants.

Nursing in Protestant countries received a great impetus

from the influence of the Humanitarianism of the eighteenth and early nineteenth centuries. Sisterhoods were established: the deaconesses of Germany in 1836, followed by a succession of English sisterhoods belonging to the Anglican Church; in 1840 the Protestant Sisters of Charity, a counterpart of the Catholic organization; in 1848 the Sisters of Mercy; St. John's House during the same year; the Sisterhood of All Saints in 1851; and St. Margaret's in 1854. Then Florence Nightingale (1820–1910) began her work of reform. Her school at St. Thomas' Hospital was opened in 1860.

All these movements had their reverberations in the United States. Deaconess-houses were founded in Pittsburgh, Milwaukee, and Chicago. The Sisters of Charity established themselves in New York, running a clinic which later became St. Luke's Hospital. There were the Sisterhoods of St. John and All-Saints in Baltimore, and the Sisterhood of St. Margaret in Boston. The Quakers in Philadelphia founded a nursing society. The Irish immigration led to the spread of Catholicism and there sprang up a long line of Catholic hospitals with Catholic nursing sisters.

The Civil War did much to stimulate nursing. About 2000 women went into nursing, and the reorganization continued after the war at an accelerated pace. In 1873 the Bellevue Hospital in New York started a school of nursing according to the principles laid down by Florence Nightingale. It was followed by the New Haven Hospital and by the Massachusetts General Hospital. In 1880 there were 15 nursing schools with 323 students. In 1900 the figures had increased to 432 schools with over 11,000 students.

By the beginning of the century nursing found itself in an altogether changed situation. The hospital had assumed greater importance. Medicine, diagnosis, and therapy had become much more complicated and made more demands on the nurses. And outside of the hospital public health work was opening new avenues of nursing service.

It was only a short time since nurses had been religious sisters. The religious origin of their profession made itself felt for a long while. The sisters gave their services in charity and mercy. Many had chosen this vocation because life had disappointed them, or as a penance for past misdeeds. Humility and self-denial seemed ideals to follow. The habit was sombre, and often as inconvenient as possible. Their living-quarters were simple, often resembling a convent. The sister's hard work was not confined to caring for the sick. She performed all the drudgery of a servant. The same hands that were expected to soothe the patient were also obliged to scrub the floors.

Times have changed. Religion now has no more to do with nursing than with any other profession. Naturally a certain ethical standard is essential in this as in every branch of healing; but much more is needed, above all intelligence and knowledge. The nurse is the physician's most valuable collaborator. She carries out his instructions and must understand the reason for them. She must adapt herself to the physician and the patient both, and still keep her self-reliance in order to be able in an emergency to act on her own initiative. It is no easy matter to be constantly in the company of invalids; and it is evident that a nurse can only stay fit, if she is not over-burdened. If any calling requires relaxation, recreation, and open-air exercise, it is certainly true of nursing. Only healthy and energetic young women with cheerful dispositions should take up nursing. Better even than the physician, they can inspire the patient with the courage of which his illness may have robbed him. They bring into the sick-room something of the healthy atmosphere of the outside world.

It is also quite plain that nurses should have a good general education. There is nothing more unpleasant, when one is lying sick and miserable, than to have a person around with whom one has absolutely nothing in common. The nurse must be able to manage the patient, and will find it much easier to exert her authority, if she can meet him on an equal cultural plane.

So gradually a new picture of the nurse is evolved, the peer of the old as regards humanity and readiness for service, but with new and less unworldly features. It is a splendid profession, good enough for the most superior women.

Since America had rebuilt its hospitals during the recent decades, and since the nursing tradition was not old enough to be hampering in its effect, an ideal opportunity was given to reorganize the profession and lead it in the pursuit of new ideals. This has been accomplished, if not universally, still to a great extent, and there is no doubt that in this respect America is far ahead of European countries.

The training of nurses has passed through phases similar to those in medical education. At first, the student learned how to take care of the sick by working under an experienced nurse. Then schools for nurses were established, which provided a theoretic foundation for the practical instruction. These schools were connected with hospitals. Of the 7000 hospitals existing in 1929, 2205 had nursing schools. It has been shown that these 2205 hospitals contain 90 percent of all available beds. In other words, only 10 percent of hospital patients are exclusively under the care of graduate nurses.

The curriculum lasts as a rule for three years. For the most part the students pay no tuition fees; or rather, they pay with work instead of money. Frequently they are given a little pocket-money. A few especially high-grade schools require a small tuition fee. Instruction includes both theory and practice. The first months are used as a probation period, to determine whether the student is suited to the nursing profession. The scientific subjects include anatomy, physiology, bacteriology, chemistry, dietetics, hygiene, sometimes psychology, specialized courses in pathology and therapy, and of course the theory and practice of nursing. The practical instruction takes place in the laboratories and in the different divisions of the hospital.

The year 1909 marked a new departure in nursing when the University of Minnesota raised it to an academic subject, and made the School of Nurses a university institute. About twenty-five universities, especially in the Middle West, followed its example. Many subjects already required for nurses were taught at the university, and it was thought an advantage for them to receive the benefits of a broader educational foundation. This type of curriculum lasts five years and is concluded by the conferring of an academic degree.

Without going quite so far, the School of Nursing of Johns Hopkins in 1889 was the first to stress the importance of a broad education for nurses. It has contributed a great deal to the development of the new type of nursing and has played the part of leader in this field also.

At the end of her course the nurse has to pass examinations which make her a graduate nurse with a state license. Nursing may be done without a license, but the certificate is a protection to the public, proving that the bearer has been given a definite training. Without this certificate a nurse cannot get a position either in a hospital or in public health service.

Only a fraction of the nurses who complete their studies every year can find hospital positions. A large number go into private practice in hospitals or in private homes. Still others enter the public health service, for which additional special training is required, lasting in general one year. We will come back to this subject later. Finally, a small fraction devotes itself to teaching. There is a marked tendency that the pupil-nurses shall not depend for their instruction on what can be given by physicians and nurses of the hospital staff during working hours; but that the responsibility for their training shall be in the hands of a special corps of teachers. The best training for this vocation is offered by Teachers College of Columbia University, which in 1898 instituted a department of Nursing and Health, where nurses can prepare themselves for teaching in a several years' course, and may also receive instruction in problems of administration. For from among the students of these courses are recruited the majority of heads of schools and superintendents of nurses.

Of course not every one of the 2205 schools can afford its own specially trained corps of teachers. For this reason in many cities central schools have been established which undertake to give scientific instruction to the several nursing schools in the neighborhood. Sometimes the pupils vary their experience by being shifted to different hospitals, as when a children's hospital takes nurses from various schools for a certain period in order to give them training in its special field.

It is not surprising, considering the large number of schools, that there are still many inequalities among them. But a certain standard, and indeed a high one is already quite general. Many schools are positively inspiring. There is nothing reminiscent of a stuffy convent or the constricting atmosphere of a sickroom; but cheerful halls, beautiful laboratories, tennis-courts, gymnasiums, swimming-pools, and a crowd of healthy gay young girls.

At present the number of nurses is very large. According to statistics, there were in 1930 213,800 licensed nurses, of whom 118,000 did private practice, 18,800 were in public health work and in industry, and 77,000 had hospital positions. To this must be added 80,000 student nurses and 150,000 practical nurses, that is, women who have not had a complete training, but who have had some nursing experience. Efforts are being made to put this category of nurse, which does fill a definite need, under some form of state regulation.

Altogether, therefore, there were in 1930 443,800 or nearly half a million women occupied in nursing or public health work.

That is a large number, and many nurses are unemployed today. They are unemployed, not because there are no invalids who need their care, but because these invalids cannot afford to pay for it. It is again a question of raising and distributing the necessary funds.

America has built up her hospitals and her system of nursing in an astonishingly short time. She has gone ahead with great energy, and has shown both initiative and good judgment. The work has been hampered neither by legal restrictions nor by lack of means. In every country, the hospital is developing into the center of all therapeutic activity, where medicine is organized and coördinated, and the invalid is offered everything that is medically possible. In America even now about eight million people a year apply for hospital treatment and during a year 700,000 children are born in hospitals. This development will go further; hospitals will come to extend their functions, till they include prophylaxis, and grow to be veritable centers for the preservation and restoration of the health of the community.

Today everything is still in a state of flux, though much has already been accomplished, and anyone travelling in America has the comfortable feeling that, in case of sudden illness, he will almost anywhere be within reach of a doctor, a hospital and a nurse, to whom he may trust himself without reservation; a feeling one does not have in every European country.

CHAPTER EIGHT

PREVENTIVE MEDICINE

WE HAVE arrived at the discussion of what is no doubt at once the most important and the least developed field of medicine, not only in America, but all over the world.

To an historian, looking back on our time several centuries from now, our hygiene will seem most primitive. I can picture this future historian writing an analysis of the medical conditions in the period following the Great War: when he gets as far as the chapter on public health, his typewriter suddenly stops. He is at a loss to understand the situation. He is able to follow the pursuit of hygiene as far back as the beginning of history. He has before him the great discoveries of the nineteenth and early twentieth centuries and can see what tremendous progress was made in the knowledge of diseases. He cannot understand why this knowledge was not used to prevent them. As he goes on reading, he finds that medicine pointed with pride to the number of communicable diseases which were under its control: the bubonic plague, cholera, small-pox, hydrophobia; but he is aware that in all countries thousands of people were still dying every year of preventable diseases, that thousands of children were crippled by rickets, though this disorder could be guarded against, that millions of people suffered from tuberculosis, though there was an accurate knowledge of this disease, that many thousands of women died annually of septic abortion because the law would not permit them to go to a doctor. He learns during his researches that when money was short, the governments curtailed their public health budget. Could people really have been so short-sighted? They spent millions every year for the cure of diseases. Did they not realize that it would be less expensive to prevent them?

He studies the status of hygiene in the various countries and is disappointed that progressive America has done no pioneer work in this field. It did just what was being done in other places, very competently and sometimes with improvements, as well as the economic system would allow. This was none too much. There was, for instance, a great enlightened city called Baltimore. In 1931, 1672 physicians were living there. It might be expected that hundreds of them would do preventive medical work. But it turns out that only a few were employed as full-time health officials. And in spite of their important work they were badly paid.

This seems to the future historian a problem in fundamentals. How did it happen that, though in the post-war period methods of disease-prevention were known, little was done about it? He perseveres in his studies for a long time and finally comes to the conclusion that the reasons were many. It was partly the fault of the physicians, who were more interested in disease than in health. A further reason, and probably one of the most important, was that public health work was largely in the hands of the government, and in most countries the governments were in a weak position. They had to defer to the voters and somehow keep them in a good temper, and, above all, never ask them for too much money. The voters prided themselves on their good sense, but they were not very clever at figures. If a man fell sick, he was sent to a hospital. There he either died or got well. The result was immediate, and one knew what had been done with the invested money. But if, on the other hand, a sum of money was granted for purposes of prophylaxis, years would pass before any results could be seen. Men lived at a rapid pace and had no time to wait. The voter's chief concern was his freedom as an individual. To be sure, he had certain obligations; he could not avoid paying taxes or sending his children to school, and his daily life was controlled by count-less police ordinances. But so far he did not recognize any obliga-tion to be healthy. He wanted to retain the privilege of being sick whenever it suited him.

The future historian unearths still other reasons which he does not disclose to me. He sits himself down and writes: "In the period following the World War, medicine was still in the first stage of its development, the age of therapy. Long years and great social upheavals were necessary before medicine could enter a new epoch, the age of prophylaxis."

Public health work in Europe has been built up gradually during the course of centuries. As early as the Middle Ages, church and state had taken measures to combat leprosy and the plague. Directions for personal hygiene survived as legacies of antiquity. Later the absolute monarchies made use of their su-preme power to enforce health by police ordinance. The philos-ophy of the Enlightenment led to a great wave of hygienic edu-cation for the masses. After a period of reaction in the beginning of the nineteenth century, a new hygiene movement arose under the stress of the Industrial Revolution, starting in England and eventually finding expression in social legislation.

In America the beginnings were very difficult. A handful of people sets foot in a new part of the world. The climate, the surroundings, everything is strange to them. They carry with them contagions, which fall on only too fruitful a soil. There are no doctors and thousands of people die. However, they soon made an effort to protect themselves. They took such measures as they had seen used in Europe. When danger threatened, a committee of sanitation was chosen from among the most re-spected citizens with full authority to give any orders that seemed necessary. The cities were all sea-ports, and the fight was first of all a war of defense against the outside world. We learned in an earlier chapter how quarantine measures were enforced everywhere. We have also seen that any promising European discoveries were adopted very quickly. It was so with smallpox inoculation, and with vaccination in the beginning of the nineteenth century. And the hygienic movement of the Enlightenment eventually had its reverberations in America. We have followed Franklin's humanitarian strivings and have watched Benjamin Rush as the advance guard of the hygienic idea. It is significant that the *Gesundheitskatechismus* (Catechism of Health) of Bernhard Christoph Faust, which was very widely read in Europe, was published in America as early as 1795, and reprinted in 1798 at the instigation of Benjamin Rush and Dr. Williamson, a North Carolina physician.

The people in the colonies were by no means inactive, but their remedies were ineffectual and the great epidemics, such as yellow fever, which swept over the country at intervals, fell on the towns like blows of fate. What was needed was a defense organized by permanent agencies, keeping watch even when no enemy was in sight.

Only after the establishment of the Union do we find the beginnings of any organized public health service. In 1798 the *Marine Hospital Service* was instituted by act of Congress, as a department which should be responsible for the medical care of the sick and disabled sailors of the Merchant Marine. In the beginning it was financed by the ship-owners, who paid twenty cents a month per man, which they were allowed to deduct from the wages. The money was collected by treasury officials, and for this reason the Marine Hospital Service is still under the Treasury Department. For the same reasons the United States Public Health Service, which originated within the Marine Hospital Service, is today a division of the Treasury Department. The first Marine Hospital was opened in Norfolk, Virginia, in 1800. In 1802 it was followed by others in Boston, Newport, and Charleston. The growing importance of shipping on the Mississippi and other inland waters led to an extension of this service to sailors belonging to the inland fleets, and a series of marine hospitals was erected in the interior of the country.

The administration was uncoördinated and lax. Hospital standards varied greatly. As we have seen, after the Civil War John Billings was put in charge of these marine hospitals and his activities led in 1870 to a reorganization of the whole department, which was built up on military lines, and from then on steadily widened the circle of its functions.

The responsibility for sick sailors would of itself turn the attention of the department to diseases brought in from outside. Quarantine regulations were the affair of the individual states. But considering the enormous significance of quarantine for the Union as a whole, the federal government could not remain indifferent to the effectiveness of the measures taken. Repeatedly since 1796, it had passed laws promising its assistance in the carrying out and strengthening of quarantine regulations. However, in 1878, the Marine Hospital Service was authorized to carry out these quarantine measures in collaboration with the state governments; and it was given far-reaching powers of control. In the same year the publication of the *Bulletin of the Public Health Service* began, which provided concrete evidence of the fact that the Marine Hospital Service was on the way to becoming a department of public health.

Till now the work of the department, in so far as it dealt with communicable diseases, had been confined to the sea-coasts. The next step was taken in 1890, by a law which authorized the department to take measures to prevent the carrying of cholera, yellow fever, smallpox, or bubonic plague from one state to another. Hereby the range of its activity was extended to the interior of the country, over the whole national territory.

Further advances were made in this direction. In 1893, a law was passed making it possible for the individual states to relinquish their quarantine stations to the Marine Hospital Service. This was accomplished step by step, and now the whole quarantine service is under the federal government. After 1890 the medical examination of immigrants was made a responsibility of the department. In 1893 the service was given authority to exercise control not only over the four infections mentioned above, but over all other communicable diseases that were being carried between one state and another. After the Spanish-American War the service was extended to Cuba, Porto Rico, and the Philippines, and eventually to the Hawaiian Islands. New problems, such as leprosy, were taken up as they became acute. It became more and more plain that such a department could work effectively only if it made scientific investigations on its own account. Laboratories and a yellow-fever institute were the next development.

In this way a department which originally had very limited functions grew into a division of public health, with far-reaching plenary powers. In 1902 its designation was changed from Marine Hospital Service to Public Health and Marine Hospital Service. At the beginning of the new century the population had a very active interest in questions of hygiene. It was the general opinion that the federal government should take over the control of sickness to an even greater extent than it had already done, and the time seemed ripe to loose the unnatural bond between the Public Health Service and the Treasury, and to unite all the federal appointments pertaining to the maintenance of public health (exclusive of the army and navy medical corps) under one independent cabinet minister. For other departments had sanitary functions as well. A branch of the Agricultural Department was in charge of the control of food and drugs and the Census Bureau collected the data for vital statistics.

However, a very sensible proposal for the unification of hygiene management met with no comprehension in Congress. Everything remained as before, except that the name of the department was changed without more ado to Public Health Service.

As at present constituted, the Public Health Service has seven important functions. First of all, it must protect the United States from diseases which may be brought in from foreign countries. For this purpose it maintains physicians abroad in touch with United States consuls, who examine emigrants before they even leave their own homes. It further enforces strict quarantine regulations in the harbors of the mainland and the islands. Its second function is to direct the enforcement of domestic quarantine, which is carried on in close collaboration with the state and local health boards. This collaboration is the third point in the program. The Public Health Service is a reference bureau, to which local administrations can at any time turn for advice, and on whose help they can call through the mediation of the President, when faced with a problem beyond their resources, and of more than local importance. The fourth function is the investigation of disease, which has already brought valuable results. Naturally research is focussed primarily on communicable diseases, but problems in child hygiene, industrial hygiene, sewerage, pollution of streams, and similar subjects receive its attention. A fifth function, which was assumed in 1902, is the supervision and control of biological products, such as sera, toxins, and anti-toxins. As its sixth function, it disseminates information on communicable diseases through a weekly bulletin and enlightens the public in matters of hygiene through newspapers, exhibitions, etc., an activity shared by many other organizations. And finally it retains its original responsibility for the Marine Hospital Service, the medical care of sailors to whom have been added recently several categories of government employees. In 1918 a special department, which we shall discuss in more detail later, was instituted for the control of venereal diseases.

The Public Health Service is under the directorship of the

Surgeon-General. His assistants, the Public Health Officers, are graded similarly to military surgeons. A special examination is required before entering the service. A new examination must be taken before every promotion, at least in the lower ranks. In addition to the active corps there is also a reserve corps which may be mobilized in special situations. There is besides a large staff of scientific and other collaborators, engineers, chemists, zoölogists, nurses, etc., who are *non-commissioned* or outside the graded ranks.

Public Health Officers ought to be familiar with every branch of hygiene. To this end they are made to serve in each division in turn. This results in the formation of a flying sanitary corps which can be called upon whenever an epidemic breaks out in any part of the country. When in 1907 some cases of bubonic plague appeared in San Francisco and a serious epidemic was threatened, federal aid was immediately invoked. The government sent out a staff of hygienists, who entered upon a remarkably energetic campaign. The city was divided into districts. The rats were exterminated. It was possible to keep the epidemic down to 160 cases with 78 deaths. The same thing occurred in New Orleans in 1920, where the epidemic was restricted to 18 cases and 8 deaths.

By means of similar campaigns, the plague, smallpox, and cholera were brought under control in the Philippines, Manila was freed from malaria and beri-beri, in 1905 a yellow-fever epidemic was stamped out in New Orleans, and in 1925 an epidemic of typhoid fever caused by infected oysters was promptly checked.

It must not be forgotten that the United States by its proximity to the tropics and Eastern Asia is particularly exposed to epidemics. It is all the more important to have at hand a well-trained corps which has moreover the authority to take any measures, no matter how drastic, which the situation may demand.

There are splendid men among these Public Health Officers. I had the privilege of observing their work with leprosy in the Hawaiian Islands, and what I saw filled me with unreserved admiration.

The Public Health Service, as has already been mentioned, is not the only government department to perform hygienic functions. Almost every branch of the administration has under it some bureau, in some way related to questions of health. Two have already been mentioned. The Children's Bureau in the Department of Labor does an important service in working out problems of child hygiene in collaboration with the separate states. The Bureau of Indian Affairs in the Interior Department in 1926 maintained 86 hospitals and 194 doctors for the medical care of the Indians. Under the same department is a Division of Mining, which has to do with the welfare of miners.

There are many other departments of the federal government which perform some sort of health service. The work is very much divided up, for reasons which can be traced in its history. The responsibility of the state for the well-being of its citizens has only very gradually come to be recognized; and as the need arose, each individual government department developed its separate hygienic function. Now that the problem of public health is so much in the foreground, a unified central bureau, a single administrative department, such as has been instituted in various European states, would not be at all out of place.

The Constitution of the United States was written at a time when there was no public health work worth mentioning. For this reason it confers on the federal government no special authority in this matter. When during the nineteenth century hygiene became more and more obviously an administrative problem, the government found itself very much restricted by the Constitution. It had to confine itself to general matters (research, information, and supervision of serum production) and questions concerning several states at once (quarantine). In addition to this, it may in emergencies come to the help of individual states with advice and money. The chief responsibility for public hygiene, however, still remains with the states, townships, and counties.

It will be remembered that during colonial times, every state did what seemed best to it in matters of health. The sea-ports, being most in danger, were the most enterprising. As early as the eighteenth century many cities appointed health commissioners. These were not physicians, but laymen whose chief duty it was to see, with the help of the police, that certain orders of the city administration were carried out. They were primarily sanitary inspectors. Sometimes they were assisted by a consulting physician.

While during the eighteenth century the war waged for the maintenance of health was purely defensive, directed against enemies from without, about 1800 it began to be a war of offense. The first point of attack was the dirt in the cities. Efforts were made to clean them up, to rid them of decaying matter and other kinds of filth. To do this effectively, it was necessary to pay some attention to sewage and to provide a water-supply. Even in ancient times it was recognized that filth was a source of danger to health. Nevertheless, it was many centuries before the Occident began to feel the need of cleanliness.

Though these efforts of individual cities were to be commended, they often remained unorganized and dependent on chance. Between 1800 and 1830 there were only 5 cities with organized boards of health. By 1873 the number had grown to 32. In 1866 New York City established its health department; Chicago one year later. Some cities were well taken care of, others very badly. And outside of the cities, in the country districts, practically nothing was done at all. There was no central office to give directions and exercise control.

It was therefore a great step forward when in 1869 Massachusetts instituted a State Board of Health. England had passed the Public Health Act in 1848, which resulted in the establishment of a number of government health departments. This movement would naturally make itself felt in America. In 1849 a commission was appointed in Massachusetts which, under the leadership of Lemuel Shattuck, drew up a model health program. However, twenty years went by before the State Board of Health of Massachusetts was finally established. The first step having been taken, California, Virginia, and Minnesota followed its example. The others fell into line, and today every state has its central Board of Health.

At present the situation is such that the administration of public health within the states is carried on simultaneously by two agencies, the State Departments of Health on the one hand, and the Municipal Departments of Health on the other, and sometimes the County Departments of Health. The division of jurisdiction differs widely among the states. Before the war the tendency was towards centralization; there was an effort to strengthen the central bureaus and subordinate the local organizations. After the war a reversion of this tendency occurred, since hygiene is seeking more and more to get hold of the individual human being, and naturally this can be accomplished more easily by a local office.

The country districts presented a special problem, owing to the great distances across the continent and the sparse population in many parts of the country. In 1920 only 109 out of 2850 rural counties had organized their own boards of health. An intensive work was set on foot, with the help of the federal government and private organizations, and by 1927 this number had increased to 337. That is of course still very small, but there will be further progress made in this direction. In the meanwhile many districts will have to be cared for directly by the State Board of Health.

In general the functions of state and local boards are identical. When possible they are executed by the local board which reports to the central office and may at times be given directions. These functions are similar in all civilized countries. First comes the task for which the agency was originally created, the supervision and control of communicable diseases. After that comes the keeping of statistics. From 1850 to 1900, at the time of the decennial census, mortality data were collected, giving a cross-section for every tenth year. But the figures obtained in this way were unsatisfactory. In 1880 continuous mortality data began to be recorded in those districts where at least 90 percent of the cases were already being statistically handled. Since 1915 birth-rate statistics have been taken. Gradually all states except two (South Dakota and Texas) could be included in these statistics. The data are collected by the local and state boards and are shipped to Washington where the statistical work is done by the Bureau of Census. The difficulties attendant on making a census are much greater in America than in Europe, where each individual is registered with the police and is moreover less likely to change his dwelling-place.

With the coming of the era of bacteriology, health agencies were confronted with new problems. Laboratories had to be erected, the first such laboratory being installed in Rhode Island in 1894. In the same year the production of diphtheria-antitoxin began in Massachusetts. At first the scientific institutes of the universities had to be resorted to. Today every state has a state laboratory, whose activities are increasing from year to year. While in the beginning the work of the laboratories was confined almost entirely to the diagnosis of communicable diseases, their activities now include the chemical and bacteriological analysis of drinking water and milk, the production and distribution of prophylactic and therapeutic sera, and numerous special lines of work, according to the needs of the individual states. Many of them have at their disposal portable laboratories in automobiles or railroad cars; a few have floating laboratories for the analysis of oysters.

The technical division is occasionally very large. It is made up of engineers whose responsibility it is to make human surroundings clean and sanitary: in other words, to supervise the water-supply, sewage, the control of rivers, lakes, harbors, bathing places, and dwellings.

Child hygiene was not taken up as an independent problem until about 1915, but since then it has assumed enormous proportions and will be dealt with as a separate subject.

The supervision of food and drugs, and finally popular education in hygiene, are further services for which the health departments are responsible.

The development of public hygiene work has led to a great demand for personnel: doctors, chemists, bacteriologists, engineers, technicians, and nurses. It is obvious that all of these require special professional training. At first they had to take it wherever it could be found, or else they entered the public health service without any particular preparation and were obliged to work their way up laboriously. For a long time the mistaken idea persisted that the knowledge of medicine was all that was needed for work in hygiene, and it would often happen, here as in Europe, that a physician who could not succeed in private practice would finally obtain a job in the public health service.

The necessity for providing opportunities for special training was recognized very early, and a way was taken which proved very successful. The movement is associated with the name of William T. Sedgwick, a biologist, who in 1883 was made director of the department of biology of the Massachusetts Institute of Technology in Cambridge, one of the best technical schools in the United States. This was the time of the great bacteriological discoveries, and Sedgwick followed them with the deepest interest. He turned to problems of hygiene and became the biological consultant of the Massachusetts State Board of Health. It is to him first of all that Massachusetts owes its model water supply and drainage system. A laboratory for research in hygiene was attached to his division of the Institute, which gradually developed into the Department of Biology and Public Health, where hygienists could take a four-years' training course.

So the first school of hygiene came to be founded and to provide a model which was to find many imitators.

In 1918 the School of Hygiene and Public Health was opened at Johns Hopkins University. It was moved into a new building of its own in 1925, (Fig. 27) with William H. Welch as director, assisted by the physiologist, William H. Howell, who later became Welch's successor. The School of Hygiene and Public Health is an independent school of the University and consequently quite apart from the medical school, though naturally relations between the two schools are very close. The object of the school is to train students in hygiene and public health, to advance research in preventive medicine, to encourage the development of a new generation of scientists, and work out methods for spreading the knowledge of hygiene.

The school is divided into departments for the following subjects: chemistry, physiology, biology, bacteriology, filterable virus, immunization, protozoölogy and medical entomology, helminthology, epidemiology, engineering, health administration, and statistics. In addition to these, special courses in personal, social and mental hygiene, as well as in sanitary legislation are held outside of these departments. In the year 1932–1933 the school contained 60 instructors and 137 students, one-fourth of whom were foreigners.

A section of the students consists of physicians who are given a certificate in public health, at the end of a year's course, and a degree of Doctor of Public Health (D.P.H.) after a two years' course. For the doctor's degree there is required, besides the examination, a dissertation and three months' practice in public health service. The school is, however, open to non-medical students. For them, the course lasts from one to three years, according to previous preparation. The school confers, in addition to the above-mentioned degree, the degree of Master or Doctor of Science in Hygiene. The whole system of instruction is as elastic as possible, in order to allow for every need of public health service, and to make it possible for young people to train themselves as specialists in a single field.

By these means the school fills a double function in that, on the one hand, it gives physicians training in hygiene and, on the other, offers to scientists who wish to devote themselves to public health work the necessary special information.

There is no doubt that these schools which do not exist yet in most European countries, contribute a great deal towards making the work of hygiene and public health more effective.

However, the work of public health agencies cannot be done by hygienists alone. The part taken by public health nurses is becoming more and more important. They form the vanguard and the intelligence department. They make their way into the homes and get in touch with individual households. It is they who keep the agencies informed and who are in the best position to further popular education. Child hygiene work is largely in their hands.

As was stated in the last chapter, there are at the present time about 20,000 nurses in public health and industrial positions. At the opening of the twentieth century, there were only a few hundred. It is obvious that for these nurses the ordinary hospital training does not suffice, and, moreover, that especially intelligent and self-reliant women are needed for this work. In

27. THE JOHNS HOPKINS UNIVERSITY SCHOOL OF HYGIENE AND
PUBLIC HEALTH

1906 the Boston District Nursing Association began to offer special courses. Columbia Teachers College followed in 1910. Since 1917 most of the important schools of nursing offer organized post-graduate courses which as a rule give the nurses a Public Health Nurse Certificate at the end of one year's course.

The facts presented in previous chapters have evidenced the decisive part played in the development of every field of American medicine by private initiative and private organizations. The state was only a secondary factor, taking over or establishing a limited number of institutions, for the most part after the burden became too great for a private agency. In the field of public health we have a different situation, since many of the problems are matters of administration which require for their execution the legislative power and the authority of the state. For this reason the state has entered the field of public health before any other department of medicine. But here, too, valuable contributions have been made by private organizations, particularly in the line of experiment.

The number of societies for the improvement of public health is extraordinarily large. Many of them have performed essential functions, and continue to do so. Especially important was the influence of the American Public Health Association, which was founded in 1872, that is, exactly at the time in which Pasteur published his great discoveries, and hygiene was approaching a new era. The Association included physicians, hygienists, and also laymen. It became a forum for the discussion of problems of hygiene, issued numerous publications, worked out standard methods for testing water, milk, and air, and for pasteurization, thereby saving much unnecessary trial and error. And, above all, it served as the nation's hygienic conscience, keeping the authorities awake to their responsibilities, and stimulating the people's interest in health.

The United States did not join the Red Cross until late in the day, in 1883; but since then the American Red Cross has proved its usefulness, not only during the war and other catastrophes, but in everyday life. In hundreds of places, especially among country communities, it has worked for the spread of hygienic ideas, by courses on home nursing, diet, and first aid.

Many organizations have extended their activities beyond the national boundaries. A division of the Rockefeller Foundation —the International Health Board—has undertaken great projects in sanitation all over the world, particularly for the purpose of controlling malaria and hookworm. Recently the Republics of the American continent have established the International Sanitary Bureau of the American Republics, which undertakes the solution of problems of general interest and distributes information.

It is quite impossible even to enumerate the countless local, state, and national organizations which in some way contribute to public health. A few will be mentioned later in another connection. All of them supplement the official public health program in the most fortunate way.

The head organization, serving as clearing house for all these endeavors, is the National Health Council in New York, comprised of delegates from the larger organizations, whose main task it is to keep its members informed of what is happening in the individual societies, in order to avoid duplication of work, and to achieve a better coördination of effort.

After getting acquainted with the organization of public health service in its main outlines, we must pass on to the observation of special lines of work in order to see how they have been approached in America, and what direction their development is now taking.

The great epidemics that during the eighteenth century used to come in from abroad and afflict the country, and which still demanded many victims during the nineteenth century—plague, yellow fever, and cholera—have been controlled by quarantine and sanitation. Smallpox, too, has lost its terrors since it can be prevented by vaccination. It is true that only eleven states require universal vaccination, as a rule enforced by admitting at school only those children who have been successfully vaccinated. In nine other states it is left to the counties and townships to decide whether they shall have vaccination laws or not. In 1920–22 America, like Europe, was visited by a widespread epidemic which, however, was of a mild nature.

During the nineteenth century *typhus abdominalis,* typhoid, was one of the most common of the communicable diseases. In 1865, out of 100,000 inhabitants of Massachusetts, 134 died of typhoid. After the bacillus had been discovered and the method of its transmission was understood, after new water-works had been built and milk was being pasteurized, there ensued a remarkable decrease in the number of cases. In 1921 there were only 2 deaths to 100,000 inhabitants in the state of New York. In the whole country the rate of mortality from typhoid and paratyphoid sank between 1900 and 1929 from 35.9 to 4.2. Typhoid and related diseases can be prevented today, especially since an effective antitoxin has been found.

In the same way the drop in the rate of mortality in the case of communicable diseases is very great. The following figures refer to the number of cases occurring among 100,000 inhabitants in 1900 and in 1929.

	1900	*1929*
Diphtheria	43.3	6.6
Scarlet fever	10.2	2.1
Measles	12.5	2.5
Whooping cough	12.1	6.3

Diphtheria immunization is not obligatory, but it is encouraged by active propaganda.

The fight against *tuberculosis* has been equally successful. In 1857 over 450 to 100,000 inhabitants died of tuberculosis in Massachusetts. And it was certainly no better in the other states. The first attempts to keep it in check were undertaken during the eighties.

A young New York physician, Edward L. Trudeau, was a victim of the disease. His brother had already succumbed to it, and his own case seemed hopeless. He, with his family, was on the way to the Adirondacks for a vacation, when he was surprised by a snow-storm. He spent two days cut off from the world, deep in the snow. But it did not hurt him in the least; quite the contrary. He decided to spend the winter in the mountains, and improved noticeably. There could be no doubt that fresh air was beneficial. His physician, Dr. A. L. Loomis, wrote up the case in 1876 and described the favorable effect of the locality. Trudeau stayed in the mountains, and there began to practise his profession. In 1884 the first tubercular cases came to him, and in the following year he opened the first sanatorium on the American continent—the Adirondack Cottage Sanitarium. In Europe health resorts had been introduced in much the same way by Brehmer, Spengler, and Dettweiler.

In 1882 the tubercle bacillus was discovered by Robert Koch. In 1887 the first tuberculosis dispensary was opened by Robert W. Philip in Edinburgh. Two years later, in 1889, an organized fight against the disease was begun in New York by a report which Hermann M. Biggs prepared for the Board of Health and which embraces the modern anti-tuberculosis program. The physicians of the city were skeptical, but the Board of Health was more far-sighted, and in 1893 began to put the Biggs program into effect by opening an educational campaign, by ordering that public institutions report tubercular cases and asking that private practitioners do the same; by sending inspectors to the homes of patients; by drawing the attention of hospitals to the necessity of separate wards; by erecting a tuberculosis hospital of its own and establishing special laboratories for investigations.

This was in New York, and just a beginning. But other localities began to bestir themselves. In Philadelphia Lawrence F. Flick founded the Pennsylvania Society for Prevention of Tuberculosis in 1892; in 1895 it was followed by a hospital for needy cases; and in 1903 by the Henry Phipps Institute, the first institute for research in tuberculosis.

Vincent Y. Bowditch was the pioneer of the movement in Boston. At his instigation the first state sanatorium was built in 1898.

Chicago, Washington and other cities followed. The necessity of sanatoria was recognized. In 1904 there existed about 100 institutions for tuberculous patients with about 10,000 beds, 57.4 percent of which were in private hands. The mortality in this year was 200, an improvement on 1890, when it amounted to 245.4, but was still very high. And there remained many localities in which hardly anything was done.

Then, in 1904, the *National Tuberculosis Association* was founded, a private society which with tremendous energy undertook to push and organize the anti-tuberculosis crusade. Great impetus was given by the International Tuberculosis Congress, held in Washington in 1908, which brought together the most prominent specialists of the world, including Robert Koch himself. The Christmas sale of tuberculosis stamps, introduced all over the country with the help of the Red Cross, not only brought in money, but provided the occasion to spread the germs of propaganda among even the most remote communities. Branches of the Association were formed all over the country. The population was educated by all possible methods and, most important of all, the government was won over, so that it assumed an ever-increasing share of the burden.

In 1931 633 hospitals and sanatoria with 80,054 beds were at the service of tubercular patients. Seventy percent of the beds

were in the hands of the state. There were in addition about
1000 fixed dispensaries, and about 2500 clinics were held by
itinerant dispensaries, especially in the country districts. There
were also about 1000 open-air schools. Seven thousand nurses
were in the service of the movement. One thousand four hundred
and seventy-one societies were dedicated exclusively to the war
on tuberculosis and were assisted by 613 additional agencies.

And what was the result? From 1904 to 1929, that is, a
period of 25 years, the death rate fell from 200 to 76 per 100,-
000. In Massachusetts it fell from 450 to 69.3 between 1860
and 1929. This is lower than the present death rate in most
European countries.

Tuberculosis, as a problem of mass disease, is as good as
solved. The stamping out of the contagion is only a question of
the time and money which are expended for the purpose.

The fight against *venereal diseases* has so far been less successful. For a long time it was hampered by a false prudery.
The ban was finally lifted by the war. With millions of enlisted
men, the problem had to be faced openly. It is a known fact
that, thanks to rigorous prophylactic measures, the American
army was freer from venereal diseases than any other participating in the war.

Interest in these problems did not die with the end of the
war, and the effort to control venereal disease was extended to
the civilian population. The U. S. Public Health Service led
the way and, as we have seen, established a separate department
in 1918. It was followed by the state and local boards of health.
While before 1914 the reporting of cases was mandatory in
only two states, by 1915 it was required in nine states, and today
is enforced everywhere with the exception of nine states.

Here, too, the efforts of the government were given effective
support by a private organization founded in 1914—the American Social Hygiene Association. Educational campaigns were

undertaken. Special dispensaries were opened, of which there are now about 600, as well as prophylactic stations.

In spite of this there have been only minor results. To be sure, the death rate in syphilis fell 29 percent between 1917 and 1930, but the death rate is not a good yard-stick for this disease. The calculation that 5 percent of the population is syphilitic is probably setting too low a figure. It has been calculated further that about a million people a day receive treatment for venereal disease; and 100,000 people die annually as the direct or indirect result of syphilis.

It is not hard to find the reasons for failures up to the present time. Venereal disease is in some ways easier to control than tuberculosis, but in other ways more difficult. Easier, because the sources of infection are or at least could always be ascertainable. More difficult, because tuberculosis is generally considered a misfortune, and syphilis a sin over which a veil is still drawn. More difficult especially because one can only get at venereal disease by far-reaching state intervention in personal affairs. That is possible in many European countries and they achieve corresponding results. American individualism resists state interference in matters of this sort.

Education by itself cannot deal with venereal disease. It is significant that in a large city which has three prophylactic stations only 10 cases a week apply for treatment. In another city with four stations only 149 cases were treated in three years. It is equally significant that in the army, which is invested with the necessary authority, the results are much better. In 1901 the rate per 1000 was 150; it sank to 45.6 in 1931.

Tuberculosis and venereal diseases are social diseases. Tuberculosis can be dealt with by financial means: by tearing down slums, taking charge of exposed children, pasteurizing milk, and improving general living conditions. Venereal diseases are bound up with the sex life, and especially with another social disease, namely, prostitution. Open prostitution has disappeared.

One is no longer accosted on the streets. Houses of prostitution have been closed. But prostitution persists in secret. It rises and falls in inverse ratio to the general economic situation. And this is a disease which must be reached, not through the police, but through education, an education which moreover has nothing whatever to do with religion.

There are many unsolved problems in this field, problems difficult to solve in America, for which money and medical efficiency do not suffice, but which demand rather a fundamental change in the point of view.

The United States extends in the south down into the subtropic zone and has to fight a number of sicknesses which Europe has been wholly or partly spared. We saw in an earlier chapter what ghastly havoc was inflicted by yellow fever during the eighteenth century. And even in the nineteenth century the southern states were in constant danger and new epidemics broke out repeatedly. That this infection has been as good as eradicated is a glorious page in the history of American medicine, and the honor belongs to the Army Medical Corps.

In 1900, after the Spanish-American War, a yellow-fever epidemic raged in Cuba, which cost more lives than the war. A commission was appointed to study the disease, with Major Walter Reed at its head. At his side stood the army physicians, James Carroll and Jesse Lazear, and a Cuban, Aristides Agramonte. The germ of yellow fever had not been discovered and no one knew how it was communicated. The general opinion was that the disease was carried from man to man directly or by means of contaminated objects. Only a few, among them in particular Carlos J. Finlay in Havana, believed it was carried by mosquitoes.

The commission began experimentally, and since at that time no animals were known to be receptive to the disease, the experiments had to be tried on human beings. This year of 1900, rich in tragedy and heroism, has an indelible place in medical history. The physicians experimented on themselves and on soldiers, Cubans, and nurses, who volunteered for the purpose. They slept in infected beds. They allowed themselves to be bitten by mosquitoes, which had already bitten yellow-fever patients. Many died, among them Lazear himself. But the sacrifices were not in vain. It was proved beyond doubt that the disease was carried exclusively by the bite of the mosquito *Aëdes aegypti* (*Stegomya calopus*). The method of control was indicated: isolation of the infected and extermination of the insects.

The fight was immediately opened, with William C. Gorgas, later Surgeon-General of the Army, in charge. Cuba was very soon cleaned up. Gorgas was then sent to Panama in 1904. His sanitation measures made possible the building of the canal for the first time. But he had a still larger purpose in mind. Yellow fever must be eliminated from the face of the earth. The Rockefeller Foundation put up the necessary funds, and Gorgas moved his forces to South America. The results were good. While as late as 1900 all the tropical and sub-tropical portions of America were still severely infested with yellow fever, twenty-five years later it was practically stamped out.

The control of *malaria* presents similar though more difficult problems. Here, too, the disease is carried by a mosquito, and it is again a question of exterminating the mosquitoes and preventing them from infecting themselves by biting malarial patients. The difficulties are greater than in yellow fever because malaria is endemic in many large sections and the single case cannot be kept under as strict observation.

The United States was formerly infected through and through with malaria. The Mississippi to the edge of the Great Lakes formed the main focus; and the Atlantic coast quite far into the north was always more or less involved. Malaria is on the decrease and is now confined to the southern states. The fight against it is largely in the hands of the departments of health. The results in the cities are good. In 26 cities, with a total of 4.5 million inhabitants, the death rate sank from 6 to every 100,000 inhabitants in 1922, to 1.6 in 1931. It is much higher when the figures for rural districts are included.

State	Year	Number per 100,000 inhabitants	
		Infected	Died
Alabama	1922	62.7	13.0
	1927	144.3	8.0
	1929	399.8	16.4
	1931	92.8	8.1
Florida	1922		22.7
	1927		15.6
	1929		32.8
	1931		13.6
Georgia	1922	65.1	20.2
	1927	79.9	10.1
	1929	230.6	23.3
	1931	65.5	10.5

The mortality of the colored population is double that of the white. The death rate for the whole Union was reckoned at 3.5 in 1929; and it is calculated that the number of malarial patients amounts to about a million. Malaria therefore still presents a very serious problem and with the tremendous expanse of the country and the constant shifting of the population will be difficult to get under control.

Still quite common is the disorder caused by the *hookworm* (*Ancylostomum*), formerly diagnosed as Egyptian chlorosis, a disease which, though not necessarily fatal, steadily undermines the vitality and the energy of the patient. It seems to have been first brought in from Porto Rico around the middle of the eighteenth century. It is a disease of the tropical and subtropical countries which found favorable conditions for its development in the southern states. The mechanism of this sickness is clearly understood; it is known that the worm-eggs enter the soil with the stools and that the larvae get into the organism through the skin. Its control is therefore theoretically simple. It is a matter of keeping the soil free from pollution. This can be done by treating diseased people with thymol and other preparations, which kill the worms in the intestines, and by building sanitary privies. Practically its control meets with great difficulties, because it requires the examination of the total population of a district, even that fraction which at the moment feels quite well. It is therefore largely dependent on the good will of the inhabitants, which in turn depends on their understanding of the procedures.

An army surgeon, Colonel Bailey K. Ashford, first attacked this problem in Porto Rico. In 1900 the Rockefeller Foundation, in collaboration with the local boards of health of the tropical and sub-tropical countries of the American continent, embarked on a campaign which led to a pronounced diminution of the disease. An investigation of school children in the southern states of the Union during the years between 1911 and 1914 showed an incidence of 59.7 percent. Under intensive treatment this sank to 39.7 between 1914 and 1918, and in 1920 was only 21.7 percent. The work has been carried on without intermission by the health agencies, but the disease has not yet been conquered.

Leprosy plays a considerable rôle in the islands—Porto Rico, Hawaii, and the Philippines—but not on the mainland, where only isolated cases occur. In 1894, Louisiana opened a leprosarium in Carville, which in 1901 was taken over by the federal government and has been run since then as a national leprosarium. Seven hundred and eighteen lepers were admitted from 1894 to 1929. In 1930 it was caring for 308 patients.

A further group of problems demanding a hygienic solution is presented by certain special dangers to which different sections of the population are exposed.

To this group belongs occupational hygiene. Industrialization has brought with it many new and serious sources of danger. It is well known that, especially in England and Germany, social legislation was achieved only after a long and determined contest. In America for a long time nothing was done to protect the workers. Human life was treated in the most brutal fashion. When a man's usefulness ceased he was put out in the streets to perish in misery, unless charity took pity on him. Immigration furnished a steady stream of strong new working power. The state restricted itself to repressing the worst abuses and to protecting women and children from too severe exploitation.

Not till this present century, since 1911, has there been any fundamental change. The workmen's compensation laws influenced employers and insurance companies to interest themselves in doing as much as possible to prevent accidents and occupational diseases. Since then many improvements have been made and, as we saw in an earlier chapter, a large number of industrial enterprises have established a comprehensive health service. At the same time we discussed the drawbacks of a system which protects the worker only while he has a job, and for this reason can never take the place of health insurance.

Children form another especially exposed group. While social health protection for adults is still in its first stages, the child hygiene movement is correspondingly advanced.

This field, too, is a very recent development. Towards the end of the nineteenth century a few schools introduced occasional visits by physicians. In 1899 Connecticut made these compulsory by law. Though the authorities had at first confined their concern to the children's souls, afterwards gradually coming to take some trouble with their intellectual training, by the twentieth century they finally began to recognize the responsibility for their physical well-being.

The World War furnished a wholesome lesson. When in 1917 three and a half million men from 18 to 30 years of age were examined to ascertain their fitness for army service, it was shown that almost half were in some way defective; and that 21 percent were totally unfit. It was shown further that a considerable part of these defects might have been prevented by proper measures taken during childhood.

After the war, the examination of larger groups of school children was undertaken; and again it proved that a very large number had some form of defect, in teeth, tonsils, vision, hearing, heart, or through a tuberculous infection. In 1930 it was calculated that 10 million persons under twenty, or more than one-fifth, were handicapped by previous or existing disease.

At the same time it was discovered that, though the absolute number of children increased from 1900 to 1930, their number in proportion to the total population was steadily decreasing. The preservation of the individual child's health seemed all the more urgent.

A conference was called by President Hoover—the White House Conference on Child Health and Protection—which investigated the prevailing status and proposed a program.

Many agencies participated in the task: the Children's Bureau, founded in 1912 as a division of the Labor Department, the state and local boards of health, and a number of private organizations, the most important being the American Child Health Association, which had been formed by merging two older societies.

The findings showing that the death rate of children is highest during the first month, and particularly in the first week, have led to the realization that preventive care should begin with the mother. For this purpose pre-natal centers are being established for pregnant women. The movement is only just beginning, but in 1929 there already existed 311 such centers, and 373 others which provided pre-natal as well as after-care for both mother and child.

The care of children of pre-school age has prospered much

better. While around 1900 there were only 20 child health centers among cities of 10,000 or over, in 1930 the number had risen to 1511. In the whole country in 1929 there were 2294 such centers, where the mothers could bring their children for examination, where they could be instructed in diet and hygiene, and from which public health nurses could be sent into the homes. About half of the centers were supported by public funds, the other half by private organizations.

At the same time so-called nursery-schools, or day-nurseries, were established in many places, where the children could be under the observation of a pediatrician, a dietitian, and a psychologist. There are now about 500 such schools.

The next step has to do with the hygiene of school children. Every child is examined on first entering school, and the examination is periodically repeated. Nurses serve as a connecting link between school and home. Where demonstrated physical defects are neglected by parents, the state must step in. School and dental clinics have been established especially for this purpose. Of course it is not merely a question of seeing to it that there is such a thing as medical care in the school. Superficial examinations do more harm than good, because they leave the impression that something has been done, though this is actually not the case.

The school is responsible, not only for the medical supervision of the children, but for their education in hygiene. The ideal of a healthy, vigorous, work-loving human being must be instilled in them. This is frequently achieved in America, and it is particularly important, since many of the pupils are descended from immigrants of diverse countries, including those most backward in hygiene. This part of education can do much to further the process of assimilation.

And finally the school ought to teach, not only theoretical, but practical hygiene. The school and all its surroundings ought to serve as a demonstration of healthy conditions. The curriculum, the whole balance of mental and physical training, ought to contribute to the well-being of the growing child and arouse in him an interest in health. It goes without saying that weak and mentally retarded children belong in special classes.

It is equally important that the school health service should not be confined to the first few years, but that the child be supervised through puberty and into adolescence. As a rule there is not enough done in this direction. To be sure, sport plays quite a rôle in the high schools, but it must be kept in mind that the main object is not the production of record-breaking athletes, but uniform physical training for the whole body of students.

Recently the universities have also introduced an intensive health service. I especially remember a beautiful hospital with numerous examination-rooms, reserved for this department at the University of California. All students are given a complete examination on entering college. The findings are put on record. Later findings are added to their cards. Space is provided for every specialty, including dentistry and psychiatry.

Medical care in schools has an important place in national health. This has been clearly seen in America. The states are not all equally advanced, but the development as a whole is making gigantic strides.

It has been realized that the care of the child should begin with the pregnant mother. Gradually, though slowly, the conviction that intervention must come even earlier is gaining ground. A single state, Wisconsin, demands a health certificate before marriage. The other states have so far shown a remarkably resistant attitude. Yet this is a hygienic factor of extraordinary importance, and at the same time a requirement which can easily be enforced.

It has been realized further that there are individuals, especially the feeble-minded, whose inheritance is so poor that they are unable to produce normal offspring. Since 1907, 23 states have enacted laws which allow sterilization on hygienic grounds. In four states these laws had to be annulled, and even in the others they are applied infrequently, because of a reluctance to intervene so drastically in personal matters. Up to 1925, 6244 sterilizations had been performed, the majority in California.

It may be that our knowledge of the laws of heredity does not as yet justify our advancing in this direction on a larger scale. But one thing is already possible: we no longer need to subject the begetting of children to the rules of chance, but can regulate it by voluntary birth-control. The birth of a child is an important matter. Women whose health has been impaired by pregnancy and labor should not conceive again. Families should not have children whom they cannot feed. Young people should not be forced to abstain from marriage for economic reasons. But sexual intercourse is a normal physiological process, on which the harmony of a marriage relation in a great measure depends. It is plain that here, too, prevention is better than cure, and birth-control better than induced abortion.

These facts seem self-evident. But they have not been recognized as such in America. Traditional puritanism, whose chief representative has now come to be the Catholic Church, forbade facing these things openly and honestly, or calling them by name. There have been and still are laws which prohibit the recommending of contraceptives.

It needed a noble, courageous, and spirited woman, Margaret Sanger, to effect a reaction in public opinion against antiquated laws and clerical obscurantism, and to open the door for birth-control—the word is her invention—even in America. With a heart sensitive to all social unhappiness, she went on her way unabashed, in spite of persecution, and the result is that today there are birth-control clinics in all the larger cities, where women can turn for counsel and medical advice, and can secure protection against a harmful pregnancy. Margaret Sanger has more lives and certainly more human happiness to her credit than many health agencies put together.

Mental hygiene, a branch of preventive medicine which originated in America, has still to be mentioned. The number of mentally sick people has grown considerably. In 1880 there were 81 mentally sick to 100,000 inhabitants; in 1923 the number had increased to 245. In 1930 almost half of the 900,000 hospital beds were needed for nervous and mentally sick patients. The yearly admissions amounted to 124,800; the average occupation, 409,000; the annual running expenses, $165,500,000. No wonder that the most serious efforts are being made to attack these disorders at their inception.

The attention of the public was turned to these problems by Clifford W. Beers's book, *A Mind that Found Itself* (New York, 1908), the autobiography of a patient. The National Committee for Mental Hygiene was founded in 1909. The same process always repeats itself. One man steps forward as the pioneer. A private organization is formed and works out a program of action; and eventually the state assumes responsibility for the problem.

So it happened again. The committee began its work under the leadership of Dr. Thomas Salmon. First of all the condition of the mentally sick people in the different states was investigated, and many obvious faults could immediately be corrected. The real work of prevention was begun after the war. The problem of crime was the first to be attacked. It was a well-known fact that crimes were often committed by psychopathic personalities. The way to prevent crime was therefore to get hold of these people in time and influence them in the right direction.

The first child guidance clinic to be organized and run on a scientific basis was founded by Dr. William Healy in 1909—the Chicago Juvenile Psychopathic Institute. It worked in collaboration with the Chicago Juvenile Court, and was the earliest organization of the kind to realize the significance of the social factor, and to put psychological and medical agencies to work in attacking the problem. It was somewhat antedated by the Psychological Clinic at the University of Pennsylvania, founded in 1896 by Dr. Lightner Witmer, which, however, was more interested in educational problems than in the question of juvenile delinquency. Others followed in St. Louis, Los Angeles, Minneapolis, St. Paul, Dallas, Cleveland, and Philadelphia. Gradually the interest shifted. Crime prevention was no longer considered the most important problem, but rather counsel, guidance, and assistance in social adaptation for youth in general. In 1927 in New York the Institute for Child Guidance was established as a center for training, research, and child guidance. Mental hygiene grew more and more to be recognized as an essential department of all prophylactic organizations, and was incorporated in the health curriculum of the schools. It is primarily due to the work of the National Committee that psychiatrists have been admitted to the court-room, the prison, and wherever loss of mental balance presents a social problem.

The first International Congress for Mental Hygiene, which took place in Washington in 1930, signified the international official recognition of a new branch of preventive medicine.

Hygiene has had, and still has, two great difficulties to contend with in America. One is the size of the continent, those tremendous thinly settled stretches of land, where the control of disease presents no special difficulties in itself, but would require so much machinery that the cost would be out of all proportion to the number of inhabitants.

The other difficulty results from the composition of the population, which till quite recently was subject to constant changes. Through the new immigration laws it has become more stable; but 10 percent of the population still consists of negroes, who have less power of resistance and are less accessible to health education. This is shown in the figures for vital statistics (to every 1,000 inhabitants in 1927):

	Total	White	Colored
Birth rate	20.6	20.2	25.0
Death rate	11.4	10.8	17.5
Excess of births	9.2	9.4	7.5

Of 100 infants born alive there died in the first year as follows:

Year	Total	White	Colored
1920	8.6	8.2	13.2
1928	6.9	6.4	10.6

In spite of these difficulties the public health movement has achieved great results within a short time. Life is easier than it used to be. Many dangers, which still threatened us a short time ago, are now kept at bay. An army of health workers is always on the watch: no mere bureaucrats, obeying orders mechanically, but well-trained specialists with plenty of initiative, constantly striving for better conditions, and able to count on the collaboration of great organizations.

And yet—and yet this is only the beginning of a beginning. Of the $3,600,000,000 which the American people expend annually for medical care only 3.3 percent, or $121,000,000, is devoted to public health ends, only 90 cents per capita.

It is true that there has been a drop in communicable diseases, but other diseases have increased.

Below are figures of deaths to every 100,000 inhabitants:

	1900	1929
Heart disease	132.1	210.8
Kidney disease	89.0	91.2
Cancer	63.0	95.9
Diabetes	9.7	18.8

Though the higher figures may result in part from more exact diagnosis and to a still greater extent from the average longer life, this does not alter the fact that they are assuming very great importance.

Work has begun on these diseases as well. Since 1913 there has been a national organization for cancer control; and since 1922 a society for the prevention of heart disease. There will be other such organizations. But it is a difficult problem, as it is a question of getting hold of the individual.

That is the task of the future. The first phase consisted in removing the causes of diseases which threatened the whole community or whole groups of the community. Tuberculosis control went one step further, since the patient was taken care of as soon as possible and his environment supervised. The last and most important step was taken in the Child Hygiene Movement, where the effort was made to forestall disease by the medical examination of healthy children, and, where dangers were recognized in time to prevent their development.

The way of future progress demands that these principles be applied to adults. The goal must be the prevention of disease by the hygienic ordering of daily life. But, if disease does break out, it must be dealt with as soon as the first symptoms appear, even when they cannot yet be felt subjectively, at a time when treatment can still assure success.

Here, too, we find promising beginnings. In 1923 the American Medical Association and the National Health Council carried on a campaign of propaganda for periodic examinations. Many people now visit a doctor as they visit their dentist, as a preventive measure. The life insurance companies, who are interested in long lives for their insured, have realized that such periodic examinations have an advantage from their own point of view, and many provide them free of charge. A special enterprise was started for this purpose: the Life Extension Institute, with numerous branches, and a personnel that runs into the thousands.

A number of private group clinics maintain a special health

extension service. One such clinic, which I visited in Chicago and which has 500 subscribers, offers for $15 a year a general medical and dental examination, blood tests and four quarterly urine analyses. For $25 there are added to these services an eye-examination, X-ray examination of the teeth, and a Wassermann test. For $50 is added the X-ray examination of the organs of the thorax, an electrocardiogram and a chemical analysis of the blood. There is no doubt that this is an extremely valuable movement. The objection often expressed in Europe that such examinations result in arousing unnecessary fears is without foundation. So soon as sickness and medicine are divested of the veil of mystery which has clung to them since the time of the shaman, so soon as sickness can be recognized as a natural process, and medicine as the appropriate treatment, no ground for fear will remain and people will realize that there is no sense in sticking one's head into the sand.

These periodic examinations are for the present restricted to a small minority of the well-to-do population. If they are to be effective, they must be extended to the population as a whole, and must become in some form obligatory. The way lies through insurance and the further development of health centers. The entire medical profession must be put at the service of preventive medicine.

Whatever branch of medicine we observe, the same problem always presents itself. We must understand quite clearly that the goal cannot be reached by propaganda alone. Popular education in hygiene is no doubt important. In America it is perhaps overdone. For what is heard too often, is not always taken seriously. At any rate, it is not enough to convince people of a theory. They must be given the means to put it into practice, and they must somehow be held to it.

The hygiene of the future will have at once an easy and a difficult task in America. Easy because the population has already a great interest in health. Everyday hygiene has permeated a far larger circle of the population than is the case in many European countries. American bath-rooms are proverbial, and nowhere else are so many articles wrapped in cellophane. This is certainly the result of propaganda, but the propaganda has worked because the American state is a government of reason, a product of the Enlightenment. Normality is its ideal. Sickness is abnormal, foolish, and senseless. We have seen how Christian Science, a typically American product, went so far as to consider disease an error in the thinking process.

Difficulties will arise from the lack of state-consciousness. It is true that patriotism is intense. All are ready to die for the flag, even if their parents were born across the water. However, to die in times of excitement is sometimes easier than everyday living. The prevailing liberalistic individualism hampers the fitting of each single citizen into the frame of the state.

Hygiene, however, means community health; it means that each person gives up individual rights and accepts responsibility for the general welfare. And here opens a whole new field of activity.

CHAPTER NINE

MEDICAL SCIENCE

In every country which has been opened to western civilization, we can distinguish three successive stages in its relation to medicine. During the first stage, the population is indeed ready to accept treatment from academically-trained physicians, but the means and the teachers to train these physicians do not as yet exist. They must either be imported, or the native sons must be sent abroad to study.

In the second stage, the point has been reached where this training can be undertaken at home. The number of physicians has increased. Many of them keep in constant touch with scientific progress abroad, make this knowledge their own, and pass it on to their pupils. But it is as yet beyond their compass to undertake independent scientific work, to attack problems of medical research on a large scale. To be sure, we find at this stage individual men who are in advance of their time, but these are isolated examples and are moreover handicapped by lack of necessary equipment.

In the final stage, research work has been introduced and is being pursued with greater and greater intensity. In the beginning, the assistance of foreign scientists, or native scientists educated abroad, will still have to be called upon, till there has been time to train a new generation to take their places.

Only when a permanent institute of research has been established, can medicine be really said to have taken root. Science is the living source from which the practice of medicine derives its daily sustenance. If the source is too distant, practice becomes parched and devitalized. Every physician and every medical institution ought to keep in constant touch with scientific research. To stand still is to regress.

America, too, has advanced along this line of development. In colonial times and even in the nineteenth century, medical students went abroad for their academic education. Then followed the founding of countless schools for the training of practitioners. Finally, with the opening of Johns Hopkins Medical School in 1893, there was established a scientific center of the first rank and with it the beginning of organized research.

From this moment America ceases to be merely a passive recipient of knowledge. It takes its place in medical science. It begins to collaborate in the solution of medical problems. Slowly at first, but always faster and faster, the process of evolution unfolds. Young men are embracing research with overwhelming enthusiasm. And today America is beginning to pay its debt to Europe.

Of course all through the nineteenth century there were certain physicians who showed an interest in science. We have seen the pioneers at work, and are aware that at an early date America was making valuable contributions to medicine. But obviously there existed at that time no centers of learning which could in any way compare with what Europe had to offer. An American of that day missed beyond everything else intellectual resonance, a mutual reverberation of ideas. The nation was deaf to his interests. Whoever gave up money-making to live for science was considered a crank. In 1876, at the end of a review of a hundred years of American medicine, John Billings wrote:

"The defects in American medicine are much the same as those observed in other branches of science in this country, and to a great extent are due to the same causes.

"Culture, to flourish, requires appreciation and sympathy, to such an extent, at least, that its utterances shall not seem to its audience as if in an unknown tongue.

"We have no reason to boast, or to be ashamed of what we

have thus far accomplished; it has been but a little while since we have been furnished with the means of investigation needed to give our observers that accuracy and precision which alone can entitle medicine to a place among the sciences properly so called; and we may begin the new century in the hope and belief that to us applies the bright side of the maxim of Cousin, 'It is better to have a future than a past.' "

The nineteenth century was a century of practitioners. It is significant that John Billings, in *A Century of American Medicine,* written in 1876 with the assistance of several collaborators, and from which I have taken the above quotation, has given separate chapters to *Medicine, Surgery, Obstetrics and Gynecology,* and *Anaesthesia,* but was able to describe the total achievements of scientific study in a single chapter entitled *Literature and Institutions.*

The contributions of this period belong for the most part to the domain of practical medicine and especially of surgery. McDowell and ovariotomy, Sims and his operation for vesicovaginal fistula, are examples which are in no way unique. America could boast of a great number of able and enterprising surgeons. One, Valentine Mott (1785–1865) in New York, a pupil of Sir Astley Cooper, was famous for his urinary calculus operations and, above all, for his ligatures of the blood vessels. He was the first man who ventured (1818), in a case of aneurysm, to tie up the arteria innominata two inches away from the heart. Another, Horatio Gates Jameson (1778–1885) of Baltimore, was one of the first surgeons who, later ligating the carotid artery, performed a total excision of the upper jaw (1820). In 1830 he attended a meeting of the Society of German Naturalists and Physicians in Hamburg and presented a lecture on the non-contagious nature of yellow fever.

The honor of having perfected the technique of thoracentesis belongs to a Boston physician, Morrill Wyman (1812–1903), who in 1850 at the Massachusetts General Hospital carried out for the first time the operation which had been previously suggested by Trousseau. Henry Ingersoll Bowditch, who was among those present, was so enthusiastic over the success of the operation that he recommended it far and wide.

Anaesthesia made possible more and more serious operations. In 1861, Erastus B. Wolcott (1804–80) in Milwaukee ventured to remove a kidney. John S. Bobbs (1809–70) from Indianapolis, as early as 1867, was successful in undertaking the cholecystotomy, or opening of the gall bladder, for the removal of gall stones.

The technical skill of Americans made them specially fitted to be surgeons, and the people, with their unusual understanding of technical achievements, followed the progress of surgery with the greatest interest. The American patient wants to get back on his feet as quickly as possible. Given the choice between an operation and prolonged internal treatment, he will not hesitate to choose the former. There is no country where so few people carry gall stones about with them. It is not surprising that great advances have been made in surgery.

Without doubt this period's most important contribution to internal medicine is the differentiation and clinical demarcation between typhoid and typhus worked out by William W. Gerhard (1809–72) in Philadelphia. Gerhard had studied with Louis in Paris and was probably the most talented of his American pupils. Abdominal typhoid and typhus were considered identical. Louis's famous book, in which he coined the name *fièvre typhoïde*, appeared in 1829. What he described was typhoid; but he believed this disease identical with the spotted fever at that time being studied in London, where both forms of fever were prevalent. Louis's book drew general attention to this group of diseases, and stimulated research in many places. Gerhard returned to Philadelphia and began by working at the Pennsylvania Hospital. Typhoid was endemic and many cases came under his observation. He was able to demonstrate that this disease was the same which he had seen with Louis in Paris. Thereupon spotted fever broke out in Philadelphia in 1836, and Gerhard, who at this time was practising at the Philadelphia Hospital, recognized this sickness as indeed identical with the typhus met with in Edinburgh, but different from what was called typhus in Paris, so that it was a question of two quite different diseases. He published his observations in 1837, in the *American Journal of the Medical Sciences*.

This discovery was in the air. Similar observations were being made elsewhere at the same time. There is, however, no doubt that it was Gerhard who finally solved the problem.

So research on practical lines was carried on even at this early date. A lasting monument to the period, the first comprehensive American medical book, was the study of the medical findings of the Civil War, the *Medical and Surgical History of the War of the Rebellion*, which was issued between 1870 and 1883 and attracted widespread attention both here and abroad.

The pursuit of theoretic studies, on the other hand, met with many more difficulties. It is true that the hospitals afforded ample material for clinical study, but experimental investigations are impossible without laboratories, and these were for a long time non-existent. There was money enough to build them, but the need for them was not yet generally felt and there were as yet no centers of research to foster such studies. In Europe, too, for that matter, laboratories are a comparatively recent product. Men like Johannes Müller, Magendie, Claude Bernard, and Pasteur, had to create their own technical apparatus and to work for a long time under very primitive conditions. But they at least had the support and interest of universities where the step from mere teaching to active research had already been accomplished, and which were prepared to assimilate new findings and to serve as the indispensable means of transmission.

In America, medical schools were as yet purely teaching institutions. Men like Beaumont and even Weir Mitchell were independent of universities. They were obliged to rely on their own resources to carry on their work, and this under very difficult conditions.

In nineteenth-century America as in seventeenth-century Europe, biological research centered not so much in the universities as in the newly-founded scientific academies. As in other fields of medicine, we find that America has rushed in a short time through all the successive stages of European development. Societies such as the Philosophical Society, founded in Philadelphia in the eighteenth century, and the various colleges of physicians and surgeons, formed on English models, the academies of medicine—storehouses of medical knowledge in various cities, the most important being the New York Academy founded in 1847, specialist societies like the Pathological Society in Philadelphia—all these became living centers of learning, forums for scientific discussion which often stimulated valuable investigations.

Circumstances specially favored the study of anatomy. It happens that physiology can be taught theoretically out of books; at least it could in the beginning, but anatomy can be learned only from the object itself, that is, from the cadaver. This was recognized even in the Middle Ages. The first scientific departments in America were institutes of anatomy. And cadavers provide material not only for teaching, but for research.

We have observed how Shippen, about the middle of the eighteenth century, strove to establish anatomical instruction in Philadelphia. He was the first professor of anatomy. His tradition persisted, carried on by his pupil, Caspar Wistar (1761–1818), who wrote an anatomical text-book and corresponded with Soemmering. His collection formed the nucleus of the Wistar Institute of Anatomy and Biology at the University of Pennsylvania. It is from him that the gorgeous wistaria vine likewise derives its name. His chair of anatomy remained for many years the most important in the country. His immediate successors,

John S. Dorsey and Philip Syng Physick, were surgeons rather than scientists. But after them came William E. Horner (1793–1853), Wistar's pupil and an inspired anatomist. The *tensor tarsi Hornerian* muscle is called after him. He wrote the first American text-book of pathology in 1829. He analyzed cholera stools and discovered that they contained intestinal epithelia.

Then in 1853 came Joseph Leidy (1823–91) who had studied with Horner, a biologist in the grand style and of astounding versatility. Anatomist, zoölogist, pathologist, botanist, palaeontologist, and above all, parasitologist: he has made important investigations in all these fields. He was a gifted draughtsman and illustrated his own books. He discovered bacteria in the intestines, grafted tumors, and surmised that a worm called ancylostomum, which he found in cats, might be a frequent cause of anaemia. His most important contribution to medicine was the discovery of another parasite, the *trichinella spiralis,* which he found in hogs. His book on amoebas is a biological classic.

Leidy, together with Louis Agassiz, who at this time was working at Harvard, represents the type of the universal biologist, a type which in Europe died out with Alexander Humboldt and Johannes Müller, to make room for the specialists.

During the last quarter of the century, the situation changed from the ground up. The German laboratory began to exert a strong influence. American medical men, who had earlier in the century flocked to Paris to visit its clinics, now turned to Germany to study its laboratories. Carl Ludwig's *Physiologisches Institut* in Leipzig became a gathering place for these young physicians, who streamed enthusiastically to Europe in search of new scientific methods which they could bring back with them to America. One of Ludwig's pupils, Henry Pickering Bowditch (1840–1911) in 1871 founded at Harvard University the first department of experimental physiology. It was followed by the one which Newell Martin, a pupil of Sir Michael Foster, founded in 1876 at Johns Hopkins University. And we saw how another of Ludwig's pupils, William H. Welch, came to Baltimore by way of New York, and how, even before the opening of the new medical school, his pathological laboratory became a center of research work.

With Johns Hopkins was established the first medical school to be founded according to the European pattern on a scientific basis. Its influence was extraordinarily far-reaching. Medical science came in contact with the university. The physician who gave up his practice in order to devote himself to science was no longer considered a crank. He found laboratories willing to make room for him, he found teachers, colleagues, and pupils. Communities for active research sprang into being.

The way for future development was shown. The medical schools were changed from institutes of learning to institutes of research. Step by step, they began to catch up with European scientific progress.

It was a slow process, however, since there were few trained men. Johns Hopkins had first to educate a new generation. This was done, but in the meanwhile many of the earlier scholars were lost to research, snowed under by problems of organization. The country's whole scientific apparatus needed to be remodelled. One school after another was reorganized. Men were wanted for this task, and Hopkins furnished a large quota. The present deans of some of the finest medical schools come from Hopkins, pupils of Welch and Osler and Martin.

The universities moved slowly; the founding in 1901 of the Rockefeller Institute for Medical Research was all the more important. The Institute is one of the foundations of John D. Rockefeller. It has nothing to do with the great organization entitled the Rockefeller Foundation, whose work extends over the whole world, nor with the General Education Board, another Rockefeller foundation which has contributed a prodigious amount to university development. The Institute for Medical Research is an independent foundation.

Even before 1900, Rockefeller had shown his interest in education by giving considerable sums to the University of Chicago. At the turn of the century, his advisor, Frederick T. Gates, became convinced that ". . . medicine could hardly hope to become a science until it should be endowed, and qualified men be enabled to give themselves to uninterrupted study and investigation, on ample salary, entirely independent of practice."

In 1901 Rockefeller gave an endowment of $200,000 for this purpose. A board of directors was put in charge, with William H. Welch as president. The original intention was to expend the income on scholarships, making it possible for the younger scientists to follow up their university studies.

But it was soon plain that the universities were not as yet adequately equipped, and that an independent research institute was desirable. A building was rented in New York and opened in the fall of 1904. The directorship and the department of pathology were put in the hands of a pupil of Welch's, Simon Flexner, who had been Professor of Pathology at the University of Pennsylvania, and is today still head of the Rockefeller Institute. The staff of collaborators came from all over the world. Associated with Flexner in pathology were two Americans, J. E. Sweet and Eugene L. Opie, the latter also a pupil of Welch's, and the Japanese, Hideyo Noguchi. Physiology and pharmacology were in charge of Samuel J. Meltzer, a native of Courland who had studied with Hugo Kroneker in Berne and had worked under Welch in New York. A Russian, Phoebus A. Levene, had been persuaded to take the position of physiological chemist.

The work was launched; and was so successful and so promising that an enlargement of the Institute had very soon to be considered. Rockefeller granted additional funds. The Institute erected a building of its own on the East River, which was opened in 1906 and added to repeatedly in the course of time. (Fig. 28). It was followed in 1910 by a hospital, in charge of which Rufus Cole was placed. It can take care of only a limited number of patients; and only cases of such diseases are admitted as are at the moment the subject of experimentation. All treatment is free.

A new department was founded in 1914, this time for research in animal pathology, with Theobald Smith, the investigator of Texas cattle fever, as director. As such an institute required large ground space for stables, it was located in the country, not far from Princeton. In 1931 this department was expanded to include plant pathology (Fig. 29).

So there came into being an institute fully equipped for the experimental study of disease in all its manifestations, in man, animal, and plant. A group of scholars representing every field of interest, medicine, biology, chemistry, and physics, was gathered together. In 1932 the staff comprised 134 scientific collaborators, associated with the Institute as members, associates, assistants, and fellows. In addition there is, of course, a large force of technical assistants.

The Institute very soon won for itself world recognition; it became an international center for medical research. When it is sometimes stated that, up to now, no sensational discoveries have originated in this Institute, it must be taken into account that this is a twentieth century foundation. The peak of sensational medical discoveries is past. Today it is a matter of going more deeply into problems, of shedding light on the finer biological mechanisms by laborious and increasingly complicated detail work.

Here the Institute has done excellent work in the most widely separated fields. It is sufficient to mention the researches of Flexner and his associates on meningitis, infantile paralysis, influenza, and encephalitis; Noguchi's work with syphilis, yellow fever, and trachoma; Alexis Carrel's revolutionizing of histology; Jacques Loeb's studies in general physiology; Karl Landsteiner's studies in blood groupings; Cole's differentiation between va-

28. ROCKEFELLER INSTITUTE FOR MEDICAL RESEARCH

The first three buildings on the left contain laboratories, next comes the Isolation Building, and finally on the right the Hospital

29. ROCKEFELLER INSTITUTE FOR MEDICAL RESEARCH
Department of Animal and Plant Pathology, Princeton, New Jersey

rious types of pneumococcus—to select only a few points. The studies and monographs of the Institute fill over 100 volumes. There is hardly a section of medicine upon which they have not touched in some way. They have made enormous additions to the sum of our scientific knowledge and, at the same time, they have already achieved important results for the practice of medicine.

In the history of American medicine, the founding of the Rockefeller Institute is not less significant a milestone than the founding of Johns Hopkins. Behind them both was the constructive energy of Welch. And, just as Abraham Flexner was the driving spirit in university reorganization (knowing, on occasion, how to strike at abuses with biting irony), so his brother, Simon Flexner, paved the way for the development of scientific medicine.

America had matured. Medical science was fostered in an increasing number of institutions, in the universities and in the new institutes of research. In 1902 the McCormick Institute for Infectious Diseases was opened in Chicago. The Carnegie Institution of Washington, founded in the same year with an endowment fund of $10,000,000, initiated a succession of biological institutes, among others one for experimental embryology in Baltimore, housed in a Johns Hopkins University building. The philanthropist, Henry Phipps, provided the endowment for an institute of research in tuberculosis, opened in Philadelphia in 1903 and in 1910 connected with the University of Pennsylvania. In 1913 Henry Phipps endowed a psychiatric clinic at Hopkins which, under the leadership of Adolf Meyer, became a research institute of the first rank.

Other endowment funds were established, which, without creating institutions on their own account, contributed considerable annual sums for medical purposes; among them the Milbank Memorial Fund, the Julius Rosenwald Fund, and the

Commonwealth Fund. In addition, many million dollars given by private individuals flowed into university endowments for the promotion of research.

A more recent endowment, the Josiah Macy Jr., Foundation in New York, deserves special mention for the character of its activities. Though its ultimate goal is also the health and welfare of mankind, it uses new methods of approach. It does not confine itself to giving large sums to hospitals and laboratories, but aims to include in its program the intellectual structure of medicine. It regards medicine not only as a technique, but still more as a social phenomenon, and is therefore ready to support historical, sociological, psychological, and even philosophical studies, insofar as they may contribute to the elucidation of medical problems.

And that is a new and very significant development. In the beginning, America was engrossed in the task of catching up with the lead taken by Europe. It had still to create its scientific equipment; it could do no more than follow in Europe's footsteps. But in the course of forty years it has covered the distance between them; it now has its own laboratories and trained men. American medicine is full-grown and able to stand on its own feet, and is looking with the impetuosity, enthusiasm, and sometimes the irresponsibility of youth, for new, untried paths.

Very interesting experiments can result. One, the Institute of Human Relations at Yale University, owes its origin to a magnificent idea.

The history of its inception is in brief as follows: Before the war psychiatry had not yet been given its legitimate place in the universities. Johns Hopkins had had its psychiatric clinic since 1913; but it stood almost alone. After the war, the Yale School of Medicine took up the problem of introducing a psychiatric department. In the meanwhile the Mental Hygiene movement had been launched, and the University as such wanted a psychiatric adviser for its 5000 students. At the same time the Connecticut Society for Mental Hygiene was on the lookout for a psychiatrist. The expedient of satisfying this threefold need by a common agency immediately suggested itself; and there was no doubt in anyone's mind that a psychiatric clinic in the usual sense, that is, a hospital for the care and treatment of cases of fully developed psychoses and neuroses, would not meet the demands of the situation. The matter ought to be approached from a more fundamental standpoint; emphasis should be laid on prevention, and with this end in view, research should center on the psychobiological aspects of men's behavior. The university already maintained a physiological and a psychological department, as well as a special department for child development research. But these institutions were not connected administratively and were at an inconvenient distance from each other. It was originally planned to bring together the already existing departments; to enlarge them with a psychiatric department as center; and to coördinate their work.

Similar tendencies became evident at this time in a parallel field. Jurists recognized the necessity of widening their range of study. The Law School added a social scientist, a psychologist, and an economist to its faculty. And now new horizons were opened. It was realized that all these branches of learning were based on the same fundamental principles and had to do with the same problem—the psycho-biological reactions of man, as an individual in relation to his physical environment and as a social unit in relation to the environment of society.

This was the origin of the idea of the Institute of Human Relations. It is intended to serve as an integrating center for the scientific study of man in relation to his environment, with biology and sociology as the fundamental sciences from which radiate on the one hand the applied fields of biology: medicine, hygiene, and nursing; and on the other the applied fields of sociology: law, economics, industry, and religion.

The Institute was opened in May, 1931, under the leadership

of the Dean of the Medical School, Milton C. Winternitz, a man of unusual energy and ability. The building contains the departments of Psychiatry and Mental Hygiene, Psychology, and Child Development Research, as well as rooms for sociological research. The physiological units are housed in an adjacent building, and across the street are found the clinics and dispensaries of the Medical School. The complete layout forms a group designated as the Human Welfare Group.

The Institute is new; and it would be foolish to look so soon for tangible results. Still, there can be no doubt that in its striving for synthesis it has provided expression for a great idea. The road it has taken may lead both medicine and the other sciences into fruitful fields.

It is moreover obvious that such an institution affords unusual opportunities for medical education. Today pre-clinical instruction at Yale is no longer confined to biological subjects, but embraces psychology and sociology, which are taught, not only theoretically, but by concrete examples. The student who feels himself sufficiently advanced to take up clinical work, reports for an examination held by the clinical faculty. It is their responsibility to decide whether the candidate has mastered the required pre-clinical studies. In the clinic itself he is taught not only diagnostic and therapy, but his attention is drawn to the psychology and the social environment of the patient. The work is done in close coöperation with the psychiatrists; and every case is considered from the point of view of its preventibility. In other words, the attempt is made to conserve for the new medicine the erstwhile advantages of the family doctor.

It would be an alluring task to assemble America's contributions to medical science during the last forty years, and to make a cross section of the research work which is now going on in so many places at once. All the more alluring, since it was my privilege to be given an intimate view of the work of many laboratories and clinics. They made on me a profound impression. It is a memorable experience to have watched Harvey Cushing in Boston perform a surgical operation. But such an attempt would reach far beyond the frame-work of this history. All the problems of medicine would have to be unfolded for discussion. It would be contrary to the character of this book, whose main purpose it is to indicate broad lines of development, to reveal general currents and tendencies, and from which nothing lies further than a striving for comprehensiveness possible only in a medical dictionary.

So in the following paragraphs I am adding only a few general observations.

By the time that the teaching of anatomy had spread beyond the confines of Philadelphia, the rudimentary problems of macroscopic anatomy and histology had for the most part been solved. For this reason, students threw all their energies into those fields which promised new discoveries; such as experimental embryology, and the study of reproduction, etiology and genetics. The extent of success can be seen in the work of T. H. Morgan, to single out only one name. Whereas the old anatomy had been an anatomy of dead bodies, the effort was now made to include the living organs, tissues, and cells. Anatomy and physiology, originally one, had become separated in the course of the nineteenth century. Today they are again united, in that the anatomist investigates, not only forms, but first of all the forces which shape them. He has his own share of experimental work; and a modern anatomical institute looks very like an institute of physiology.

Two great fields of research are open to the student of physiology. On the one hand is physiological chemistry, which in America has made tremendous strides. All over the country we find efficient and well-equipped institutes of physiological chemistry. The advances in chemistry have stimulated other lines of research; primarily pharmacology, but in addition pathology, internal medicine, and pediatrics, in which a German forty-eighter, Abraham Jacobi (1830–1919) did pioneer work. On the other hand there is neurophysiology, which today is receiving special attention. Experiments are often tried out on monkeys, and many institutes have monkey wards. Yale maintains its own monkey farm in Florida.

Neurophysiological investigations have had a pronounced effect on clinical medicine, clinical neurology, brain and nerve surgery, and of course on psychiatry, which is now in process of full development. Very recently, after overcoming the usual opposition, the psychoanalytic movement has also been able to establish itself; and Freud, Adler, and above all Jung, have their groups of disciples.

At many medical schools physiology is taught by biologists instead of by medical men. This may have its dangers, since there is always a tendency for the various branches of medicine to develop away from each other. But things are evened up, because the modern clinician does his work primarily from the physiological standpoint, so that the contact between the physiological institute and the clinic is preserved.

Pathology and bacteriology are seldom separated; logically enough, since bacteriology is after all a department of etiology. Pathologists as a rule have at their disposal less dissection-material than is provided at European institutes. This lack is partly made up for by a more intensive examination of available material and by the preservation of all organs.

The attention given to tropical pathology and its fruitful results have been mentioned several times. There were several reasons why America found this an attractive field. In the first place, the proximity of the tropics lent practical importance to this work. In the second place, at the time that America was ready for scientific research, the pathogenesis of diseases like anthrax, diphtheria, and tuberculosis had already been clarified to a large extent by European investigators. Tropical pathology, on the other hand, was still virgin soil, all the more promising since the island possessions afforded a wide range of research.

Among the specialties obstetrics, gynecology, ophthalmology, the treatment of ear, nose and throat, and urology can look back on a longer past. They have their assured place in the scientific system and each contributes its part to present progress. Various improvements in radiology and X-ray technique originated in America. We need only to be reminded of the names of Coolidge and Bucky. Pioneers have introduced the use of X-ray for the diagnostic examination of the intestinal canal, the ventricals of the brain, and the gall bladder. But on the whole it seems to me that research in medical X-ray is pursued more actively in Europe. American dermatology is still behind the times; and legal medicine is in its very beginning.

Research is more specialized here than in Europe. For instance, many of the younger scientists who are masters in their own narrow field understand nothing whatever of allied activities; nor do they show the slightest interest in them. To offset this, there is a marked tendency to keep the specialist in his place. He is a small cog in a big machine and he never gets to be anything else. At the same time, the machine as a whole, the department or the institute, is probably less specialized and one-sided than a corresponding European institution.

Science is at the present time very popular in America. The people have faith in it. To advertise a product, it is sufficient to state that it is scientific. Science has been embraced with tremendous enthusiasm, and with sincere idealism. Even in America, scientists do not make money. Young people's salaries are often smaller than those in Europe. In most universities it would be considered unethical for a professor to patent an invention, whether for his own benefit or for that of his university. Exploiting one's profession is unheard of; universities must be kept free of mercenary ties.

Research is a word to conjure with, rolled on the tongue of

the youngest student. Sometimes he may think he is carrying on research when he is merely counting the buttons on his own coat and comparing them with his neighbor's; in the first enthusiasm he does not always differentiate between the essential and the non-essential. There are scientific tasks, countless as the sands of the sea, which are in themselves scientific and yet have no scientific significance. A great deal of energy is wasted in this way.

American science has the enormous advantage of having at its disposal vast sums of money. Research workers are given the best apparatus and the animals best suited for experimentation. They can undertake expensive journeys; and their work is made much less arduous through the help of an adequate corps of assistants. The American office secretary is unexcelled and has made a substantial contribution to the advance of science. Undertakings requiring a large outlay are today hardly possible except in America. The present crisis has of course reduced available funds, but a sound program can be financed even at this time.

Of course certain disadvantages often attach to large gifts of money, especially when they have come from endowed foundations. The donors naturally want to be shown results. They want to know whether their money was given in the right place. But scientific research needs time to mature, and investigations that last for years may lead to a negative conclusion. The donor has not always the patience to wait. So it may happen that the machine threshes dry straw, merely because the money is there to keep it going.

One characteristic of American research is the cheerful optimism and a certain gay spirit of enterprise which animates the majority of scientists. They attack problems even when these offer slight prospect of solution, and when sensible people shake their heads. They try a shot and very frequently hit the mark.

Research finds many followers; and great pains are taken to train the next generation for scientific work. From the day

30. WILLIAM H. WELCH
1850–1934

of his enrollment the young student is closely observed, and the development of each individual is followed with great attention. A young man with the divine fire in his breast can be assured that all doors will be open to him.

In 1884, William H. Welch (Fig. 30) came to Baltimore. Johns Hopkins Hospital was established. The School of Medicine was opened. Generations of young people passed through Welch's laboratory, were initiated by him into the mysteries of science, and carried the seeds of learning throughout the country. The new century opened. The Rockefeller Institute and the Carnegie Institution were founded. On every board, on every committee, Welch had his place, a small rotund man, always ready to help, always obliging, honored and loved by everyone. Then came the World War, and hygiene came to be a burning question. Turning to a great new set of problems, Welch created the School of Hygiene and Public Health and became the driving force in the building up of public health work. Years passed. One day he looked up from his work and saw, no matter where his eyes fell, new hospitals, new laboratories, doctors, nurses; everywhere teeming life. The seed had borne splendid fruit. One thing only was missing. And he, who had lived and shaped a good bit of history, created the Institute for the History of Medicine at Johns Hopkins University.

Its opening was solemnized on October 18, 1929. This was something more than another new institute. A symbolic act had been accomplished. Here there was now a place from which to look, not only as formerly into the future, but also back into the past; a place designed for reflection, in which to study the direction of evolution, to bring unconscious tendencies to consciousness, to bridge the gap between medicine and life, designed, too, for the fuller training of physicians, bringing them closer to humanity and sharpening their social conscience. Here was another mile-post in American medicine. This day marked the close of one period and the beginning of another.

The Institute opened on October 18, 1929. Six days later the market crashed in New York. After the headlong *fugato*, comes the *fermata*, comes reflection and the return to the spirit.

On April 8, 1930, William H. Welch celebrated his eightieth birthday. The whole country, indeed the whole world, paid honor to him and his work, and through him to American medicine.

☆ EPILOGUE ☆

HISTORY IS MARCHING on unceasingly and at a tremendous speed. This English edition, prepared but one year after the German edition, required quite a few additions, and I have no doubt that by the time it is in print, new trends in American medicine will be noticeable. This book embraces a very short period and yet the way from the medicine-man to world medicine was a long one. Extraordinary achievements have been performed in an exceedingly short time. A few decades were sufficient to provide America with the best technically equipped medicine in the world. Yet great tasks are still ahead, problems difficult to solve, as they lie not in the technical and scientific, but in the social field, where traditions and prejudices must be dealt with. If this historical study can contribute to a clearer understanding of our present-day situation, it has more than fulfilled its task.

I am greatly indebted to many institutions and personalities. The Saxon Ministry of Education granted me a leave of absence from the University of Leipzig, in the winter of 1931–1932, which made possible my trip through the United States and as a result, this book. A grant of the Josiah Macy Jr., Foundation in New York enabled me to purchase literature without which I could not have started writing this book abroad.

I wish to thank my American colleagues, who unselfishly gave me so much of their time to show me around their departments and hospitals, to answer my questions and to provide me with literature and photographs.

And finally I thank my co-workers, Fielding H. Garrison and John Rathbone Oliver, who were good enough to read the original manuscript, for numerous valuable suggestions. This book kept me busy for more than four years. While I was writing it a new task arose. I felt that now I would have to study the development of Russian medicine. America and Russia—both gigantic territories, both young in civilization. In 1620 the Mayflower landed in Plymouth and in 1689 Peter the Great was enthroned. In the beginning of the 20th century the great development of American medicine started, and in 1917 a new era began for Russia. Both countries were unhampered by traditions, and both had very similar problems to face. However, the difference in the economic structure and in the underlying philosophy necessarily led to different solutions.

The United States of America and the Union of Socialist Soviet Republics today are the two countries that are experimenting in the medical field and are seeking new forms of medical service. They, first of all, will determine the future of medicine. In writing this book, whenever I discussed a problem, I endeavored to find out what the Russians were doing in such a case. The literature on the subject was very poor, and consisted mostly of the superficial impressions of travelling physicians.[1] I did not find what I wanted, namely, a study on the philosophic and economic background of Soviet Russia that could explain the medical developments and trends. So I will try to fill in that gap myself. Two years ago I began learning Russian, studying Russian history, literature, philosophy, the Soviet institutions. A research trip through Russia will follow. A book on Russian medicine will integrate this study on American medicine, and both together will make evident what the actual course of medicine is.

HENRY E. SIGERIST

Johns Hopkins University
October, 1934

---

[1] In the meantime Sir Arthur Newsholme and John Adams Kingsbury published their *Red Medicine* (New York, 1933), a valuable first attempt.

The following bibliography makes no pretense whatever of being complete. It contains mainly the books which I have consulted myself, and should enable the reader to pursue the subjects in which he is most interested.

GENERAL LITERATURE ON THE HISTORY OF AMERICAN MEDICINE

The most important publication on the whole subject is:
Francis R. Packard, *History of Medicine in the United States*, New York, 1931, 2 vols.; a large, worth while compilation of material, which however does not go beyond the 19th century.
Also:
James Gregory Mumford, *A Narrative of Medicine in America*, Philadelphia and London, 1903.
E. H. Clarke, H. J. Bigelow, S. D. Gross, T. G. Thomas, J. S. Billings, *A Century of American Medicine*, Philadelphia, 1876.
Fielding H. Garrison, *"A Century of American Medicine,"* in: *A Century of Progress*, New York, 1933, see also the corresponding chapters in: Fielding H. Garrison, *An Introduction to the History of Medicine*, Philadelphia and London, 4th ed., 1929.

BIOGRAPHICAL MATERIAL

James Thacher, *American Medical Biography, or Memoir of Eminent Physicians who have Flourished in America*, Boston, 1828.
Stephen Williams, *American Medical Biography*, Greenfield, Mass., 1845.
Samuel D. Gross, *Lives of Eminent American Physicians and Surgeons of the Nineteenth Century*, Philadelphia, 1861.
William B. Atkinson, *The Physicians and Surgeons of the United States*, Philadelphia, 1878.
Irving A. Watson, *Physicians and Surgeons of America*, Concord, 1896.
Richard French Stone, *Biography of Eminent American Physicians and Surgeons*, Indianapolis, 2nd. ed., 1898.
Howard A. Kelly, *A Cyclopedia of American Medical Biography*, Philadelphia and London, 1912, 2 vols.

Howard A. Kelly and Walter L. Burrage, *Dictionary of American Medical Biography*, New York and London, 1928.

Dictionary of American Biography, New York, 1928 etc. (11 volumes up to 1934)

HISTORY OF MEDICINE IN DIFFERENT STATES

California: Henry Harris, *California's Medical Story*, San Francisco, 1932.

J. Marion Read, *A History of the California Academy of Medicine*, 1870–1930, San Francisco, 1930.

Canada: Maude E. Abbott, *History of Medicine in the Province of Quebec*, Montreal, 1931.

W. B. Howell, *Medicine in Canada* (Clio Medica), New York, 1933.

Colorado: *Medical Coloradoana, a Jubilee Volume in Celebration of the Semi-Centennial Anniversary of the Colorado State Medical Society*, 1871–1921, Denver, 1922.

Connecticut: G. W. Russell, *An Account of Early Medicine and Early Medical Men in Connecticut*. Proceedings of the Connecticut State Medical Society, 1892.

W. R. Steiner, *The Evolution of Medicine in Connecticut, with the Foundation of the Yale Medical School and its Notable Achievements*. Historical Address at the Centennial Celebration of the Yale Medical School, June 15, 1914.

Delaware: *The Delaware State Medical Society and its Founders in the 18th Century*. Paper presented at the Annual Meeting of the American Academy of Medicine, 1885.

Illinois: *Early Medical Chicago: an Historical Sketch of the first practitioners of medicine in the city, with the present Faculties and Graduates since the organization of the Medical Colleges of Chicago*, Chicago, 1879.

History of Medicine and Surgery and Physicians and Surgeons of Chicago, Chicago, 1922.

Iowa: *Medicine in Iowa, from its early settlement until 1876*. Journal of the Iowa Medical Society, I, 1911–1912.

Maryland: Eugene Fauntleroy Cordell, *The Medical Annals of Maryland, 1799–1899*, Baltimore, 1903.

John R. Quinan, *Medical Annals of Baltimore, from 1608 to 1880*, Baltimore, 1884.

Massachusetts: Samuel A. Green, *History of Medicine in Massachusetts*, Boston, 1881.

Henry R. Viets, *A brief History of Medicine in Massachusetts*, Boston and New York, 1930.

Michigan: C. B. Burr, *Medical History of Michigan*, Minneapolis and St. Paul, 1930, 2 vols.

Minnesota: A. S. Hamilton, *The Early History of Medicine in Minneapolis*. President's Address before Hennepin County Medical Society, Jan. 7, 1918.

A. S. Hamilton, *A Historical Survey of the Minnesota Academy of Medicine*, President's Address, Minnesota Academy of Medicine, Sept. 10, 1924.

Missouri: E. J. Goodwin, *A History of Medicine in Missouri*, St. Louis, 1905.

New Hampshire: O. P. Hubbard, *The Early History of the New Hampshire Medical Institution, with a Sketch of its Founder, Nathan Smith*. Washington, D. C., 1880.

New Jersey: Stephen Wickes, *History of Medicine in New Jersey, and its Medical Men, from the Settlement of the Province to A.D. 1800*, Newark, 1879.

New York: James J. Walsh, *History of Medicine in New York*, 1900, 3 vols.

North Dakota: J. Grassick, *North Dakota Medicine, Sketches and Abstracts*, Grand Forks, N. D., 1926.

Pennsylvania: Theodore Diller, *Pioneer Medicine in Western Pennsylvania*, New York, 1927.

G. W. Norris, *The Early History of Medicine in Philadelphia*, Philadelphia, 1886.

Frederick P. Henry, *Standard History of the Medical Profession of Philadelphia*, Chicago, 1897.

Virginia: Wyndham B. Blanton, *Medicine in Virginia in the Seventeenth Century*, Richmond, 1930.

Wyndham B. Blanton, *Medicine in Virginia in the Eighteenth Century*, Richmond, 1931.

Wyndham B. Blanton, *Medicine in Virginia in the Nineteenth Century*, Richmond, 1933.

Wisconsin: Louis Frederick Frank, *The Medical History of Milwaukee, 1834–1914*, Milwaukee, 1915.

BIBLIOGRAPHY OF SEPARATE CHAPTERS OF THE BOOK

I. THE SOIL.

A. Brigham, *The United States of America*, London, 1927.
F. Machatschek, *Allgemeine Länderkunde von Nordamerika*, Hannover, 1928.
Indian Medicine:
Handbook of American Indians North of Mexico, edited by Frederick Webb Hodge, Smithsonian Institution, Bureau of Ethnology, Bulletin 30, Washington, D. C., 1907–1910, 2 vols., and many other publications in the same series.
Eric Stone, *Medicine Among the American Indians*, New York, 1932.
Clark Wissler, *The American Indian*, New York, 2nd ed., 1922.
D. and M. R. Coolidge, *The Navajo Indians*, Boston and New York, 1930.
George J. Engelmann, *Labor Among Primitive Peoples*, St. Louis, 1882.
Max Bartels, *Die Medizin der Naturvölker*, Leipzig, 1893.
L. Lévy-Bruhl, *La mentalité primitive*, Paris, 1922.

2. COLONIAL TIMES

Justin Winsor, *Narrative and Critical History of America*, 1886–89, 8 vols.
Kretschmer, *Die Entdeckung Amerikas*, 1892, 2 vols.
G. Friederici, *Charakter der Entdeckung und Eroberung Amerikas durch die Europäer*, Stuttgart, 1925.
Herbert L. Osgood, *The American Colonies in the Seventeenth Century*, New York, 1904–1907, 3 vols.
Herbert L. Osgood, *The American Colonies in the Eighteenth Century*, New York, 1923–1924, 4 vols.
The Ingenious Dr. Franklin, Selected Scientific Letters of Benjamin Franklin, edited by Nathan G. Goodman, Philadelphia, 1931.
Charles Tourtourat, *Benjamin Franklin et la médecine à la fin du XVIIIe siècle*, Paris, 1900.
William Pepper, *The Medical Side of Benjamin Franklin*, Philadelphia, 1911.

3. THE UNITED STATES

Edward Channing, *History of the United States*, New York, 1915–1921, 5 vols.

James Truslow Adams, *The Epic of America*, Boston, 1931.
Ernst Daenell, *Geschichte der Vereinigten Staaten von Amerika*, 3rd ed. of A. Hasenclever, 1923.
Evarts B. Greene, *The Foundations of American Nationality*, New York, 1922.
James Bryce, *The American Commonwealth*, London, 1911, 2 vols.
Frederick Jackson Turner, *The Frontier in American History*, New York, 1920.
Charles E. and Mary R. Beard, *The Rise of American Civilization*, New York, 1927, 2 vols.
Cambridge History of American Literature, 1917–1921, 4 vols.
André Siegfried, *Les Etats-Unis d'Aujourd'hui*, Paris, 1927.

4. PIONEERS

John Morgan (1735–1789): *The Journal of Dr. John Morgan of Philadelphia, from the City of Rome to the City of London, 1764*, together with the fragment of a Journal written at Rome, 1764, and a Biographical Sketch, Philadelphia, 1907.—A short but clear biography in: *The North American Medical and Surgical Journal*, 1827, IV, 362–386.—W. S. Middleton, *John Morgan, Father of Medical Education in North America*, Annals of Medical History, 1927, IX, 13–26.—J. Carson, *A History of the Medical Department of the University of Pennsylvania from its Foundation in 1765*, Philadelphia, 1869.
Benjamin Rush (1745–1813): J. C. Lettsom, *Recollections of Dr. Rush*, London, 1815.—William Pepper, *"Benjamin Rush,"* Journal of the American Medical Association, 1890, XIV, 593–601.—A good deal of material in: Frederick P. Henry, *Standard History of the Medical Profession in Philadelphia*, Chicago, 1897.—Thomas G. Morton, *The History of the Pennsylvania Hospital, 1751–1895*, Philadelphia, 1897.—Harry G. Good, *Benjamin Rush and his Services to American Education*, Berne, Indiana, (1918).
Ephraim McDowell (1771–1830): Samuel D. Gross, *"Origin of Ovariotomy: Brief Sketch of the Life and Services of the Late Ephraim McDowell,"* North American Medico-Chirurgical Review, 1860, IV, 1028–1053.—Mary Young Ridenbaugh, *The Biography of Ephraim McDowell, M.D., "The Father of Ovariotomy,"* New York, 1890.—August Schachuer, *Ephraim McDowell, "Father of Ovariotomy" and Founder of Abdominal Surgery*, Philadelphia and London, 1921.

Daniel Drake (1785–1852): E. D. Mansfield, *Memoirs of the Life and Services of Daniel Drake, M.D., Physician, professor and author,* Cincinnati, 1855.—William Pepper, *"Daniel Drake: or Then and Now,"* Journal of the American Medical Association, 1895, XXV, 429–436.—Otto Juettner, *Daniel Drake and his Followers,* Cincinnati, 1909.—Robert Peter, *The Medical Department of Transylvania University,* Filson Club Publications No. 20, Louisville, Kentucky, 1905.

William Beaumont (1785–1853): *"William Osler, A Backwood Physiologist,"* in: *An Alabama Student and other Biographical Essays,* 2nd impression, Oxford, 1909, pp. 159–188, reprinted as the introduction to a facsimile of Beaumont's work, which was published in Boston in 1929 on the occasion of the 13th International Physiological Congress.—Jesse S. Meyer, *Life and Letters of Dr. William Beaumont,* St. Louis, 1912.

Samuel David Gross (1805–1884): *Autobiography of Samuel David Gross, M.D.,* Philadelphia, 1893, 2 vols.—C. W. G. Rohrer, *"Professor Samuel D. Gross; America's foremost surgeon,"* Johns Hopkins Hospital Bulletin, 1912, XXIII, 82–94.

James Marion Sims (1813–1883): J. Marion Sims, *The Story of my Life,* New York, 1884.—R. Olshausen, *Uber Marion Sims und seine Verdienste um die Gynäkologie,* Berlin, 1897.—W. D. Ward, *"The Life and Work of Dr. J. Marion Sims,"* The American Journal of Obstetrics, 1906, LIV, 192–203.—A. Martin, *Zeitschrift für Geburtshilfe und Gynäkologie,* 1913, LXXIII, 946–948.

Oliver Wendell Holmes (1809–1894): John T. Morse, *Life and Letters of Oliver Wendell Holmes,* Boston and New York, 1896, 2 vols.—William Osler, *"Oliver Wendell Holmes,"* in: *An Alabama Student,* Oxford, 1909.—J. H. Mason Knox, Jr., *"The Medical Life of Oliver Wendell Holmes,"* Johns Hopkins Hospital Bulletin, 1907, XVII, 45–51.

Silas Weir Mitchell (1829–1914): Anna Robeson Burr, *Weir Mitchell, his Life and Letters,* New York City, 1930.—S. Weir Mitchell, *Memorial Addresses and Resolutions,* Philadelphia, 1914, with an essay by William H. Welch, *S. Weir Mitchell, Physician and Man of Science,* pp. 97–127.—Charles W. Burr, *The S. Weir Mitchell Oration,* Philadelphia, 1920.

John Shaw Billings (1838–1913): Fielding H. Garrison, *John Shaw Billings, A Memoir,* New York and London, 1915.

Sir William Osler (1849–1919): The bibliography of Osler's works and literature on him up to 1926 can be found complete in: Bulletin No. IX of the International Association of Medical Museums and Journal of Technical Methods, Sir William Osler, Memorial Number, Appreciations and Reminiscences, Montreal, 1926.—The most exhaustive and monumental biography is: Harvey Cushing, *The Life of Sir William Osler*, Oxford, 1925, 2 vols.—An interesting short biography is: Edith Gittings Reid, *The Great Physician, a Short Life of Sir William Osler*, London, New York, Toronto, 1931.

5. MEDICAL EDUCATION

The best sources of recent statistics are:
Final Report of the Commission on Medical Education, Office of the Director of Study, 630 W. 168th Street, New York, 1932.—*The Journal of the American Medical Association* also publishes in August of every year an Educational Number, in which the latest statistics can be found.
Of basic importance are:
Abraham Flexner: *Medical Education in the United States and Canada*, a Report to the Carnegie Foundation for the Advancement of Teaching, Bulletin No. 4, New York, 1910; *Medical Education, a Comparative Study*, New York, 1925; *Universities, American, English, German*, New York, London, Toronto, 1930.
Early literature: N. S. Davis, *History of Medical Education and Institutions in the United States*, Chicago, 1851.—John H. Rauch, *Medical Education, Medical Colleges and the Regulation of the Practice of Medicine in the United States and Canada*, 1765–1891, Illinois State Board of Health, Springfield, Illinois, 1891.
History of specific schools: J. Carson, *A History of the Medical Department of the University of Pennsylvania, from its Foundation in 1765*, Philadelphia, 1869.—George M. Gould, *The Jefferson Medical College of Philadelphia, 1826–1904*, New York, Chicago, 1904, 2 vols.—Thomas Francis Harrington, *The Harvard Medical School, a History, narrative and documentary*, edited by J. G. Mumford, New York, Chicago, 1905, 3 vols.—William H. Welch, "The Relation of Yale to Medicine." Address delivered Oct. 21, 1901, at the Two Hundredth Anniversary of the Founding of Yale College, *Yale Medical Journal*, 1901, VIII.—Samuel Bard, *Two Discourses dealing with Medical Education in Early New York*, New York, 1921 (Facsimile of two discourses of 1769 and 1819).—J. C. Dalton,

History of the College of Physicians and Surgeons of the City of New York, Medical Department of Columbia College, New York, 1888. —R. and J. Peter, *Transylvania University, a History of the Medical Department,* Louisville, Kentucky, 1905.

On Dentistry especially: William J. Gies, *Dental Education in the United States and Canada,* a Report to the Carnegie Foundation for the Advancement of Teaching, Bulletin No. 19, New York, 1926.

6. THE PHYSICIAN AND THE PATIENT

The most important sources are to be found in the publications of the Committee on the Costs of Medical Care of Chicago, Chicago University Press:

1. *The Five-Year Program of the Committee on the Costs of Medical Care.* 1928.

2. *The Extent of Illness and of Physical and Mental Defects Prevailing in the United States: A Compilation of Existing Material.* By Alden B. Mills. 1929.

3. *A Survey of Statistical Data on Medical Facilities in the United States: A Compilation of Existing Material.* By Allon Peebles. 1929.

4. *Hospital Service for Patients of Moderate Means: A Study of Certain American Hospitals.* By Niles Carpenter. 1930.

5. *Medical Care for 15,000 Workers and their Families: A Survey of the Endicott Johnson Workers Medical Service, 1928.* By Niles Carpenter. 1930.

6. *A Survey of the Medical Facilities of Shelby County, Indiana:* 1929. By Allon Peebles, 1930.

7. *Capital Investment in Hospitals: The Place of "Fixed Charges" in Hospital Financing and Costs.* By C. Rufus Rorem. 1930.

8. *Private Group Clinics: The Administrative and Economic Aspects of Group Medical Practice, as represented in the Policies and Procedures of 55 Private Associations of Medical Practitioners.* By C. Rufus Rorem. 1931.

9. *A Survey of the Medical Facilities of the City of Philadelphia:* 1929. Being in part a Digest of the Philadelphia Hospital and Health Survey, 1929. By Nathan Sinai and Alden B. Mills. 1931.

10. *A Study of Physicians and Dentists in Detroit:* 1929. By Nathan Sinai and Alden B. Mills. 1931.

11. *The "Municipal Doctor" System in Rural Saskatchewan.* By C. Rufus Rorem. 1931.

12. *A Survey of the Medical Facilities of San Joaquin County,* California: 1929. By Nathan Sinai et al. 1931.

13. *A Survey of the Medical Facilities of the State of Vermont.* By Allon Peebles. 1932.

14. *The Costs of Medicines: The Manufacture and Distribution of Drugs and Medicines in the United States and the Services of Pharmacy in Medical Care.* By C. Rufus Rorem and Robert P. Fischelis. 1932.

15. *Midwives, Chiropodists, and Optometrists: Their Place in Medical Care.* By Louis S. Reed. 1932.

16. *The Healing Cults: A Study of Sectarian Medical Practice: Its Extent, Causes, and Control.* By Louis S. Reed. 1932.

17. *Nursing Services and Insurance for Medical Care in Brattleboro, Vermont: A Study of the Activities of the Thomas Thompson Trust.* By Allon Peebles and Valeria D. McDermott. With an Evaluation of the Nursing Program, by Violet H. Hodgson and Katharine Tucker. 1932.

18. *The Medical Service of the Homestake Mining Company: A Survey of a Community Medical Service Operated under Industrial Auspices.* By Louis S. Reed. 1932.

19. *University Student Health Services: A Study of Organization, Services Rendered, and Costs in Cornell University, Yale University, the University of Michigan, the University of Minnesota, the University of California, and Oregon State Agricultural College.* By Don M. Griswold and Hazel I. Spicer. 1932.

20. *A Community Medical Service Organized under Industrial Auspices in Roanoke Rapids, North Carolina.* By I. S. Falk, Don M. Griswold and Hazel I. Spicer. With Reports on Certain Phases of the Organization, by David Riesman and George B. Muller. 1932.

21. *Organized Medical Service at Fort Benning, Georgia.* By I. S. Falk. With Reports on Certain Phases of the Organization, by David Riesman and George P. Muller. 1932.

22. *The Fundamentals of Good Medical Care: An Outline of the Fundamentals of Good Medical Care and an Estimate of the Service Required to Supply the Medical Needs of the United States.* By Roger I. Lee and Lewis Webster Jones, with the assistance of Barbara Jones. 1933.

23. *Surveys of the Medical Facilities in Three Representative Southern Counties.* By C. St. C. Guild. With a Statistical Appendix on the Method of selecting Representative Counties. By I. S. Falk. 1932.

298   *Bibliography*

24. *The Incomes of Physicians: An Economic and Statistical Analysis.* By Maurice Leven. 1932.
25. *The Ability to Pay for Medical Care.* By Louis S. Reed. 1933.
26. *The Incidence of Illness and the Receipt and Costs of Medical Care among Representative Families: Experiences in Twelve Consecutive Months during 1928–1931.* I. S. Falk, Margaret C. Klem, and Nathan Sinai. 1933.
27. *The Costs of Medical Care: A Summary of Investigations on the Economic Aspects of the Prevention and Care of Illness.* By I. S. Falk, C. Rufus Rorem, and Martha D. Ring. 1933 (one volume with 648 pages, summarizing the earlier investigation).
28. *Medical Care for the American People: The Final Report of the Committee on the Costs of Medical Care.* 1932.

Various other organizations have collaborated with the Committee on the Costs of Medical Care and have issued the following publications:

The American Dental Association

The Practice of Dentistry and the Incomes of Dentists in Twenty States. By Maurice Leve   1932.
The Cost of Equipping a Dental Office. By Dorothy Fahs Beck. 1932.
A Study of Dental Clinics in the United States: 1930. By Miriam Simons Leuck. 1932.
A Further Study of Dental Clinics in the United States. By Miriam Simons Leuck. 1933.
The Costs of Dental Education. By Miriam Simons Leuck. (In preparation.)
The Way of Health Insurance. By A. M. Simons and Nathan Sinai. 1932.
Summary of the Facts Pertaining to Dentistry Contained in the Published Reports of The Committee on the Costs of Medical Care. By Dorothy Fahs Beck. J. Amer. Dent. Assoc., 1932, pp. 230–251.

The American Medical Association

"The Costs of Medical Education, Students' Expenditures." By R. G. Leland, J. Am. Med. Assoc., 1931, pp. 682–690.
"Income from Medical Practice." By R. G. Leland, J. Am. Med. Assoc., 1931, 1683–1691.

The Metropolitan Life Insurance Company

The Cost of Medical Care. By Lee K. Frankel. 1930.

A Study of Sickness Cost and Private Medical Practice. By Donald Armstrong. 1932.

A Study of the Cost of Medical Care among the Employees of the Metropolitan Life Insurance Company. (In preparation.)

The National Bureau of Economic Research

The Purchase of Medical Care through Fixed Periodic Payment. By Pierce Williams. 1932.

The National Tuberculosis Association

Medical Service in Industry. (In preparation.)
The Cost of the Lack of Care in Tuberculosis. (In preparation.)

The Milbank Memorial Fund

International Studies on the Relation between the Private and Official Practice of Medicine, with Special Reference to the Prevention of Disease. By Sir Arthur Newsholme. 1931. 3 vols.
Medicine and the State. By Sir Arthur Newsholme. 1932.

Julius Rosenwald Fund

The Public's Investment in Hospitals. By C. Rufus Rorem. 1930.
Paying your Sickness Bills. By Michael M. Davis. 1931.
The Crisis in Hospital Finance. By Michael M. Davis and C. Rufus Rorem. 1932.
Negro Hospitals: A Compilation of Available Statistics. With an Introduction by Michael M. Davis. 1931.
Economic and Social Status of Patients of the Public Health Institute of Chicago. By Bernard Regenburg. 1931.
The Middle-Rate Plan for Hospital Patients—A Year's Experiment in Keokuk, Iowa. By Mary Ross. 1931.
The Middle-Rate Plan for Hospital Patients—The First Year's Experience at the Baker Memorial of the Massachusetts General Hospital, Boston, Mass. By C. Rufus Rorem. 1931.
How do Physicians and Patients like the Middle-Rate Plan for Hospital Care? The Second Year's Experience of the Baker Memorial Unit of the Massachusetts General Hospital, Boston. By C. Rufus Rorem, Clyde D. Frost, Elizabeth Richards Day. 1932.
"State Medicine" Abroad and its Relation to Hospitals. By E. H. Lewinski Corwin and Michael M. Davis. 1931.

300 *Bibliography*

Annual Medical Service in Private Group Clinics. By C. Rufus Rorem. 1932.

Physician's Fees and Hospital Bills. By Michael M. Davis. 1932.

The Quality of Care rendered by the University of Chicago Clinics. By Emmet B. Bay. 1932.

Sickness Insurance in the United States. By C. Rufus Rorem. 1932.

Growth of Clinics in the United States. By Margaret Lovell Plumley. 1932.

Syphilis as an Economic Problem. By Leon Bromberg and Michael M. Davis. 1932.

Medical Advertising. By Mary Ross. (In preparation.)

Economic Aspects of Medical Care; a List of Reading References as revised. January, 1934.

See, also:

Harry H. Moore, *American Medicine and the People's Health,* New York, London, 1927.

Julian P. Price, *The Young Doctor Thinks Out Loud,* New York and London, 1931.

Recent Social Trends in the United States: Report of the President's Research Committee on Social Trends, New York and London, 1933. 2 vols.

Mayo Clinic: *Sketch of the History of the Mayo Clinic and the Mayo Foundation,* from the Division of Publications, Mayo Clinic, Philadelphia and London, 1926.

American Medical Association: N. S. Davis, *History of the American Medical Association, from its Organization up to January, 1855,* Philadelphia, 1855.

Sectarian Medicine

Morris Fishbein, *Fads and Quackery in Healing,* New York, 1932.

Homeopathy: *Transactions of the World's Homeopathic Convention held at Philadelphia . . . 1876.* Vol. II. History of Homeopathy, Philadelphia, 1880.

Osteopathy: *Autobiography of A. T. Still,* Kirksville, Mo., 1897.—A. T. Still, *Philosophy and Mechanical Principles of Osteopathy,* 1902. —E. R. Booth, *History of Osteopathy and Twentieth Century Medical Practice,* Cincinnati, 1924.—McConnel and Teall, *The Practice of Osteopathy,* Kirksville, Mo., 1920.

Chiropractic: D. D. and B. J. Palmer, *The Science of Chiropractic,* Davenport, Iowa, 1906.—William Carver, *Carver's Chiropractic Analysis*, Oklahoma City, 1915.

Christian Science: Mary Baker Eddy, *Science and Health, with Key to the Scriptures*, Boston, 1875, in innumerable editions.—Sybil Wilbur, *Life of Mary Baker Eddy*, 1929.—Lyman P. Powell, *Mary Baker Eddy, a Life-Size Portrait*, 1930.—Edwin Franden Daken, *Mrs. Eddy, The Biography of a Virginal Mind*, New York, 1929.

7. HOSPITALS AND NURSING

Hospitals

History: Thomas G. Morton, *The History of the Pennsylvania Hospital*, *1751–1895*, Philadelphia, 1897.—J. W. Croskey, *History of Blockley, A History of the Philadelphia General Hospital, from its Inception, 1731–1928*, Philadelphia, 1929.—*An Account of the New York Hospital*, New York, 1820.—E. H. Pool and F. J. McGowan, *Surgery at the New York Hospital One Hundred Years Ago*, New York, 1929.—*A Psychiatric Milestone*, Bloomingdale Hospital Centenary, 1821–1921, privately printed by the Society of the New York Hospital, 1921.—Robert J. Carlisle, *An Account of Bellevue Hospital, with a Catalogue of the Medical and Surgical Staff from 1736–1894*, New York, Society of the Alumnae of Bellevue Hospital, 1893.—N. I. Bowditch, *A History of the Massachusetts General Hospital*, Boston, 1851; 2nd ed., with a Continuation to 1872, Boston, 1872.—*Massachusetts General Hospital*, Memorial and Historical Volume, 1921.—G. W. Myers, *History of Massachusetts General Hospital, June, 1872 to December, 1900*, Boston, 1929.—*The History of Boston City Hospital, from its Foundation until 1904*, edited by D. W. Cheever and a Committee of the Hospital Staff, Boston, 1906.

Present situation: The publications of the Committee on the Costs of Medical Care (listed above).—The publications of the American College of Surgeons: Manual of Hospital Standardization, and yearly reports: Hospital Standardization Report and Year Book, Chicago (40 East Erie Street).—Transactions of the American Hospital Association, yearly, Chicago (18–20 East Division Street).—Proceedings of the Annual Congress on Medical Education, Medical Licensure and Hospitals, yearly, American Medical Association, Chicago (535 North Dearborn Street).—Edward F. Stevens, *The American Hospital of the Twentieth Century*, Revised Ed., New York, 1921.

—James Clark Fifield, *American and Canadian Hospitals*. A Reference Book giving Historical, Statistical and other Information . . . Minneapolis, 1933.

Henry Ford Hospital: *Henry Ford, My Life and Work*, New York, 1926, W. L. Graham, *"The Henry Ford Hospital*," Detroit, Michigan, in: *Collected Papers by the Staff of the Henry Ford Hospital* (First Series, 1918–1925), New York, 1926.

Middle-Rate Plan: Publications of the Julius Rosenwald Fund (listed above).

Nursing

Most important: *Nursing and Nursing Education in the United States*, Report of the Committee for the Study of Nursing Education, New York, 1923.

Lavinia L. Dock, *A History of Nursing*, New York and London, 1907–1912, 4 vols.

Lavinia L. Dock and Isabel Maitland Stewart, *A Short History of Nursing*, New York, London, 3rd ed., 1931.

Minnie Goodnow, *Outlines of Nursing History*, Philadelphia and London, 4th ed., 1928.

8. PREVENTIVE MEDICINE

U. S. Department of Commerce. Bureau of Census. Mortality Statistics (yearly).

U. S. Department of Commerce. Bureau of Foreign and Domestic Commerce. Statistical Abstracts of the United States (yearly).

H. I. Bowditch, *Public Hygiene in America*, Boston, 1877.

Harry H. Moore, *Public Health in the United States*, New York and London, 1923.

Laurence F. Schmeckebier, *The Public Health Service, its History, Activities and Organization*, Baltimore, 1923.

Robert D. Leigh, *Federal Health Administration in the United States*, New York and London, 1927.

C. E. A. Winslow, *State Board of Health of Massachusetts, A Brief History of its Organization and its Work, 1869–1912*, Boston, 1912.

William Travis Howard, *Public Health Administration and the Natural*

History of Disease in Baltimore, Maryland, 1797–1920, Washington, 1924.

Mazyck P. Ravenel, *A Half Century of Public Health*, New York, 1921.

Charles V. Chapin, *A Report on State Public Health Work based on a Survey of State Boards of Health*, n. d. (c. 1916).

Health Departments of States and Provinces of the United States and Canada, *Public Health Bulletin No. 184*, 1929.

Tuberculosis: S. A. Knopf, *History of the National Tuberculosis Association*, New York, 1932.—Stephen Chalmers, *The Beloved Physician, Edward Livingston Trudeau*, Boston, 1916.—C. E. A. Winslow, *The Life of Hermann M. Biggs*, Philadelphia, 1929.—Philip P. Jacobs, *The Campaign against Tuberculosis in the United States*, New York, 1908. Philip P. Jacobs, *The Control of Tuberculosis in the United States*, New York, 1932.

Venereal Diseases: George Walker, *Venereal Disease in the American Expeditionary Forces*, Baltimore, 1922.—Edward L. Keyes, *"The Present Status of Venereal Disease Prophylaxis, Social and Medical,"* J. Soc. Hyg., 1933, XIX, 1–13.

H. H. Howard, *The Control of Hookworm Disease by the Intensive Method*, New York, 1919.

E. S. Gosney and Paul Popenoe, *Sterilization for Human Betterment*, New York, 1929.

Collected Papers on Eugenic Sterilization in California, a Critical Study of Results in 6000 cases, with an introduction by E. S. Gosney. The American Betterment Foundation, Pasadena, Calif., 1930.

Margaret Sanger, *The Sixth International Neo-Malthusian and Birth Control Conference*, New York, 1925–1926, 3 vols.

Margaret Sanger, *My Fight for Birth Control*, New York, 1931.

Mary Ware Dennett, *Birth Control Laws*, New York, 1926.

White House Conference on Child Health and Protection, in course of publication since 1931.

Mental Hygiene, Quarterly Magazine of the National Committee for Mental Hygiene, begun in 1917.

George S. Stevenson and Geddes Smith, *Child Guidance Clinics, a Quarter Century of Development*, New York, 1934.

Prolonging Life as a Function of Life Insurance, Five Years' Experience of the Life Extension Institute, New York, 1919.

Eugene Lyman Fiske, *Health Building and Life Extension*, New York, 1923.

9. MEDICAL SCIENCE

Handbook of Scientific and Technical Societies and Institutions of the United States and Canada, 2nd Ed., *Bulletin of the National Research Council*, No. 76, 1930.

Simon Flexner, *The Rockefeller Institute for Medical Research*, New York. Rufus Cole, *The Hospital of the Rockefeller Institute*, New York. Theobald Smith, *The Department of Animal Pathology of the Rockefeller Institute*, Princeton, N. J., in: *Forschungsinstitute, ihre Geschichte, Organization und Ziele*, Hrsg. von L. Brauer, A. Mendelssohn Bartholdy, A. Meyer, Hamburg, vol. II, 1930, pp. 458–505. (In the same volume, pp. 437–457: Rudolf Wigand, Die Naturwissenschaftlichen und medizinischen Forschungsinstitute der Vereinigten Staaten von Nordamerika.)

The Rockefeller Institute for Medical Research, History, Organization, Present Scope of the Scientific Work, Buildings and Equipment, Publications, New York, 1932.

The Human Welfare Group. New Haven, Connecticut, General Hospital Society, Yale University, 1929.

Bulletin of Yale University. Institute of Human Relations (yearly).

Abel, John Jacob, 129
Adams, Samuel, 53
Adler, Alfred, 282
Æsculapius, 200
Agassiz, Louis, 273
Agramonte, Aristides, 252
Andral, Gabriel, 111
Aristotele, 15
Arlt, Carl Ferd. von, 126
Ashford, Bailey K., 255
Ayllon, 17

Balboa, 14
Bard, Samuel, 204
Barton, Benjamin Smith, 82
Beaumont, William, 96 ff., 104, 172, 271
Beers, Clifford W., 261
Bell, John, 89
Bernard, Claude, 118, 271
Bigelow, Henry J., 117
Biggs, Hermann M., 248
Billings, John Shaw, xii, 121 ff., 128, 130, 234, 268 f.
Billroth, Theodor, 102
Blackwell, Francis, 31
Bobbs, John S., 270
Boccaccio, 84
Boerhaave, Hermann, 31, 41, 91, 127, 205
Bohun, Lawrence, 33
Bond, Thomas, 47 f., 79
Bowditch, Henry Ingersoll, 270
Bowditch, Henry Pickering, 273
Bowditch, Vincent Y., 249
Boylston, Zabdiel, 38 ff., 42
Bravo, Francisco, 15

Brehmer, Hermann, 248
Broedel, Max, 160
Broussais, François J. V., 111
Brown, John, 84 f.
Brown, Samuel, 93
Brown, Thomas, 129
Bucky, 283
Buffalo Bill, 69

Cabot, John, 22
Caboto, Giovanni, 22
Cabrillo, 19
Calvert, Cecil—Lord Baltimore, 25
Calvert, George—Lord Baltimore, 25
Cardenas, 19
Carey, Matthew, 84
Carminati, 98
Carrel, Alexis, 276
Carroll, James, 252
Cartier, Jacques, 21
Cervantes, 130
Charles I, 25
Charles V, 15
Cheselden, William, 91
Cicero, 15
Cohnheim, Julius, xii, 128
Cole, Rufus, 275 ff.
Coligny, Admiral, 20
Columbus, Christopher, 13 f., 16, 18
Coolidge, 283
Cooper, Sir Astley, 269
Coronado, 19
Cortez, Hernando, 14, 17, 223
Crawford, Jane Todd, 87 ff.
Crawford, Thomas, 87
Cullen, William, 76, 84
Cushing, Harvey, 281

D'Abano, Pietro, 77
Dare, Virginia, 23
Davis, Jefferson, 66
Davis, S. N., 134
Davy, Sir Humphry, 116
Delaware, Lord, 33
Dettweiler, Peter, 248
Dorsey, John S., 273
Douglas, William, 42
Drake, Daniel, 90 ff., 103, 121, 132, 134 f.
Drake, Francis, 22
Dudley, B. W., 101
Dupuytren, Guillaume, 111 f.

Eastman, 139
Eddy, Mary Baker, 200 f.
Edison, Thomas, 51
Elizabeth, 22, 23, 26
Emerson, Ralph Waldo, 64, 117
Endicott, John, 34 f.
Eugénie, Empress, 109
Evans, Thomas W., 165

Fauchard, Pierre, 166
Faust, Bernhard Christoph, 233
Fergusson, William, 101
Finlay, Carlos J., 252
Fletcher, Robert, 122
Flexner, Abraham, 138 f., 196, 277
Flexner, Simon, 275 ff.
Flick, Lawrence F., 249
Ford, Henry, 213
Foster, Sir Michael, 273
Fothergill, John, 42
Fracastoro, Girolamo, 77
Frank, Johann Peter, 95
Franklin, Benjamin, 39, 48 ff., 53, 56, 76, 82 f., 120, 233
Frederick II, 43
Frerichs, Friedrich Theodor, 125
Freud, Sigmund, 282
Fuller, Samuel, 34

Fulton, Robert, 61

Galileo, 30
Garrison, Fielding H., 122, 287
Gates, Frederick T., 275
Gerhard, William W., 270 f.
Gies, William J., 168
Gilman, Daniel Coit, 127 f.
Goforth, William, 90 f.
Gorgas, William C., 253
Gourgues, Dominique de, 21
Gram, Hans Burch, 195
Grant, General, 67
Griffitts, Samuel P., 82
Gross, Samuel David, 100 ff., 109

Hahnemann, Samuel, 195
Haller, Albrecht von, 91, 105, 122
Halsted, William Stewart, 129
Hamilton, Walten H., 189 f.
Harris, Chapin A., 166
Harvey, William, 30, 77
Hawkins, John, 22
Hawthorne, 117
Hayden, Horace H., 166
Heale, Giles, 33
Healy, William, 261
Hebra, Ferdinand von, 126
Henrietta Maria, 25
Hippocrates, 40, 82
His, Wilhelm, 129
Holmes, Oliver Wendell, 111 ff., 167
Hoover, Herbert, 257
Hope, 76
Hopkins, Johns, 127
Horner, William E., 103, 273
Howell, William H., 243
Hudson, Henry, 27
Humboldt, Alexander von, 273
Humphrey, Dr., 89
Hunter, John, 41 f., 76, 101
Hunter, William, 76 f.
Hutchinson, James, 82
Hyrtl, Josef, 117

Jackson, Andrew, 63
Jackson, Charles Thomas, 116
Jackson, James, 206
Jacobi, Abraham, 63, 282
Jaeger, Eduard von, 126
James I, 23 f.
Jameson, Horatio Gates, 269
Jefferson, Thomas, 39
Johns, John, 204
Jung, C. G., 282

Kelly, Howard A., 129
Knopp, Nicholas, 43
Koch, Robert, 248 f.
Kronecker, Hugo, 275
Kuhn, Adam, 79, 82

Lafayette, 56, 72
Landsteiner, Karl, 276
Langenbeck, Bernhard von, 101 f.
Larrey, Dominique Jean, 111
Laudonnière, René de, 20
Lazear, Jesse W., 252 f.
Lee, Robert E., 67
Leidy, Joseph, 273
Leighton, David, 80
Leon, Ponce de, 16
Levene, Phoebus A., 275
Lincoln, Abraham, 67, 96
Linné, Carl von, 79
Lisfranc, Jacques, 111
Lloyd, James, 42
Loeb, Jacques, 276
Long, Crawford Williamson, 115 f.
Longfellow, 73, 117
Loomis, Alfred L., 248
Louis XIV, 21, 52
Louis, Jean, 47
Louis, Pierre C. A., 111, 270 f.
Lovell, Joseph, 96
Ludwig, Carl, xii, 128 f., 160, 273 f.

Magendie, François, 271
Mall, Franklin Paine, 129

Mance, Jeanne, 204, 223
Marat, 51
Martin, Newell, 128, 273 f.
Mather, Cotton, 38 f.
Mayo, Charles H., 178
Mayo, William J., 178
Mayo, William W., 178
McDowell, Ephraim, 87 ff., 96, 104,
116, 172, 269
Meltzer, Samuel J., 275
Menendez, 20 f.
Meyer, Adolf, 277
Middleton, Peter, 204
Mitchell, Silas Weir, 117 ff., 271
Molière, 37
Mongolfier, 51
Monroe, Alexander, 76
Montagu, Lady Mary Wortley, 38
Montaigne, 130
Morgagni, Giovanni Battista, 76 f.
Morgan, John, 75 ff., 82 f., 85, 87,
96, 101
Morgan, T. H., 281
Morton, William Thomas Green,
116 f.
Mott, Valentine, 101, 269
Müller, Johannes, 271, 273

Napoleon I, 48, 57, 61
Napoleon III, 67, 109, 165
Narvaez, Panfilo de, 17
Nélaton, Auguste, 101
Nicot, Jean, 24
Nightingale, Florence, 224
Noguchi, Hideyo, 275 f.

Oliver, John Rathbone, 287
Opie, Eugene L., 275
Osler, Sir William, 124 ff., 274

Paget, Sir James, 101
Palmer, B. J., 198
Palmer, D. D., 198
Pasteur, Louis, 118, 125, 245, 271

Penn, Thomas, 78
Penn, William, 28, 31
Philip, Robert W., 248
Philipp II of Spain, 22
Phipps, Henry, 249, 277
Physick, Philip Syng, 101, 273
Pineda, 16
Pizarro, 14, 18
Plutarch, 48, 130
Poe, Edgar Allan, 73 f.
Politzer, Adam, 126
Pontiac, 59
Pott, John, 34

Quimby, Phineas Parkhurst, 200 f.

Raleigh, Sir Walter, 23 f.
Réaumur, René A. F. de, 98
Redman, John, 76 f., 81 f.
Reed, Walter, 252
Reichert, Edward Tyson, 119
Remsen, Ira, 128
Ribaud, Jean, 20
Ricord, Philippe, 112
Ridgeley, Frederick, 93
Rizzoli, F., 101
Robinson, G. Canby, 143
Rockefeller, John D., 139, 274 f.
Rokitansky, Carl, 125
Rousseau, Jean-Jacques, 48, 55
Rush, Benjamin, 75 f., 79, 81 ff., 91, 96, 233
Russel, Walter, 33
Rutherford, Daniel, 76

St. Martin, Alexis, 97 ff.
Salmon, Thomas W., 261
Sanger, Margaret, 260 f.
Schmiedeberg, Oswald, 129
Schnitzler, 126
Schurz, Carl, 63
Sedgwick, William T., 242 f.
Semmelweis, Ignaz Philipp, 114 f.
Shattuck, Lemuel, 240

Shippen, William, Jr., 41, 78 f., 81 f., 272
Simon, Gustav, 107
Sims, James Marion, 100 f., 105 ff., 269
Skoda, Josef, 125
Smellie, William, 41 f.
Smith, Joe, 60
Smith, Nathan, 110
Smith, Theobald, 276
Soemmering, Samuel von, 272
Soto, Hernando de, 18
Spengler, Karl, 248
Stafford, Dr., 35
Stevens, 98
Still, Andrew T., 196 f.
Stromeyer, Georg Friedrich Louis, 101
Strümpell, Adolf, 126
Sudhoff, Karl, xi
Sutter, General, 65
Sweet, J. E., 275
Sydenham, Thomas, 31, 84, 87

Tecumseh, 59
Thacher, Thomas, 37
Traube, Ludwig, 125
Trousseau, Armand, 270
Trudeau, Edward L., 248
Twain, Mark, 73

Vaca, Cabeza de, 17 f.
van Buren, John, 205
van Helmont, J. B., 98
van Swieten, Gerhard, 91
Verrazzano, 21
Vesalius, Andreas, 77
Vespucci, Amerigo, 14
Virchow, Rudolf, 125
Vizcaino, 19
Voltaire, 38, 48, 77

Waldseemüller, 14

Warren, John Collins, 101, 110, 116 f., 206
Washington, George, 39, 54 ff.
Welch, William H., xi f., 128 f., 130, 243, 274 ff., 285 f.
Wells, Horace, 116
Whistler, James McNeill, 74
Whitman, Walt, 73
Whitney, Eli, 62
Whytt, Robert, 76
Wilkinson, Will, 33

Williams, Roger, 26 f.
Williamson, Hugh, 233
Wilson, Woodrow, 72 f.
Winternitz, Milton C., 280
Winthrop, John, 35
Winthrop, John, Jr., 35 f., 120
Wistar, Caspar, 82, 272 f.
Witmer, Lightner, 262
Wolcott, Erastus B., 270
Wotton, Thomas, 33
Wyman, Morrill, 269

abortions, 230
academies, 272
aëdes aegypti, 253
Alabama, 61, 166
Algonquins, 3
American Association for the Advancement of Osteopathy, 197
American Child Health Association, 257
American College of Physicians, 174
American College of Surgeons, 174, 208 ff., 222
American Dental Association, 167
American Dental Convention, 167
American Institute of Homoeopathy, 196
American Journal of Dental Science, 166
American Medical Association, 96, 134 f., 148, 152, 162, 174, 192 f., 264
American Medical Association of Vienna, 174
American Medical Directory, 193
American Philosophical Society, 50, 80, 272
American Physiological Society, 118
American Public Health Association, 245
American School of Osteopathy, 197
American Social Hygiene Association, 250
American Society of Dental Surgeons, 166
amulets, 12
anaesthesia, 101, 115 ff., 206, 270
anatomy, 42, 117, 157, 272 f., 281

ancylostomum, 254 f., 273
anti-Federalists, 56
Apaches, 59 f.
apothecaries, 45, 79
Arizona, 1, 2, 61
armada, 22
Army Medical Corps, 96, 122
Aztecs, 14

bacteriology, 158, 282
Baker Memorial Unit, 214 f.
Baptists, 60
Bellevue Hospital, 128, 205 f., 224
Bellevue Hospital Medical College, 206
beri-beri, 237
birth control, 259 ff.
birth rate, 263
Blackfeet, 59
Bloomingdale Hospital, 205
Boston, xiv, 27, 39 ff., 54
Bowdoin, 110
Bureau of Indian Affairs, 238
Burlington, 110

Caesarian operation, 10
California, 1, 53, 61, 65
Cambridge, 40
Canada, 52
cancer, 222, 264
Carnegie Foundation, 138, 168
Carnegie Institution of Washington, 277, 285
Census Bureau, 235, 241
Charleston, 29
chemistry, 281
Chicago, 64, 68 f.

Chicago Juvenile Psychopathic Institute, 261 f.
Chicora, 16
Child Health Centers, 258
Chippewas, 4, 6
chiropractic, 198 f.
choleccystotomy, 270
cholera, 99, 205, 230, 234, 237, 247, 273
cholera infantum, 86
Christian Science, 200 ff., 266
Cibola, 19
Cincinnati, 90 ff.
Cincinnati College, 94, 103
Civil War, 66 f.
clerical medicine, 34, 37
climate, 1, 2
college, 143 ff.
College of Philadelphia, 78 f., 81 f., 131
College of Physicians of Philadelphia, 80
Colorado, 1, 2, 19, 62, 65
Columbia College of Physicians and Surgeons, 131, 141 f.
Columbia Teachers College, 228, 245
Columbia University, 131, 149, 165, 174
Comanches, 10, 59
Committee on the Costs of Medical Care, 187 ff., 221
Commonwealth Fund, 278
compensation laws, 185, 256
Connecticut, 26
contraceptives, 260
Cornell University, Medical College, 142 f., 205
Cost: tuition, 165; medical care, 180 ff., 186 ff.; hospitals, 215 ff.
cotton, 24; gin, 62
County Departments of Health, 240
County Medical Societies, 192
Cuba, 71, 235, 252

Dakotas, 4
Dartmouth College, 110, 131
deacons, 223
deaconesses, 224
death rate, 263
Declaration of Independence, 54 f.
dentistry, 116, 165 ff.
dermatology, 283
diabetes, 263
diphtheria, 32, 241, 247, 282
dispensaries, 207
Dominicans, 17
Duke University, 139
dysentery, 32

Edinburgh, 41, 76, 111
education, foreign, 146 ff.; medical, 40 ff., 77 ff., 131 ff., 280
Egyptian chlorosis, 254
embryology, 277, 281
Endicott-Johnson Corporation, 186 f.
England, colonial policy, 22 ff.
Enlightenment, 39, 55, 83 ff., 132, 266
Erie Canal, 62
examinations, 160 f.
excess of births, 263

Federalists, 56
fetish, 4, 9
Florida, 16, 18, 20 f., 52, 62
Forts: Caroline, 20; Crawford, 99; Dearborn, 64; Mackinac, 97; Nassau, 27; Orange, 27
Foundations, 63, 277 f., 287
France, colonial policy, 20 ff.
Franciscans, 17
frontier, 58, 69, 75
full-time system, 140

General Education Board, 139, 274
genetics, 281
gold rush, 65
group medicine, 176 ff., 188 ff.

Guanahani, 13
Guatemala, 14
gynecology, 107 ff.

Hahnemannian Society, 196
Haidas, 7
Halve Maene, 27
Harvard University, 40, 110 f., 115, 131, 167, 206, 273
Hawaii, 71, 235, 238, 255
Health Centers, 265
health departments, federal, 233 ff.; state and local, 239 ff.
Health Extension Service, 265
health insurance, 182 ff.
heart disease, 263
Henricopolis, 47
Henry Ford Hospital, 213 f.
Henry Phipps Psychiatric Clinic, 277
Holland, colonial policy, 27
homeopathy, 143, 195 f.
Honduras, 14
Hopis, 11
hospitals, 46 ff., 123, 204 ff.; number, 211; frequency of use, 229; cost, 212 ff.
hospital standardization, 210
hot springs, 9
Howard University, 143
Hupas, 7
hydrophobia, 230
Hygeia, 193
hygiene: personnel, 241 ff.; schools of, 243 f.; country districts, 240; industrial districts, 256; child, 238, 242, 247, 256 ff.; mental, 261 f.; popular education, 242, 265; information, 236

iatreion, 46
iatrochemists, 30
iatrophysicists, 30
Illinois, 61
illustration, medical, 160

immigration, 62 f., 69 ff., 235, 262
imperialism, 71
Incas, 14
Index Medicus, 123, 192
Indians, 2 ff., 17 ff., 24, 27 ff., 34, 52 f., 58 ff., 64, 99; medicine, 4 ff.; surgery, 9 ff.; obstetrics, 10 f.
industrial insurance, 185 f.
industrialization, 62
infant death rate, 263
influenza, 32
inhalation-anaesthesia, 101, 115 ff., 206
insane, 86, 205
Institute for Child Guidance, 262
Institute of Human Relation, 278 ff.
Institute of the History of Medicine, 141, 159 f., 285
insulin, xiii
insurance, 182 ff., 215
internal medicine, 158 f., 270, 281
International Health Board, 246
interneship, 162
Iroquois, 11

Jamestown, 23, 33
Jefferson Medical College, 94, 102 f., 105, 118
Jesuits, 21
Johns Hopkins Hospital, 123, 126, 128 ff., 138 f., 285
Johns Hopkins School of Hygiene and Public Health, 243 f., 285
Johns Hopkins School of Medicine, 127 f., 138 ff., 149 ff., 154 ff., 267, 285
Johns Hopkins University, 127 f., 146 ff., 273, 277, 285
Josiah Macy, Jr., Foundation, 287
Journal of the American Medical Association, 193
Julius Rosenwald Fund, 278

Kansas, 19, 59
Kentucky, 60, 87
kidney disease, 263
King's College, 110, 131, 204
Klamaths, 5

laparatomy, 10
laughing gas, 115 f.
lectures, 155
legal medicine, 283
leprosy, 232, 235, 255
libraries, medical, 120 ff.
licenses, 44 f., 162 ff.; chiropractors, 199; dentists, 166 f.; nurses, 227; osteopaths, 197 f.
Life Extension Institute, 264 f.
lightning-rod, 48, 51
Louisiana, 21, 52, 61
Lourdes, 200

Maidus, 7 f.
Maine, 61
malaria, 237, 246, 253 f.
Manitou, 3 f.
Marine Hospital Service, 123, 233, 236
Marine Hospitals, 233 f.
Marxism, 71
Maryland, 25, 57
Massachusetts, 26, 46, 54; State Board of Health, 240
Massachusetts General Hospital, 112, 206, 214 f., 224, 269
Massachusetts Institute of Technology, 242 f.
Massachusetts Medical Society, 41
Massachusetts Metaphysical College, 201
Mayflower, 26 f., 32 ff.
Mayo Clinic, 178 ff., 219
Mayo Foundation for Medical Education and Research, 180
McCormick Institute for Infectious Diseases, 277

McGill University, 126, 130
measles, 32, 247
Medical Arts Building, 175 f.
Medical Center, 142
Medical College of Ohio, 94, 103, 121
medical laws, 43 ff.
medical schools: number, 143; list, 143 ff.
medical students, preparatory training, 146 ff.
medicine man, 4 ff., 17, 20
Meharry Medical School, 143
Mennonites, 52
mental disease, 261 f.
Mental Hygiene, 261 f.
Methodists, 60
Mexico, 1 f., 10, 14, 17 ff., 60 f., 65, 67
middle-rate plan, 214 f.
Milbank Memorial Fund, 277
Missions, Spanish, 19, 53
Mississippi River, 16, 18 f., 21, 52 f., 56, 59, 61, 92, 234, 253
Monroe Doctrine, 72
Mormons, 60
Mount Vernon, 54, 57
Municipal Departments of Health, 240

National Board of Medical Examiners, 163
National Committee for Mental Hygiene, 261
National Health Council, 246, 264
National Tuberculosis Association, 249
Naturopathy, 199
Navajos, 6 f.
Negroes, 24, 29, 66, 68, 83, 107, 143, 262
neurology, 118 f., 282
Nevada, 61
New Amsterdam, 27, 36, 44

New England, 1, 25 ff., 34 ff., 53, 66
New Hampshire, 26, 110
New Haven Hospital, 224
New Jersey, 28, 45, 135
New Mexico, 1 f., 19, 61
New Orleans, 47, 61
New Spain, 15, 20
New Sweden, 27
New Thought, 201
New York, 27, 32, 40, 45, 47, 57, 66, 69
New York Academy of Medicine, 272
New York Hospital, 48, 142 f., 205
New York Public Library, 123
New York University Medical College, 206
Nicaragua, 14
normality, 266
North Carolina, 25, 60
Northwestern University, 141
number, regulation of university classes, 150 ff.
nursery schools, 258
nurses, 224 ff., 250; schools, 224, 227 f.; number, 228; Public Health, 244

omens, 12
open air schools, 250
operative surgery, 159
osteopathy, 197 ff.
ovariotomy, 87 ff., 269

Panama Canal, 71 f., 253
Paris, 77, 109, 111, 125, 133
pathology, 103 f., 128, 158, 282
Pawnees, 59
pediatrics, 282
Pennsylvania, 28, 52
Pennsylvania Hospital, 47, 204 f., 270
periodic examinations, 222, 265

Peru, 10, 14 ff.
pharmacology, 157 f.
Philadelphia, xiv, 27, 32, 40, 47, 54, 56, 68 f., 75 ff., 84 ff., 90 f., 102 f., 118, 120
Philadelphia Dispensary, 207
Philadelphia General Hospital, 205, 271
Philippines, 71, 235, 237, 255
physician, 169 ff.; training, 146 ff.; number, 169 ff., 175; distribution, 170 ff.; country, 171 f.; specialists, 173 f.; costs, 175, 180 ff., 186 ff.
physiology, 97 ff., 273, 282
Pilgrim Fathers, 26
pioneers, 75 ff.
plague, 24, 230, 234, 237, 247
Plymouth, 26, 34
poor-houses, 47, 205 f., 235, 254 f.
Porto Rico, 71, 235, 254 f.
practical nurses, 228
practice, country, 171 f.; city, 171 ff.
prenatal care, 257
prenatal center, 257
Presbyterian Hospital, 141 f.
preventive medicine, 230 ff.
primitive medicine, 8 ff., 61
printing, 120
Private Group Clinics, 176 ff., 265
prostitution, 251
Protestant Sisters of Charity, 224
psychiatry, 159, 278 f., 282
psychoanalysis, 282
psychobiology, 159
psychology, 279 f.
Public Health Act, 240
Public Health Nurses, 244 f., 250, 258
pueblos, 2
puerperal fever, 112 ff.
Puritans, 25 ff., 31, 34

quackery, 136, 195 ff.
Quakers, 27 f., 224

quarantine, 37, 45, 123, 232, 239, 247

Quarterly Cumulative Index, 192

radiology, 283
railroads, 68 f.
Red Cross, 245, 249
religious medicine, 201
Rhode Island, 26 f.
rickets, 230
Rights of Man, 55, 83
Rockefeller Foundation, 253, 255, 274
Rockefeller Institute for Medical Research, 274, 285
Royal Society, 36, 38
Russia, 71, 288

St. Augustine, 20
St. John's House, 224
St. Luke's Hospital, 224
St. Margaret's, 224
St. Thomas' Hospital, 224
Salamanca, 15
Salerno, 43, 180
San Francisco, 65, 69
sanitoria, 248 f.
sassafras, 33
scarlet fever, 32, 42, 247
school health service, 259
scurvy, 31
sects, medical, 136, 201 f.
shamans, 4 ff., 265
ship-surgeons, 33, 44
Sioux, 5, 10, 59
Sisterhood of All Saints, 224
Sisters of Charity, 224
Sisters of Mercy, 224
slavery, 24, 27, 66 ff.
smallpox, 31 f., 37 ff., 46, 230, 233, 237, 247; inoculation, 38 f., 42, 233
social insurance, 184
Social Service Departments, 222

Social Service Workers, 222 f.
South Carolina, 20, 25, 29, 66
specialization, of physicians, 173 f.; of research, 283
spotted typhus, 270 f.
State Board Examinations, 136 f., 146, 152, 162 f., 198 f.
State Board of Medical Examiners, 136 f., 163
State Departments of Health, 240
statistics, medical, 124; vital, 241, 263
steamboat, 61
stegomyia, calopus, 253
sterilization laws, 260
students, medical, number, 143; choice, 150 f.
Surgeon-General's Library, 122; Index, 122
surgery, 9 f., 41, 79, 100 ff., 159, 269
sweat-bath, 9
Sweden, colonial policy, 27

taboo, 3, 5
Tennessee, 60
Texas, 16, 61
Texas cattle fever, 276
thoracentesis, 269
tobacco, 24
toxalbumen, 119
Transylvania University, 93, 101, 121, 131
Treaty, of Ghent, 57; of Paris, 52; of Versailles, 56
trepanning, 10
trichinella spiralis, 273
tropical pathology, 282
tuberculosis, 181, 212, 222, 230, 248 ff., 257, 282
Tulane University, 139
Twanas, 6
typhoid, 32, 110, 237, 247, 270 f.
typhoid, related diseases, 32, 247

U. S. Public Health Service, 233 ff., 250

university, 148 ff.

university extension, 149

University, of Chicago, 139, 149, 275; Illinois, 143; Iowa, 139; Maryland, 89, 166; Michigan, 220; Minnesota, 227; Missouri, 178; Pennsylvania, 81 f., 118, 131, 272, 275, 277; Rochester, 139, 141; *see also* Columbia, Cornell, Duke, Harvard, Howard, Johns Hopkins, McGill, New York, Northwestern, Transylvania, Tulane, Vanderbilt, Washington, Western Reserve, Yale

Utah, 2, 61

vaccination, 233, 247; enforcement, 247

Vanderbilt University, 139, 143

variolation, 38 f., 42

venesections, 9

Vermont, 60

vesico-vaginal fistulas, 107, 269

Vienna, 125 f., 173 f.

Virginia, 23 ff., 30 ff., 44 ff.

Washington, 57

Washington University, 139, 143

Western Reserve University, 141, 219

whooping cough, 247

William H. Welch Medical Library, 141

Winnebagos, 9 f.

Wisconsin, 9

Wistar Institute, 272

wistaria, 272

women medical students, 151

Women's Hospital of the State of New York, 108

World War, 72, 141, 256

xenodochia, 47

Yale University, 40, 110, 131, 141, 189, 278 ff., 282

yellow fever, 32, 84 ff., 205, 233 f., 237, 247, 252 f., 269

Yucatan, 16

Zunis, 11